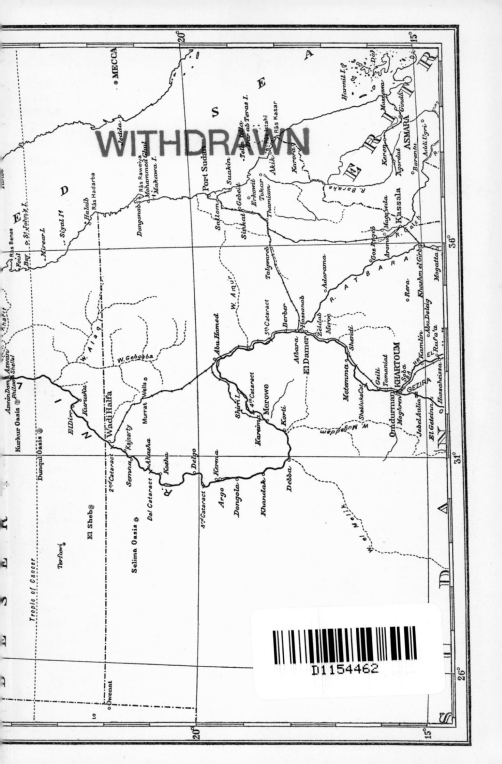

NOTE ON THE AUTHOR

Dr. H. E. Hurst is Scientific Consultant to the Egyptian Ministry of Public Works, and was formerly Director General of the Ministry's Physical Department. He has been in the service of the Egyptian Government for forty-six years.

He is *Grand Officier de l'Ordre du Nil, Commandeur de l'Ordre d'Ismail* and *Membre de l'Institut d'Egypte.*

THE NILE

a general account of the river
and the utilization of
its waters

BY

H. E. HURST
C.M.G., M.A., D.Sc., F. Inst. P.

CONSTABLE · publishers · LONDON

LONDON

PUBLISHED BY
Constable and Company Ltd.
10–12 Orange Street, W.C.2

INDIA *and* PAKISTAN
Orient Longmans Ltd.
BOMBAY MADRAS CALCUTTA

CANADA
Longmans, Green and Company Ltd.
TORONTO

SOUTH *and* EAST AFRICA
Longmans, Green and Company Ltd.
CAPE TOWN   NAIROBI

First published 1952

PRINTED IN GREAT BRITAIN BY THE WHITEFRIARS PRESS LTD.
LONDON AND TONBRIDGE

To all those with whom I have
worked in the service of the
Egyptian Government

Note on Spelling of Arabic Words

The Arabic language contains several sounds which do not occur in English, and also the pronunciation of some letters varies in different parts of Egypt and the Sudan, so that sometimes several spellings of a word are in use in English. The author has tried to be reasonably consistent, but has not troubled too much where alternative spellings are common; e.g. Mohammed or Muhammad, gebel or jebel, wadi or wady, Sudan or Soudan.

H. E. H.

SANDFORD-ON-THAMES,
September, 1951.

CONTENTS

ix

LIST OF PLATES

LIST OF PLATES

Where no source is mentioned the photographs were taken by
the author.

LIST OF FIGURES IN THE TEXT

MAPS.   SCALE I : 9,000,000

NORTHERN HALF OF THE NILE BASIN INSIDE THE FRONT COVER
SOUTHERN HALF OF THE NILE BASIN INSIDE THE BACK COVER
Reduced from a map produced by the Egyptian Survey Department.

INTRODUCTION

OF all the rivers in the world the Nile probably interests the greatest number of people. The lives of twenty million people in Egypt and the Northern Sudan depend upon it entirely, for without the Nile their country would be a desert. It is interesting to geographers because of its length, and the fact that unlike other great tropical rivers it flows from south to north and so passes through countries with a variety of climates. Parts of its basin are still very little known and even untraversed, and this is an attraction to travellers. For historians and archæologists there is a record in Egypt, written on the monuments and in the tombs, stretching back 7,000 years to the very beginnings of civilization. To engineers and scientific men the hydrological studies which have been made on the Nile are of theoretical and practical interest, and are the basis of the great scheme of projects which has recently been drawn up for the full utilization of the waters of the Nile for irrigation. In these days the river has also a personal interest to many from Great Britain, the British Empire and the United States who served in its basin during the two world wars.

Despite its great interest there are very few modern books on the subject. Some of the large amount of information collected by the Egyptian Government has appeared in reports of the Ministry of Public Works, but these are very technical and have not a wide circulation, so that they are not easily obtainable by the general reader.

I have therefore written this book to meet the needs of all these groups of readers for an accurate account of the Nile without a mass of technical details. It is based on my work extending over forty years on the collection and study of data about the Nile.

It was an accident that I went to Egypt and became connected with the Nile, and it occurred in this manner. In 1903, having taken first class honours in Physics at Oxford, I became a lecturer and demonstrator under Professor J. S. Townsend in the Electrical Laboratory of the University. In 1906 Captain H. G. Lyons, then Director-General of the Survey of Egypt, came to Oxford to receive an honorary degree and met Townsend at dinner at New College. The next day Townsend told me that Lyons was looking for scientific people to work in Egypt and suggested that I might apply. As a result I was appointed to the service of the Egyptian Government and was stationed at Helwan Observatory.

The work was new to me and I found it very interesting. During the five years I was there I worked mainly on terrestrial magnetism and was in charge of the magnetic survey of Egypt and the Sudan, but I was also concerned with meteorology, astronomy, sub-soil water and survey work. My first connection with the Nile was in 1913, when I became head of the Meteorological Service which also recorded data about the Nile. Finally in 1915 all the work of a physical nature done by the Survey, and the hydrological work of the Ministry of Public Works, were combined to form a new department of the Ministry, the Physical Department, of which I became the head. At this time Sir Murdoch MacDonald was proposing projects on the Nile for the increase of cultivation in Egypt and the Sudan, and the presentation of the hydrological side fell on the new department. This began our connection with Nile Projects and my colleagues and I were able to develop the hydrology and put it on a scientific basis. This involved travelling over a large part of the Nile Basin and doing a good deal of research, the results of which are recorded in Physical Department Papers published by the Ministry of Public Works. In 1946 I retired from the post of Director-General of the Physical Department and have since been retained as Scientific Consultant to the Ministry. Before I retired my colleagues and I published proposals for a combination of projects for the fullest use of the Nile waters for irrigation.[1] This combination was based on a new theory of the storage of water in good years to meet the shortage in bad years, as Joseph did with the corn in Egypt some thousands of years ago. The theory occupied my spare time for a number of years, and in the course of working it out a lot of time was spent in examining a long series of records of such natural events,

[1] *The Nile Basin.* Vol. VII. *The Future Conservation of the Nile.* Hurst, Black and Simaika. Cairo: Ministry of Public Works, 1946.

as rainfall, the thickness of the rings in the big trees of California, and the thickness of the annual layers of mud, known as varves, in the beds of ancient lakes. Just recently a beginning has been made on these projects by the commencement of work on the Owen Falls Dam on the Nile at its outlet from Lake Victoria. This is a joint undertaking of Uganda and Egypt, to provide power for the one and an enormous storage reservoir for the other. The Egyptian Council of Ministers has also approved the other parts of the programme.

The importance of scientific studies of the Nile was well known to His Majesty the late King Fouad, who took a keen interest in the subject, and this interest has been continued by His Majesty, King Farouk. During my forty-five years' service in the Egyptian Government I have served under twenty-five different Ministers of Public Works, many of whom had been irrigation engineers. If they were not engineers they still had agricultural interests and understood well the importance of studies of the Nile. It is a pleasure to recall the courteous treatment and assistance which I have received from all of them. The same cordial relations have existed between myself and other senior officials of the Ministry and of the Physical Department, without whose assistance this book could not have been written. I can only add that I have enjoyed my work in Egypt, which has provided me with a continued succession of new and interesting problems to solve.

Chapter One

GENERAL SURVEY OF THE BASIN

THIS book is about one of the great natural features of the world, which has played a large part in the early development of the human race. The Nile is the dominating feature of the north-east quarter of Africa and affects all of Egypt, the Sudan and Uganda, one-third of Ethiopia, and parts of Kenya, Tanganyika, Ruanda-Urundi and the Belgian Congo. Its annual cycle is produced by the prime source of all our energy, the sun, which evaporates water from the South Atlantic Ocean and this, by pressure differences and the earth's rotation, is driven 2,200 miles across Africa to the highlands of Ethiopia, where it falls as rain. The water runs off the hillsides scouring away much earth, and runs by little rivulets into hundreds of little streams which find their way into the Sobat, Blue Nile and Atbara, and so into the Mediterranean, to be again in part drawn up into the atmosphere and again circulated to who knows what part of the earth.

All along the Nile's 4,160 miles from its most remote source near lake Tanganyika to the Mediterranean and over the 1,100,000 square miles of its basin and even outside, people are affected to some extent by the river or by water which helps to form the river. In East and Central Africa transport, power, crops and drinking-water are concerned; in the Sudan transport, drinking, and some irrigation; while in Egypt it is the whole life of the country, and away from the river only a few nomads exist. The Nile can also be harmful by flood and drought, and the attempts to mitigate the effects of these by the control of the river will be described in this book. By chance the river flows through several states, but to get the best out of it, it must be treated as a whole, as was done in the Tennessee Valley.

This book will describe what has been done towards control of the river and what is proposed, and also to some extent the scientific bases of the work, and the following short introduction will make it easier to understand the more detailed account which forms the remainder of the book.

4

First let us look at the maps of the basin, of which the one covering the northern half is inside the front cover of this book, and the one of the southern half at the end. Then think that if one could walk without hindrance or delays at ten miles a day along the river bank from the Rosetta mouth of the Nile to the most remote source of the White Nile near Lake Tanganyika, it would take 416 days or about fourteen months, and one would gradually climb up to a height of about 6,000 feet above sea level. I say, if one could walk along the river bank, for in places this could not be done because of swamps, and sometimes forest might make it difficult, while if one followed up the Blue Nile it would be quite impossible to keep to the river bank when one entered Ethiopia, because the river here flows through a tremendous canyon 3,000 feet deep, with every one of its tributaries likewise in a deep valley. However, if one persevered, keeping as near the river as one could, descending into tributary valleys and climbing up again, one would ultimately come to the reputed source of the Blue Nile, a sacred spring on a mountain side 9,000 feet above the sea. But I would not like to give an estimate of how long the journey would take, though the actual distance by river is only about three-quarters of that to the White Nile source. In making these journeys one would pass from Egypt with a history going back 5,000 years—and even at that remote date showing a civilization which must have taken a further long period to develop—to the Sudan, Ethiopia, Uganda, and parts of Kenya, Tanganyika and the Belgian Congo where, at the most, the known history only covers some hundreds of years. In these regions most of the country was unknown to the outside world a hundred years ago.

This long river, certainly the second and perhaps the longest in the world, flows from south to north over 35 degrees of latitude, and has a basin covering a great deal of the north-east corner of Africa, and including more than a million square miles of territory. In this great extent are the relatively temperate climates of the Lake Plateau and Ethiopia, temperate only because of their altitude, the hot climate of the Sudan plains, and the delightful winter climate of Egypt and the northern Sudan.

On the high country in the tropics there is a considerable rainfall, but in the plains the rain decreases, until somewhere

north of Khartoum it is negligible, and the river enters that belt
of desert which stretches right across Africa from the Red Sea
to the Atlantic Ocean, and even eastwards into Asia, and which,
except for the fertile strip along the river, extends northwards
to the Mediterranean Coast. (See rainfall map, p. 177.) In the
southern regions the rainfall allows of the growth of sufficient
crops to feed the population and provides grazing for their
cattle. But in the central Sudan rainfall is capricious, and irrigation, made possible by the building of the Sennar Dam, was
started about twenty-five years ago on the Blue Nile. Some more
irrigation is made possible by pumps and by the flooding of
areas along the river in the neighbourhood of Dongola. In
Egypt, however the whole of the cultivation is dependent on
irrigation, and the irrigated area is much greater than in the
Sudan. Water forms a main topic of conversation in the villages
of Egypt and is often the cause of serious quarrels. With the
system called perennial irrigation five million out of Egypt's
six million acres of cultivation produce two and sometimes
three crops a year.

All this is possible because of the regular habit of the Nile to
rise in flood at about the same time each year. This is due to
the apparent annual movement of the sun north from the equator
from March to June and back again from July to September, in
other words to the inclination of the earth's axis to the plane of
its orbit round the sun. By this movement the major circulation of the atmosphere is affected so that a belt of rain follows the
sun northward with a delay of about two months. Rain begins
to fall on the highlands of Ethiopia in March or April, and by
June the Blue Nile is well on the rise. By the end of August or
beginning of September it has reached its maximum and begins to
fall again. In flood the Blue Nile is a tremendous stream flowing
full, and in places over-topping its banks, but by April it has
decreased to one-fortieth of its flood discharge, and has so
shrunk that it wanders about amongst the sands of its bed and
can be forded in many places in its upper reaches.

Fortunately several causes make the White Nile a more steady
stream than the Blue, so that its contribution prevents the Main
Nile from falling to the same small proportions as the Blue. The
main cause is that the White Nile has the great lakes Victoria and

Albert behind it, and from these issues a discharge which does not vary greatly with the seasons. The discharge of the White Nile itself does vary, however, with the season, because about half its water comes from its Ethiopian tributary, the Sobat. But still it only falls to about 40 per cent. of its flood discharge, and provides four-fifths of the whole Nile discharge when it is at its lowest.

For a river the habits of the Nile are regular, but the Biblical story of Joseph indicates correctly that there are high years and low years. However, the work of British and Egyptian irrigation engineers in building dams and barrages on the river, has very much lessened the ill effects both of very high floods and of very low ones. In the present century the Aswan Dam and the Gebel [1] Aulia Dam on the White Nile have enabled enough water to be stored from the time of plenty each year to increase the low stage discharge in Egypt by 50 per cent. At the same time the barrages which cross the river at Assiut and below Cairo hold up the low river level high enough for the water to enter the main canals and so supply the perennial area of Egypt. In the Sudan the Sennar Dam enables a gross area of about 1,000,000 acres to be cultivated, of which one quarter is under crop when the Blue Nile is low.

An important tributary of the Nile in flood time is the Atbara coming from northern Ethiopia; but after the flood it is dry for half the year. From the mouth of the Atbara to the sea, a distance of 1,700 miles, there are no more tributaries and the river decreases in volume, slightly because of evaporation, but considerably because of the amount of water taken from it for irrigation in Egypt. The Nile in flood can be controlled only a little, but in the low period from February to July in Egypt it is completely controlled, and all its water, together with what has been stored from the preceding time of high levels is used for irrigation. A great deal will be said later about irrigation and of the interesting problems to which it gives rise, particularly of the means suggested for making full use of the waters of the Nile for irrigation in Egypt and the Sudan.

The relative volumes of the Nile tributaries are shown in the

---

[1] This is pronounced Gebel in Lower Egypt and Jebel in Upper Egypt and the Sudan, and means mountain.

table below in numbers which can easily be remembered. They represent approximately the average quantities flowing in a year, and the unit is 12 milliards or 12,000,000,000 cubic metres or tons. This large number does not convey very much about the actual size of the quantity involved, but some idea can be given by saying that the unit of 12 milliards if spread evenly would cover all the land of Egypt between the deserts on either side of the Nile Valley and the Mediterranean sea, to a depth of 36 centimetres or 14 inches. Put another way, the unit would cover the county of Yorkshire to a depth of 2½ feet.

The Annual Discharge of the Nile

Unit 12 Milliards of Cubic Metres or Tons.

Bahr el Jebel downstream of Lake Albert	2
Bahr el Jebel downstream of the Sudd	1
River Sobat at its mouth.	1
White Nile at Khartoum	2
Blue Nile at Khartoum	4
River Atbara	1
Main Nile entering Egypt at Wadi Halfa . . .	7

To put the table into words—two units leave Lake Albert and are reduced to one after passing through the swamps of the Sudd Region; the Sobat coming from Ethiopia then adds one, making two for the whole White Nile; then the Blue Nile adds four and the Atbara one, so the total for the Main Nile flow is seven units. These are round numbers in which smaller tributaries and ordinary losses incurred in travelling are ignored, but they give the general picture of the relative importance of the largest tributaries.

To sum up, the major part of the Nile water comes from Ethiopia and nearly all of the remainder from the Lake Plateau of Central Africa. Only a very small part of the rainfall over the Southern Sudan ever reaches the Nile, and this is out-weighed by the large quantities lost in the swamps.

8

Chapter Two

EGYPT

ARRIVING in Egypt by air, as one often does these days, the first thing one sees is the low sandy coast west of Alexandria. As one crosses it the dark blue Mediterranean passes through lighter shades of blue, blue green and pale green as the water shallows on the flat beach. Once past the coast line there are many traces of the battle of Alamein in the form of tracks and outlines of camps, and one remembers that time of anxiety and disquieting rumours in July, 1942, when it was reported in Cairo that Germans had cut the desert road from Cairo to Alexandria and would probably be in Cairo the next day. The desert road, a black line, is soon crossed and the edge of the Delta is reached. The country is a patchwork of green and brown rectangles, cut up by ditches, small water courses and larger canals. The newer channels are straight while the older, which follow the courses of ancient natural channels, are winding, though the windings have been kept within bounds by training works. Very soon the Rosetta branch of the Nile is recognizable by its width and winding course. In the summer and autumn it is a muddy stream filling its trough from bank to bank, while from February to July many sand banks narrow the course of the river, which in fact is hardly flowing at all, being shut off above by the sluices of the Muhammad Ali Barrage at the head of the Delta, and below by those of the new Edfina Barrage near its mouth. Thus it was in August, 1942, when I was asked by the military authorities to report upon its state and whether it would be possible in case of emergency to send enough water down to make the river a serious obstacle. Rommel had then nearly reached Alamein. At the time it was possible in the upper half of the river's course from the Barrage to the sea, to wade across in many places without being wetted above the waist. Its flow might have been increased by taking water from the main canals, but this would have damaged the crops and caused dismay to the farmers, so it could have been only a last resort.

Fortunately after a week or so I was told that my report had become only of academic importance as the enemy had been halted at Alamein. It was very creditable that in these critical days my Egyptian colleagues remained calm and seemed to be less disturbed than I really was myself.

Continuing the journey across the Delta one crosses the other branch of the Nile, the Damietta Branch, and the desert on the eastern side becomes visible as one approaches Cairo air port. This is on the desert on the outskirts of the city, which is itself built partly on the desert at the foot of the bare rocky Mokattam Hills. About ten miles to the westward are the Pyramids on the edge of the desert on the other side of the valley, and visible from most places in the country round Cairo. At Cairo the narrow valley of the Nile begins, and from there to Khartoum it is never much more than about twelve miles wide, and sometimes hardly more than the width of the river itself, just a green thread in the brown desert. From ancient times there have been cities on the eastern bank of the Nile in the area known as Old Cairo on the southern outskirts of the present city. This latter is relatively modern since it was begun only about a thousand years ago. It has increased greatly in size in the last fifty years and now contains more than two million people, making it the largest city in Africa. During my time it has extended in all directions and the centre has been filled with tall buildings rising to seven or eight stories and more (one of nineteen is now being built), many of which stand on a basis of fine shops. The centre of the town is to some extent cosmopolitan with a mixed sort of architecture on European models. Most of the palaces built a century or two ago have made way for more modern buildings, but some old Arab houses still remain in the Musky quarter and towards the Citadel, and many of the mosques are old, the earliest dating back to the ninth century. The Citadel built by Salah el Deen, the Saladin of the Crusades, overlooks Cairo from the east, and is, with the aqueduct which ran from the river to the Citadel, among the oldest buildings, other than mosques, now remaining.

The latest development of Cairo is the industrial quarter to the north, where during and since the war many factories have been built and industries new to Egypt have been introduced.

It remains to be seen how many of these can develop in competition with Europe and America, since industry requires a great deal of scientific and technological research behind it, and only a small amount of this has yet been done in Egypt. What research is done is almost entirely under the auspices of the Government, either in government departments or in the Universities, and a body has been formed to co-ordinate research. The development of the arts and sciences has always received encouragement from King Fuad and King Farouk, by the foundations of various societies and institutes devoted to special objects, and by the invitations to international learned bodies to hold congresses in Egypt. In particular one may mention the support given to the Egyptian Royal Geographical Society in the form of subventions from the privy purse for the production of special publications relating to Egypt, to some of which this book is indebted for information.

Of the population of about twenty millions in Egypt about four millions live in the towns. In size Alexandria follows Cairo with a million and, because of its position as a port, has a large proportion of foreigners and people of mixed origin. These foreign and hybrid peoples have been responsible for the introduction of many foreign words into Arabic, the language of the country. In household matters, marketing, cooking and so on, many Italian words are in use in Alexandria which are not common in Cairo and would be unknown in the villages. As an example of foreign words I am reminded of my cook who said " Arabic is a very rich language. It has always two names at least for everything. For example, rubber in Arabic is ' lastica ' and also ' kowitch ' (caoutchouc)." I agreed with him that Arabic is a rich language, but pointed out that these two words " lastica " and " kowitch " were not Arabic but " effrangi."

Alexandria stretches along the coast for twenty miles with the port at the western end, and the royal palace of Montaza with its delightful gardens at the eastern. Cairo is the centre of Government, but in normal times the King and the Council of Ministers transfer to Alexandria for the hottest months, and many of the inhabitants of Cairo also take holidays there to enjoy the bathing and the cool breeze from the sea. Some description of climate will be found in Chapter XI.

Alexandria is at the tail end of the Mahmoudiya Canal which brings fresh water from the Nile and forms a link in water transport from Alexandria inland. The western branch of the Nile enters the sea a short distance east of Alexandria and a few miles north of Rosetta. Owing to the silt which it carries in flood time the river is continually pushing its mouth further seawards and the silt gives a muddy appearance to the sea-water for some miles off the coast. The way in which a delta is formed is, however, better seen with smaller rivers, where after rain the muddy water entering the sea can be seen from the air to spread out as a cloud whose density gradually decreases towards its edge. This is often seen along the Mediterranean coast of Europe and is known also in lakes. I have seen it in Lake Albert, where nearly every small stream coming down from the escarpment forms a tiny delta. In one case the muddy water was a jet pushing slowly into the lake in a sort of spiral and diffusing gradually.

Between Alexandria and the Rosetta Mouth is Aboukir Bay, the scene of what is called the Battle of the Nile, where Napoleon's fleet was destroyed by Nelson, so putting an end to the oriental schemes of the man whom Trevelyan calls " the most ambitious spirit since Alexander the Great." The port of Rosetta is visited by small sailing ships trading round the Eastern Mediterranean and was much more important in former times than it is now. A mile or two above the town is the site where an earth bank or sudd across the river used to be constructed each year. This was completed when the flow in the river was shut off at the Delta Barrage and all the water went into the canals because it was needed for cultivation. The bank prevented salt water from running many miles inland, and also enabled seepage and drainage back into the river trough from the Barrage northward to be collected and used for irrigation of small areas further north along the river. It has now (1951) been replaced by a masonry barrage at Edfina which shuts out the sea and whose sluices give control of the river upstream at the time of the year when this is necessary. (See Plate II.) The construction of such an earth bank, which still continues on the Damietta Branch, is a delicate operation, since it must be done in a time limited at the beginning and at the end; at the beginning because the river must have fallen until its velocity has decreased enough to allow of earth deposited

in it remaining in place. Also enough time must have elapsed after
the flood for the earth on its banks, which will be used to make
the sudd, to have become sufficiently dry to be easily workable. It
is limited at the end by the time when there ceases to be excess
water over the needs of the cultivation. The foundation of the
bank is a timber frame work filled with bags of earth which is
gradually pushed out from both sides, the bank being made up
to its proper section by tipping more and more earth. The
critical time comes when both parts of the bank nearly meet.
The weather then becomes particularly important as a storm may
hold up the work and drive a lot of salt water up the river. The
salt must then be, as far as is possible, washed out with fresh
water. As the gap gets less the discharge down the river is
reduced so as not to wash away earth from the bank, and on the
proper timing of the reduction depends the successful closing
of the gap. After the bank is closed and trimmed off, no more
Nile water escapes directly to sea since it must first irrigate the
crops, and then some may percolate through the ground into
the drains and so into the sea.

When the river rises in flood again six months later and the
natural supply is enough for the needs of the cultivation the head
sluices at the Delta Barrage are opened up, the trough of the
river fills, and the water rises behind the Sudd. When a suitable
level is reached upstream of the Sudd a number of cuts are made
in it and the water begins to trickle through the cuts. Gradually
enlarging them the rush of water becomes stronger, while fish
try to swim up the jets or jump the barrier, and large lumps of
the bank give way as they are undermined. The timber frame-
work breaks up and bits of it are retrieved by boats waiting
downstream. In about twenty-four hours the whole obstruction
has gone, and for the next six months the river flows unhindered
to sea.

In the past it has been cheaper to make Sudds every year
rather than control the flow by permanent masonry barrages
with sluice gates, but now a barrage has been built at Edfina
above the town of Rosetta, and another is projected near the
mouth of the Damietta Branch at Faraskour. There is no doubt
that these permanent and graceful works, with the considerable
saving of water and the delicate control of the two branches

which they give, are essential and worthy gateways through which this marvellous river may make its way to the sea.

One cannot talk of Egypt without mentioning the people and their mode of life. Egypt is a thickly populated country and its nineteen million inhabitants occupy about six million acres of cultivated land. The two large towns Cairo and Alexandria contain roughly three million people, while there are five other towns each with more than 100,000 inhabitants. Something like 60 per cent. of the workers are engaged in agriculture. They include women, children, and an uncertain number of casual labourers, for wives and families often help the men in the lighter work of tending cattle and harvesting crops. Industry, transport and commerce occupy about 16 per cent. of the male workers, but the numbers are increasing. Two and a half per cent. occupy posts in the public services, which are much desired and form a principal object of education. Academic education is going ahead rapidly although about 80 per cent. of the total population are still illiterate. There is great danger of the scheme of education becoming top-heavy with two existing universities in 1946 containing more than 15,000 students and two more universities projected. The result of this might well be more students than the available teaching staff could cope with, or the country afterwards employ in suitable work at a reasonable remuneration. This would undoubtedly lead to the existence of a body of discontented young men who would be a source of instability and trouble. It may be noted that the number of law students was greater than the number of those in any one of the three faculties of science, medicine or engineering.

Of the holdings of agricultural land more than half are less than half a feddan,[1] forty or fifty are more than 2,000 feddans and the average size is about 2¼ feddans. In spite of the fertility of the land, the families existing on half a feddan or less have a low standard of life, their food being bread and vegetables with meat very occasionally. To meet the demands for meat of the poorer people about 25,000 camels a year are slaughtered, of which many are imported from the Sudan and Arabia.

In the country people live in villages and hamlets. A village

---

[1] One feddan = 1·04 acres. This statement is a little deceptive since the same man sometimes owns more than one plot.

is controlled by a headman called an omda, under whom may be several sheikhs, including those of outlying hamlets attached to the main village. The omda transacts the business of the village, looks after law and order through the village watchmen and is in touch with the mamur, an official of the Ministry of the Interior in charge of the district. The mamurs are under the Mudir or governor of the province.

The omda's house is the meeting place where proclamations of new regulations and laws are made, disputes are settled and inquiries held, and it usually falls on the omda to entertain any official who comes to the village on business. His house is generally the largest in the village and built of burnt brick. In the more prosperous villages many of the houses are also of burnt brick, but many are still made of unburnt brick or of mud, sometimes of one and sometimes of two stories; the roof, which is flat, is a store for maize stalks which are used as fuel. Disastrous fires sometimes occur through this practice because of sparks from a fire in a courtyard being blown by a strong wind. As this usually happens while the men are away in the fields the village is often well alight before anything can be done. These village fires are more frequent in April and May when the wind accompanying " Khamseen " weather blows strongly from the south, an unusual quarter.

Another feature of the life of villages and towns is the cafés where people collect to drink coffee or, a recent introduction, tea also. There they may play games of tric-trac or be entertained by story tellers, conjurers or singers, but now much entertainment comes from the radio which has penetrated every village of any size. So the fellah, who often has never been outside his own district, is introduced suddenly, and without any background for comparison, to perplexing ideas as to what is happening in countries whose names he hardly knows.

Since so many holdings are tiny and the farmers extremely poor, agricultural implements have remained primitive except on the larger estates owned by more wealthy people where mechanization is being gradually introduced. The universal tool is the fass with which a great deal of the land is cultivated. (See Plate IV.) The fass first of all functions as a spade for digging the ground and making ditches, and later as a hoe for ridging up and weeding.

It resembles a wheelwright's adze, but with a larger head and longer handle. The plough is still made of wood shod with iron and may be drawn by oxen, buffaloes, or even by such a combination as a donkey and a camel. Reaping is usually done by hand with a curved knife much smaller than the ordinary sickle, and this is the usual tool used in the fields for cutting berseem (clover) for cattle, rushes for mat making, or corn.

There is no pasture land as in Europe and the principal fodder crop, berseem, is on the ground for a few months only. During this time it will yield five or six cuttings, so rapid is its growth. The usual way of feeding cattle is to tie each to a peg in the ground, the tethering rope being of such a length as to allow a certain area of berseem to be eaten, and the peg is moved from time to time according to the needs of the animal.

Life in the country is regulated by the sun, and the people and their cattle go out to the fields soon after sunrise, to return about sunset. Very often children look after the cattle and small tots can be seen riding on buffaloes or leading camels. It was explained to me by a fellah that the reason a small boy can take charge of a camel is that a camel's eye magnifies, and so he thinks the boy is much larger than he really is and is afraid of him.

The townspeople, excepting those of Cairo and Alexandria, are engaged mainly in the ordinary crafts which supply their own and the needs of the countryside. Industry on a larger scale is mostly centred on Cairo and Alexandria. Looking down the census of occupations in the Annuaire Statistique one finds all the ordinary trades, carpenters, tailors, shoemakers, etc., represented, with large items for servants, waiters, workmen, and a final item " others." During and since the recent war, many industries have started or developed to manufacture articles formerly imported. In some cases these continue enterprises started by the British Army during the war.

A description of the character of a people apart from their customs and mode of life is difficult. One can be led into generalizations, and if these are sufficiently general to be correct, one often finds that they apply to people anywhere and are the characteristics of human nature. Also it is impossible for one who has spent most of his life in a country and has enjoyed living and working there to give a fair and unbiased account of its inhabitants, so I offer only a few remarks on the subject. One characteristic is the general cheerfulness and kindliness of the people. Hospitality is practised everywhere, and two or three labourers sitting down to a meal of bread and vegetables in a field will invite the passer-by to join them. The invitation is generally politely refused, but a hungry man can always get a meal in the country. Kindness is always shown in misfortune, and kindness to children often becomes indulgence. Family ties are strong, and assistance for relations, whether they deserve it or not, is a matter of principle which, although it often leads to what foreigners consider abuses in the matter of appointments, cannot be entirely evaded even by the most enlightened and upright. The kindly instinct can be illustrated by the answer of a student in a law examination when asked what punishment he would inflict in a certain case of theft. He replied that the penalty was three months' imprisonment, but that the man was a poor man with a large family and he would temper justice with mercy and let him off with a caution. In ordinary dealing politeness is more noticeable and more formulæ are employed than in the West. A humorous remark of an obvious nature will often solve a difficulty, and a little cheerful encouragement will make people work diligently. For example, passing through the Customs, where formalities may sometimes be drawn out, a customs officer on one occasion asked me if I had brought any presents from England. To this I replied that I was a Government official and how should I find money to buy presents. The officer laughed and passed my baggage immediately.

When I first went to Egypt hotels in provincial towns, unless they were tourist resorts, were often uncomfortable and not very clean. I can well remember in early days arriving about eight o'clock on a winter night and engaging a room at an hotel in a town of some importance. The hotel did not provide meals, for which one went to a café. Fortified by a good meal and some wine I returned to the hotel, where my servant as a precaution had made up my bedding on my camp bed. After giving instructions to be called at 6 a.m. I went to sleep. Next morning I was called, and as it seemed cold and not very inviting for rising an hour before sunrise I was meditating whether to delay or not. However, as I surveyed the ceiling and saw what were dropping from it on to my bed, my mind was rapidly made up. Apparently my presence could only just have become known as nothing had got inside the bed and I was not bitten. This state of affairs has changed and reasonable hotels can now be found in all towns of any size. In the Fayum there are two hotels on the shore of the lake where one can spend a pleasant time visiting the many places of interest in the neighbourhood.

In Upper Egypt the two sides of the river are very different from each other. The eastern desert is rugged and mountainous and is much cut up by deep valleys (wadis), down which occasional heavy rains cause torrents to flow (Plate I). Such rains are only occasional and in the south several years may pass without any water coming down to the river. The desert cliffs in many places come close to the river and there is little cultivation. In fact it is only between Assiut and Luxor that the cultivation on the east bank covers any considerable area. Owing to the scanty population and the rough nature of the country the east bank often provides hiding places for the lawless from the thickly populated west bank. The chief towns and cultivation are all on the west, and naturally the railway is also on this side until it crosses the river at Nag Hammadi on the first bridge over the Nile south of Cairo.

The western desert is not cut up by deep wadis, in fact there are no wadis, and though there are occasional shallow drainage lines these do not bring down torrents like those on the east. This desert is lower and more undulating, but is nevertheless sharply divided from the valley, because cultivation ceases as soon as the land begins to rise above the level which can be flooded. In the eastern desert water is to be found in many places in the wadis where it remains in wells and holes for months after rains. The plateau increases in height as one travels from the Nile to the Red Sea, along which is a range with peaks reaching 7,000 feet. There is occasionally rain on this coastal range and this helps to keep up the water levels in wells and holes. After rain, and within a few days, small herbs begin to appear in favoured places along drainage lines, giving the desert a greenish tinge, while in the wadis small bushes and tufts of

I.   A WADI IN THE EASTERN DESERT

II.   THE EDFINA BARRAGE NEAR THE MOUTH OF THE ROSETTA BRANCH, THE
LATEST WORK ON THE NILE

(*By courtesy of Hamed Suleiman Pasha*)

grass renew their greenery, and grazing is provided for the camels, sheep and goats of the very small number of Bedawin who inhabit it, and who move from place to place according to the location of the grazing.

The western or Libyan desert stretches away west of the Nile right across Africa and is one of the most desolate regions in the world. Wells are few and far between, though a hundred miles or so west of the Nile Valley there is a chain of large depressions, the oases, in which water is near the surface and where there are villages and cultivation. Tracks lead from the Nile Valley to the oases and from one oasis to another, and in the days before cars, when I did most of my own desert travelling, camels were the only means of transport, and caravans kept to the regular tracks. The advent of cars has led to the development of a technique of desert travel beginning with the first war, and since then the western desert has been well traversed and remarkable journeys have been made by surveyors, and by soldiers in the second world war.

The most famous desert track is the Arbain Road from Darfur in the Sudan to the Nile at Assiut. This was the route for caravans of slaves from Equatorial Africa and was so-called because the journey took forty days, arbain in Arabic meaning forty. Like most routes in the western desert generations of travellers have made a series of parallel tracks covering several hundred yards in width. Most of the desert near the Nile is not sandy but gravelly, and a track once made lasts for years. I well remember when in the desert west of Aswan on a route not commonly travelled, being puzzled by the occurrence of what looked like the track of a bicycle without any tyre markings. On inquiring of my Bedawin camel men, I was told that it was the track of the measuring wheel of Dr. Hume of the Geological Survey, who had been there a year or two before. On the western side of the Nile, however, there are places where blown sand is encroaching on the cultivation, which acts as a sort of a trap for the sand. West of Mir near Deirut some distance outside the present dividing line between cultivation and sand there is a well which shows by successive strata of masonry that it has been built up in stages since ancient Egyptian times to keep its mouth above the advancing sand.

c 2

Perhaps the following story is a relic of some old tradition, which may also be the origin of the idea that an underground river flows beneath the chain of the oases. Some little distance south of the Aswan Dam, is Shemet-el-Wah, which means the bay of the oasis, and here there is said to be a whirlpool. A merchant trading up and down the river was shipwrecked at this point and amongst his belongings which disappeared was a wooden bowl from which he was accustomed to eat. The following year, having taken to trade on land, he was in the oases of the western desert, when one day, sitting by a well, his bowl suddenly floated up from the depths of the well in front of his eyes. This tale was told to me by a boatman in Nubia, but I was never able to trace its origin.

The idea of an underground river beneath the oases is no doubt connected with the theory that at some previous geological epoch the Nile or one of its branches passed through the oases to the Mediterranean and this was shown on some maps as late as about 1880. Dr. John Ball, one of the pioneers of desert surveys and studies, examined the matter carefully in recent times and concluded that neither the Nile nor any branch of it ever passed through the Libyan Desert to the sea.

He also made a considerable study of the levels of the water in wells scattered over this desert and was able to draw a map showing the existence of a general sheet of water under the desert sloping from the south-west to the north-east and reaching sea-level south of the latitude of Cairo, while in the extreme south-west corner of Egypt near Gebel Owenat it was 400 metres above sea-level. His general conclusions have been confirmed by Mr. G. W. Murray who has recently reviewed the question.[1] This extensive sheet of water is in the porous rock underlying the desert and the conclusion is that it derives its present supplies from the northern fringe of the tropical rains which reach the highlands of Ennedi and Tibesti in French Equatorial Africa. The water must flow very slowly through the rock, however porous, and so seasonal changes and even the effect of high and low years would be damped out at distances as far from its source as Egypt. This agrees with the fact that

---

[1] 'The Artesian Water beneath the Libyan Desert.' Congress of the Royal Egyptian Geographical Society. Cairo: January, 1951.

the level of the water surface in the oases varies very little unless disturbed by heavy draft from wells. It is probable that this underground water is what might be called fossil water and dates back to a time when there was much more rain over northern Africa than there is now and the water was not far below ground level. As the rainfall decreased and desiccation set in, the water level would gradually fall until it reached a steady state in equilibrium with the new conditions. Now the very small flow, which must take place owing to the slope of the water table, is kept going by the rainfall on these south-western highlands. Where there are depressions, as in the oases, the ground level is near the water level, which is easily reached by wells. In places the level of the water is even above the ground level and so it overflows, enabling the neighbouring land to be cultivated. This is the case at many places in the oases where even ponds and lakes are occasionally found. The high level of the underground water in the south of Egypt rules out the suggestion which has been made, that the water in the oases may be some of the large quantity which is lost in the swamps of the southern Sudan.

The Fayum, which is sometimes called an oasis, lies to the west of the Nile, about forty miles south of Cairo. It is separated from the Nile Valley by a narrow strip of desert, but it is unlike the oases further away in that its water supply comes by a canal from the Nile. It is a depression of considerable area, the bottom of which is filled by Lake Karun (in ancient times called Lake Moeris), and most of the remainder is cultivated. The lake lies about 150 feet below sea level and is brackish, a fact which I soon discovered the first time I was camped near it, as my servant made porridge with lake water. The lake has no outlet and receives the drainage water from the cultivated land. Its level is kept fairly steady by evaporation balancing the inflow so that it is steadily becoming more saline. It has now become so salt that some of the fish formerly living in it have died out, notably the Nile perch, while sea fish which have been put in, red mullet and soles, are thriving.

In the morning the view over the Fayum from the eastern side is delightful, with the green cultivation, the blue lake and the brown desert hills behind. The level of the lake has had its ups and downs as is proved by the existence of lake beaches at different levels, and also by the remains of an ancient causeway and quay at Dimay, well above the present lake. The history and prehistory of the Fayum, as well as its geology and the variations of the lake have been closely investigated.[1] The Fayum depression was not always connected with the Nile Valley, but some time in the early Paleolithic period the Nile broke through and filled the depression, leaving a beach high above the present cultivation and lake level as evidence. The examination of the beaches at different levels and the classification of the stone implements found in them gives a history of the ups and downs of the lake, of which it had several in prehistoric times. By the end of the Neolithic period the lake had fallen approximately to sea level as shown by some neolithic settlements on a beach at about this level. The existence of pottery and implements of predynastic and dynastic times along with the neolithic remains shows that this level of the lake persisted over a long period.

About 2000 B.C. the channel into the Fayum was enlarged by one of the rulers and the lake rose to a level approaching that of the Nile so that Nile water flowed into it in flood and some of it went back to the river later. The lake thus acted to some extent as a regulator of the river downstream, helping to reduce the crest of a high flood and slowing the rate of fall of the river when the crest was past. Of these two the reduction of a high flood would probably be the more important. Some historic evidence for this work is to be found in Herodotus who visited Egypt about 450 B.C. and had the story from the priests. One wonders what happened to the inhabitants of the lake shores when the rise of about 60 feet was taking place. Ball calculates that this might have taken place in four or five years and thereafter there would be an annual rise and fall of about eight feet, making a change of area of the lake of about 50,000 acres. Presumably this area could be cultivated as basin land is cultivated to-day to give one crop each year, but, as a great width of land would be inundated, the cultivators would have to leave their permanent homes each year to follow the receding water. In the last 2,000 years the lake has fallen from 60 feet above to

---

[1] *Contributions to the Geography of Egypt.* Ball. Cairo Government Press, 1939. *The Desert Fayum.* Caton-Thompson and Gardner. London, 1935.

its present level of 150 feet below the sea. The level of the lake depends on the balance between inflow and evaporation. A large inflow required a large lake to evaporate it, and as the inflow into the present lake has been reduced to the drainage of the Fayum only, the size of the lake has diminished correspondingly. A great deal of interesting information about the Fayum and its lake will be found in Dr. John Ball's book, " Contributions to the Geography of Egypt."

The Fayum is unlike any other part of Egypt owing largely to the fact that it is the only cultivated land in Egypt which has a visible slope. This produces a variety of scenery, and the land drains, of which there are several, have cut for themselves valleys well below the general land level, which makes them a little like streams found in other countries, and quite unlike the drains of small slope found elsewhere in Egypt. The considerable slope on the Fayum drains is made use of to turn mills for grinding corn, while the fall on some of the canals is applied to turn large water wheels, by which a portion of the water is raised to irrigate land at higher levels. Some of these may be seen on the canal which passes through the principal town, Medinet Fayum.

From Aswan until north of the Nag Hammadi Barrage a distance approaching 250 miles, irrigation is on the basin system, which we will describe later, except for small areas irrigated by pumps. North of this perennial irrigation begins, but there are still basins along the desert edge to within twenty-five miles of Cairo. At Assiut the Ibrahimia Canal, the largest in Egypt and one of the big canals of the world, takes off the river on the west bank above the Barrage, and this feeds the whole of Middle Egypt and the Fayum. It finally ends in the small canal whose surplus water escapes into the Rosetta Branch of the Nile north of the Muhammad Ali Barrage at the head of the Delta. One of the branches of the Ibrahimia Canal is the Bahr Yusef, an old channel which follows a winding course along the edge of the cultivation near the desert until it finally enters the Fayum which it supplies with water.

Bahr is a name given to a body of water and usually means a river or some sort of channel, so that Bahr Yusef is Joseph's Channel. I don't think it is known who Joseph was or when he lived, though there was a tradition 700 years ago that he was the man who first drained the great lake in the Fayum and made the place habitable, a task in which he was assisted by angels. The present Bahr Yusef branches off the modern Ibrahimia Canal at Deirut, but in former times it extended much further south along the desert edge. Thousands of years ago when the Nile in flood topped its banks or broke through them to flood the country, owing to the slope downwards of the land from the river to the desert, a good deal of water would be trapped between the river bank and the desert as the river fell. This water would drain away northwards gradually forming a drainage channel in the low ground along the desert edge. Possibly Chief Engineer Joseph at some stage improved this channel so as to supply the Fayum, or even to lead the surplus water back to the Nile.

About three-quarters of the way from Cairo to Aswan is Luxor, and many will remember that here there was formerly a change of the gauge of the railway, and for the last part of the journey the gauge was reduced to one metre. Standard gauge now extends all the way to Aswan and the journey has been shortened by several hours and is more comfortable. Luxor, the ancient Thebes, was the capital of Upper Egypt in the days of the Pharaohs. Their monuments still remain in the temples of Luxor and Karnak on the east bank of the river, and in the temples and the famous tombs of the kings and queens on the other side of the Nile. Luxor contains more ancient remains to interest the ordinary visitor than any other place in Egypt. The discovery of the tomb of Tutankhamun with its wonderful treasure of objects of all kinds, including the gold and enamel mummy case, will be well remembered. These can now be seen in the Cairo Museum of Ancient Egyptian Antiquities.

It is rare for the archæologist to find a tomb which has not been visited by robbers soon after its occupant and his belongings had been deposited, but in the case of Tutankhamun, although robbers had entered, they had got away with very little. A more spectacular find was made at Luxor in 1881 by M. Maspero and M. Emile Brugsch of the Department of Antiquities, whose suspicions were aroused by the occasional sale of objects of a particular period, which pointed to the existence of some tomb as yet undiscovered by the authorities. All these objects were traced to one agent, but the inquiry did not get much further until a quarrel amongst the gang over prices led to an informer betraying the source of the treasures. Here in a single rock chamber, outside the Valley of the Kings, was found a great collection of mummies of kings and their belongings. It appeared that thousands of years ago the guardians of the tombs, disturbed by thefts which were taking place, and afraid for the safety of the sacred bodies of the kings themselves, had removed the whole lot by night to a new hiding place and then filled it in. This cache, containing objects dating from 1700 B.C. to 1000 B.C., had remained undiscovered until the middle of the nineteenth century and was then revealed only by accident. Amongst the remains were the coffins and mummies of Seti I, Rameses II and Rameses III.

The river from Aswan to Cairo is a great highway for all kinds of merchandise, transported either by sailing boats or by tugs and barges. The sailing boats are mostly rigged with one or two short masts sloping forward and each carrying a long yard with a triangular sail. Coming along with a good breeze their high white sails make a fine sight. They vary in size from small felukas used for crossing the river, or going from one village to the next, and capable of taking four or five people, up to large vessels which may carry as much as 200 tons. Fortunately in Egypt the prevailing wind is from the north while the river flows from the south, so that boats can sail upstream with the wind and drift down with the current.

I made use of one of these boats when I was on magnetic survey in Nubia in 1909 to transport my three men, my camp equipment and myself. I had hoped that it would also transport my horse, but the beast fell into the water at the first attempt to get him up an indifferent gangway, and refused to try it a second time. This was a pleasant journey made in November when the weather was delightful. Stations were about twenty-five miles apart, where observations took about two days, and then we struck camp, loaded the boat and sailed or drifted downstream to the next point, usually camping at night. The horse was ridden along the bank and my time was divided between computation in the boat and riding the horse. One afternoon I mounted him when we were not far from the village of Derr, which is a centre of a district, a calling place of the post-boat and a police post, in fact a place of some importance in Nubia. Knowing the laziness of the reis (captain) I gave strict instructions that on no account was he to stop before reaching Derr, where we should stay the night. I had not ridden very far when I came to a cliff which descended to the water's edge. There was a track over the rocks round its foot which had obviously been used by generations of donkeys stepping in each other's tracks, with the result that a groove had been worn in the rocks, negotiable by a donkey, but not by a horse. After trying this and finding it impossible, with difficulty I got my horse back to where the rocks began. By this time it was nearly sunset. My boat was visible in the distance, so I fired several shots in the hope of attracting attention, but without effect. Afterwards the reis said that they heard the shots but thought I was shooting duck, and in any case they had my strict instructions not to stop before reaching Derr. I made inquiries about an alternative track inland and found that there was one said to be " not extremely far." A guide was found and we started on foot leading the horse. Fortunately it was a moonlight night, for the track was rough and rocky, winding up into the hills and seeming to go straight inland. I don't know whether the guide lost his way, but it was not until about nine o'clock that at last we came down a hill into Derr, to find some of my men, a policeman, and a lot of villagers coming out to search for me, wondering whether I had been waylaid by thieves or fallen over a precipice. There was great relief at my safe arrival, and many congratulations and pious expressions—el hamdulillah bi salama—thanks be to God that you have arrived in safety.

The river from the Delta Barrage to the Sudan boundary at Wadi Halfa, a distance of 800 miles, is always navigable though there are sometimes difficulties when it is low. It is a pleasant journey, made in very comfortable ships, which used to be full of tourists, and may be again when money is not so scarce. The stretch from Aswan to Halfa is particularly attractive in the winter as the days are usually sunny and warm and not too hot, though the nights may be cold. At that time of the year the reservoir is full, and looking south from the Aswan Dam the desert hills rising abruptly from the water recall the Italian Lakes. The Dam is built at the head of the First Cataract, which extends for a couple of miles northwards, and is caused by a barrier of granite through which the river has cut its way in a number of channels separated by many rocky islands. In flood time many of the rocks and islands are partly submerged by the muddy waters and most of the sluices of the Dam are open so that only a slight control is exercised on the river.

After the flood when the reservoir is being filled or emptied, only a regulated amount of water is allowed to pass, and the islands, channels and rapids of the cataract appear clearly. At this time of the year there is a good deal of activity on the part of villagers living downstream of the Dam, who are mostly fisher-men. Each pool in the rocks, or each little run, is the preserve of somebody, where he will make a trap of stones, into which it is easy for the fish to find their way by little passages but difficult for them to escape again. These traps are visited in the early morning and the catch is brought to the market on the bank at Karore village. This is an interesting place to visit, but one must be early to see it or the fish will have been bought by contractors and taken away.

Nile fish are of many varieties and some are good eating, particularly the Nile perch (*lates niloticus*) and the bulti (*tilapia*). The Nile perch gives good sport on rod and line at Aswan from about April to June, but is not caught when the water is muddy or in the winter. The record fish caught on rod and line there weighed about 160 pounds. They can be caught with a live bait, or by spinning with a dead fish or an artificial bait. Another fish which gives good sport on lighter tackle is the tiger fish (*hydrocyon*), but it is almost useless for eating because of the many floating bones. The fishing is in the turbulent water below the Dam and the fish seem to be trying to make their way upstream.

When the river is being regulated only a limited number of sluices are open, and these are usually in sets which are changed from time to time to avoid erosion of the apron of the Dam downstream. When there is a change-over many pools are left in the rocks below those sluices which have just been closed, and there is then great activity on the part of men, women, girls and boys, wading with baskets, nets and hands, chasing fish wherever they are to be found. If they think too many days have passed without a change of water, a deputation will wait on the Resident Engineer in charge of the Dam to ask that something be done to help the fishing by changing the sluices.

From Cairo to a little south of Luxor the cultivated land is usually several miles wide but towards Aswan it narrows to less than a mile, and in places the desert hills which are never far away are close to the river. These conditions persist for a long way south of Wadi Halfa, and in fact there are only a few places north of Khartoum where there is very much cultivation.

South of Aswan there are many temples on the west bank beginning with the well-known Philæ on an island near the Dam, and finishing with the rock temple of Abu Simbel excavated in the face of a great cliff. Both of these are imposing works, though Philæ is now almost completely submerged when the reservoir is full, and can only be seen as it was before the Dam was built during the height of the summer. The original proposal was to build the Aswan Dam almost to its present height, but the outcry from archæologists and many others at the idea that Philæ would be submerged resulted in the building of a low Dam which held up only a small quantity of water. Within a few years of the finishing of the Dam the need for expanding cultivation in Egypt led to its heightening, with a consequent increase to about two and a half times in reservoir capacity.

The heightening of the Dam raised a difficult problem of construction. Masonry, like everything else, expands when it gets hot and contracts when it cools, and the Aswan Dam, a mile and a quarter long, is no exception. It increases its length in summer and shrinks again in winter, by a matter of a few inches. This movement has caused a number of fine cracks which open in the winter as the masonry shrinks and close again in the summer. Lest anyone should think that these transverse cracks endanger the stability of the Dam it should be mentioned that all dams have fine cracks, and the Aswan and similar dams are designed so that if they were divided into sections by cross-cuts, each section, would stand up by itself. The problem was to build the new work on to the old so that the two would unite and ultimately become as homogeneous as is possible in such a great work. The heightening of the Dam required that it should also be thickened by building a layer five metres thick on to its back and then heightening the composite structure. Fig. 1 is a sketch showing a section of the Aswan Dam as it is to-day,

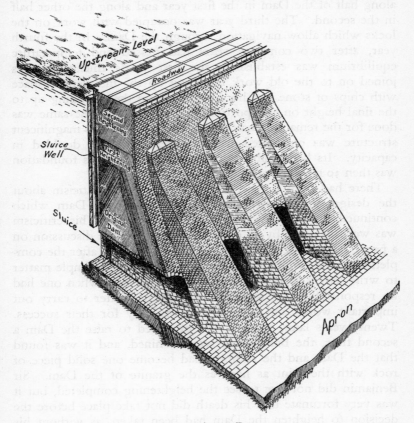

FIG. 1. Aswan Dam.

and indicating the stages of heightening. The wells in which the sluice gates are suspended are shown, but not the gates or the winches on the top of the Dam which raise and lower them. The problem was solved by Sir Benjamin Baker, the consulting engineer and designer of the original Dam. The plan adopted was to join the thickening to the old work by steel bars, but to keep the two apart until enough time had elapsed for the new work to have arrived at the same temperature equilibrium as the old. This was done by leaving a space of several inches between the Dam and the thickening and building the thickening along half of the Dam in the first year and along the other half in the second. The third year was occupied with work on the locks which allow navigation through the Dam. In the fourth year, after two complete years had passed and temperature equilibrium was established, the first year's thickening was joined on to the old work by filling up the intervening space with chips of stone and liquid cement and then building up to the final height on this portion. In the last year the same was done for the remaining half of the work, and so this magnificent structure was completed while its reservoir was doubled in capacity. Its height above the average level of its foundation was then 30 metres or about 100 feet.

There had been a good deal of irresponsible criticism about the design and construction of the heightened Dam which continued for years after the first heightening. This criticism was well answered by an eminent engineer in the discussion on a paper read to the Institution of Civil Engineers after the completion of the heightening. He said that it was a simple matter to write letters to the papers or deliver lectures when one had no responsibility; it was quite a different matter to carry out important works and take all responsibility for their success. Twenty years later, when it was proposed to raise the Dam a second time, the Baker joint was examined, and it was found that the Dam and the addition had become one solid piece of rock with the joint as hard as the granite of the Dam. Sir Benjamin did not live to see the heightening completed, but it was very fortunate that his death did not take place before the decision to heighten the Dam had been taken, as without his advice and the great weight carried by his opinion, the Egyptian authorities might not have felt justified in undertaking such a new adventure.

The Dam was again heightened twenty years later by still another method, originally suggested by Sir Murdoch Mac-Donald who was consulting engineer for the second heightening. This was modified by an International Commission and finally consisted of buttresses which leaned on the back of the Dam, and were separated from it by stainless steel plates to allow of the buttresses contracting and expanding freely. The heightening was built on the top of the old work. The reservoir now has five times its original capacity and a height of about 38 metres or 125 feet above average foundation level while it raises the river level as far back as the Second Cataract, a distance of 220 miles. There has been talk of a third heightening and designs were made with the object of providing a reservoir of such size that in the event of a dangerously high flood arriving, the levels in Egypt could be lowered by allowing the reservoir to fill up and hold the crest of the flood. When the natural river discharge had fallen to a safe amount the impounded flood waters would be discharged. This project was not accepted, largely to avoid having too many eggs in one basket, and the Cataracts south of Wadi Halfa have been examined to find a new dam site suitable for flood protection and for the provision of hydro-electric power. Such a site has been found in the Fourth Cataract. At the present time work is underway for the building of a station to make use of the power which could be generated at the Aswan Dam. This scheme has been discussed many times during the past thirty years, and it is a misfortune that it was not completed before the second war, when the power might have been very useful in producing fertilizers and so increasing the yield of food crops.

Before the enlarged reservoir was filled a careful archæological survey was made of the country between Aswan and Halfa, since the submergence would lead to the destruction of mummies and fragile objects which might be buried there. At the same time the many temples were repaired and strengthened so as to withstand the flooding which would take place annually. All these temples are on the west bank of the Nile and, with one or two exceptions, so are those lower down the river. The construction of the Aswan Dam and its two heightenings resulted in reducing considerably the amount of land which could be cultivated in Nubia and compensation was made for this to the owners. In addition some land above reservoir level was brought into cultivation by means of pumps. The people of Nubia are of a different race from the Egyptians and speak as well as Arabic a language of their own. The able-bodied men migrate to the towns of Egypt as servants, leaving the women, children and old men to look after household affairs. In spite of the reduction of cultivable land most of the people, when their houses were rendered useless, merely moved uphill and built others out of the reach of the inundation. They subsist largely on remittances from their relatives working in Cairo and Alexandria, which allow them to import food from outside.

Chapter Three

IRRIGATION IN EGYPT

I. ANCIENT HISTORY

HAVING given some description of the country of Egypt, an account will now be given of irrigation which enables the country to be inhabited. Some of the information was picked up from my old friend H. Hindmarsh, formerly Director-General of Projects, during the many years we have been shooting snipe and duck together.

How frequently it happens in England that we are in trouble about water. Heavy rains cause floods and then we read that in some areas houses are surrounded by water and people marooned, while there are pictures of boats in the streets taking supplies to those who are cut off. On the other hand, if no rain falls for a few weeks there is a drought, the water stored in reservoirs is depleted and restrictions on consumption are imposed everywhere. At the same time the grass and other crops in the fields dry up and this leads to a milk shortage as well. In Egypt, thanks to the Nile and to the fact that it is regulated, it is rare that there is great damage either from floods or droughts, and the farmers know that they can count on having water at the proper times running on their lands in the exact quantities required. As the poet Tibullus wrote, " Father Nile . . . because of thee Egypt never sues for showers nor does the parched blade bow to Jove the rain-giver." In this respect Egypt is one of the most fortunate countries in the world. However it was not always so, and I shall describe how irrigation arose in prehistoric times and was gradually developed; and how in recent times it has expanded rapidly owing to great engineering works and to scientific studies, which have given an increasing control over the river, and how it is proposed to extend this control until the maximum advantage is obtained from the Nile waters.

To the eye the cultivated land of Egypt lying between its deserts is flat, but careful measurements with an engineer's level show that it has a small slope downwards from south to north, and a slightly greater slope downwards from the river banks to the deserts on either side. The south to north slope of the land is slightly greater than that of the river and is about 5 inches to the mile, or 1 in 13,000. Without a slope water would not flow and irrigation canals would not work, in spite of the opinion of an officer of high rank during the first war who said the surface of a canal could not be anything but level, because a water surface is always level. The slope towards the desert is not so regular but is of the order of 8 inches to the mile. It arises because the fertile land of Egypt has been brought down as mud from Ethiopia by the river, and when in former times the uncontrolled muddy water flooded the land, at first more mud tended to be dropped near the river bank and so a slope of the land was created. Afterwards the slope reached a state of equilibrium since the rise of the river bank increased the velocity of the water just beyond it and so less mud was dropped near the bank and more farther away. It is estimated that the bed of the river and the land of Egypt have been rising at a rate of 3 or 4 feet in a thousand years.

The rainfall is negligible except on the coast where it amounts to about 6 inches in the year, most of which falls in the winter, so that cultivation depends entirely on irrigation. Before giving some account of irrigation as it is to-day it will be interesting to try to see what the country was like before and how irrigation developed. For this we have to go a long way back, to Palæo-lithic or Old Stone Age times, and make use of the evidence from geology and the distribution of stone implements. This evidence is not very complete and conclusions are liable to be altered as fresh finds are made. Moreover, authorities are not in entire agreement on such matters as ancient climate or the interpretation of the geological evidence as to the history of the Nile, but in any case we can say what seems probable about these distant events without claiming anything approaching certainty.

As one flies from Cairo southwards the architecture of the desert below appears with the clearness of a relief model. The big wadis of the Eastern Desert with their tributaries all sharply cut are evidence of erosion by torrents. (See Plate I.) On the western side of the Nile, however, there is not this sharp relief, nor is there any sign of large drainage systems leading to the Nile. The country as a rule is more rounded and the topography shows evidence of having been shaped by the wind, which has removed the traces of former water action. Most of the carving of the Eastern Desert was finished more than half a million years ago and in the next period of geological history, the Pleistocene, which corresponds with the Ice Age of Europe and North America, rainfall declined. Sometime about the middle of this period the first traces of man appear in Egypt as indicated by the flint implements brought to sharp edges by hammering with other stones. These primitive tools are widely scattered over the deserts where people could not now exist, and afford evidence of a wetter climate over the Egyptian corner of Africa. The early people must have been hunters living on the many varieties of game which roamed the wide areas which are now desert, and using their sharpened stones for breaking up the kill. Since those times the climate has become drier, and desert conditions must have prevailed, at any rate in the Western Desert, for a very long time, during which the depressions forming the oases have been scooped out by the wind. There have, however, been occasional periods of more rain when men and animals roamed the plains before they were finally forced to concentrate in such favoured spots as the Nile Valley or the oases in the Western Desert. In the Eastern Desert life is still possible for a small number of nomads, where the wadis concentrate the effects of the rare falls of rain and enable scanty vegetation to persist and afford grazing for their camels and goats. But in years when no rain falls they are driven to the Nile Valley. There is evidence that people inhabited the Western Desert along the southern border of Egypt until predynastic times perhaps 6,000 years ago. In the days of heavier rainfall where the deserts were inhabited, the water table would be much nearer the surface than it is now, and with the cessation of rainfall it would tend to sink, at first by evaporation from the surface. This, however, would slow down and ultimately the only losses would be by percolation into the Nile Valley or the sea, or in the few depressions where the subterranean water is close to the surface and is drawn upon for irrigation.

When the rainy period ceased and the water table began to sink, life would still be possible in many depressions in Southern Egypt where the water table was at ground level. With the

D 2

concentration of the population in the Nile Valley a more settled kind of life would begin, though at first hunting would still be a principal occupation. Game would only disappear with the existence of a considerable population, for conditions at first would be very like those in the dry season in the Central Sudan, where the game comes down to drink at the river in the early morning or evening and then retires inland. In Egypt the fringes of the valley were swampy and would afford grazing for the game until the human population with its domestic animals got too numerous. This lasted through predynastic times (about 4500 B.C. to 3400 B.C.) and into times whose history is known. Hunting scenes on the walls of tombs of important men depict the lion, leopard, wild ox, giraffe, ostrich and several kinds of antelope, while plants and trees are shown which no longer grow in Egypt. To find these animals and plants now one must go as far south as the Central Sudan.

It is now necessary to go back a little in time. During the period when the Wadis were being eroded, quantities of sand and gravel were carried by a river of steeper slope than the present Nile and were deposited at its mouth to form a delta. In later times, perhaps 10,000 years ago in what is called the recent geological period, the mud began to be deposited which forms the present cultivable land of Egypt, and which is still extending seaward. This fine material has been washed down off the plateau of Ethiopia by the rains which produce the Nile flood, but formerly a steeper and more rapid stream carried it further out to sea.

It seems reasonable to suppose that since the beginning of the present soil formation of Egypt the Nile rose in flood and fell again every year much as it does now. This only involves the assumption that the major circulation of the atmosphere was similar to what it is now, and consequently that the belt of tropical rains, then as now, moved northwards annually with the sun as far as the Ethiopian plateau and then back. In predynastic times, say 5000 B.C., we can imagine the Nile rising and falling with sometimes a larger and sometimes a smaller flow, unaffected by the handiwork of men. It would wind about in its valley slowly changing its course, and since there was nothing to restrain it, in every year except those of very low flood it would overflow its banks, flooding the valley to the desert edge on either side. When it fell after the flood some of the water would make its way back to the river and some would remain in the depressions along the desert edge. This is very similar to the present behaviour of the Blue Nile in the Sudan north of Roseires, where the river overflows into flats called mayas, from which some water returns later to the river, but some remains in the lower parts of the flats for months afterwards, providing drinking places for the game. All along the desert edges in Upper Egypt there would be pools in which swamp vegetation, papyrus, reeds and other aquatic plants would flourish just as they do on the Nile in the Central and Southern Sudan. There would also be lakes due to the meandering of the river. Such swampy pools full of water-birds are shown in the pictures of wild-fowling in some of the tombs of dynastic times (after 3400 B.C.). The higher land from which the water had drained would probably be quickly covered by grass and small herbs, providing grazing for game and for the animals which the inhabitants managed to domesticate, as for example the ass and the ox. The people were probably hunters and herdsmen living on the desert edge in flood time and moving on to the flood plain when it dried and became green.

The same would apply to the Delta, but in early times the river had several branches instead of the two existing to-day and there were no doubt cross channels as well and lakes left by the river cutting across bends, so that much of the Delta must have been washed over by the flood nearly every year leaving a large amount of swamp. Consequently it could not have been inhabited to the same extent in early times as Upper Egypt, where the desert above water level was inhabitable during the flood.

Judging by the pictures in the tombs the game must have survived into dynastic times, but possibly only in favoured spots where there was access to water. Some game animals, the ibex, wild sheep, gazelle, still survive in the Eastern Desert, and the oryx and addax have only disappeared from Egypt in recent times and are still found in the deserts of the Northern Sudan.

At some stage in these primitive times people began to cultivate the wild grasses whose seeds they gathered, and the edible roots which they dug, and they would plant these in the wet ground left after the flood had subsided, where they would germinate and mature on the water left in the soil. Here at some remote time, whose date cannot be estimated, was the first irrigation by the annual rise of the Nile, coincident with the beginnings of agriculture. In the depressions, which would be filled by the flood, water would remain for months after the land had drained. When the normal flood crop was harvested another crop might be obtained in some places by using water from depressions. At first the water would be carried in pots or skins, then primitive lifting appliances would be devised to pour water into little channels to conduct it on to the fields, and so began the germs of perennial irrigation. In the beginning the annual inundation was uncontrolled and the water flowed on and off the land as the river willed. Under these conditions in low years the higher parts of the land would not be flooded, and in years when flood levels only lasted a short time the water would not remain on the land long enough to produce the desired effect of wetting it thoroughly, so gradually attempts were made to improve matters by some control measures. It was not possible to make much improvement in a time of low flood until modern times, but some control of the water must have taken place in very early times.

2. BASIN IRRIGATION

The basin system of irrigation was used throughout Egypt until towards the middle of the nineteenth century and is still carried on in Upper Egypt on about 1,000,000 acres. In this system the land is divided into basins of from 1,000 to 40,000 feddans (acres) by the construction of a longitudinal bank, as near the river as it can safely be placed, and cross-banks between this bank and the edge of the desert. When the Nile rises, water is let into these compartments through short canals with regulating sluices, flooding the land to a depth on the average of from 1 to 2 metres. The water is held there for from forty to sixty days and after the river has fallen sufficiently is drained back again. During this time it drops its silt and this process, repeated for thousands of years, has formed basins of which the surface is so perfectly graded by the deposition of the silt that it drains completely leaving no pools behind. In the basin area the villages are on mounds above flood level and become islands when the basins are flooded, so that in many cases a village can only be reached in a boat.

The beginnings of flood control leading to the system of Basin Irrigation, which was the only system until the nineteenth century, perhaps began in some of those places where a narrow tongue of Nile alluvium projects into the higher desert land. It would be easy to put a bank across the mouth of this, leaving a narrow passage by which the flood water could enter. When the maximum level was reached and the water began to fall the gap would be closed with earth and stones. The water could thus be held on the land for a sufficient period, after which it could be run into some near-by depression to be kept for later use by others. A village might undertake a work of this size, but its extension to large basins between the river bank and the desert, like those of to-day, could only be undertaken by an organized government, which however existed from very early times in Egypt.

Tradition has it that Menes (c. 3400 B.C.), the first King of Egypt, was the first to build banks to control the Nile. This would be a colossal undertaking and it seems likely that control would be gradual, arising from beginnings in places where the topography was favourable. Moreover the state of civilization at the end of the predynastic period would seem to indicate that people had already settled in villages for a long time preceding. Such villages would at first be on the desert edge, as they could only exist on the flood plain of the Nile if they were protected against the annual inundation by being embanked, and it may well be that attempts to control the river by embanking developed along with the embanking of villages. I would hazard the suggestion that the first attempts might have been made on the eastern bank where the close approach of the desert hills to the river in many places offers favourable conditions. The success of banking off some narrow tongues as already suggested, might lead some energetic and powerful personage to embank a small bay in the hills, where at both ends the high land came close to the river. This would be done by making a bank alongside the river channel from headland to headland leaving a gap by which the water could enter. When enough water had entered, as before, the gap would be closed and the water retained as long as was necessary, after which an opening would be made back to the river. The attempt to deal in this way with less favourable spots, where the headlands were further from the river, would lead to the construction of cross banks as well as the longitudinal bank along the river. In some such way as this one can imagine the beginnings of the basins of to-day.

The building of villages on mounds must be of great antiquity, since only by this means could the villagers live near the land which they cultivated. Away in the north of the Delta, where thirty years ago a lot of the land was marsh in winter time, the remains of old village sites deserted long ago can be seen from a distance in the clear air. These are called " Kom " meaning a hill, and are used by the fellahin as a source of manure, since their soil, formed partly by the disintegration of the houses, and lived on for hundreds, if not thousands of years, is impregnated with nitrates.

In the early years of the twentieth century when I arrived in Egypt, the country west of Cairo was basin land from the Upper Egypt railway line to the desert, and each year from September to November became a lake with villages and palm trees rising out of the water. In the bright sunlight and the temperate weather of autumn in Egypt this was a wonderful sight with the desert hills and the Pyramids in the background.

The basins are usually in chains of four or five which are filled from a short canal, and the whole programme is carefully organized and run to a time-table beginning with the southern basins. In former times the canal inlets were blocked with earth and stones when the required level in the basins was reached, but now each inlet has its masonry regulator by which inflow can be controlled and a sound system has replaced haphazard operations. After standing for the required time, the escape is opened and the water is drained back to the river. In a low year when it has not been possible to reach the proper level a chain of basins is topped up by escaping the water from the upstream set into it instead of allowing it to flow back direct into the river. An interesting phenomenon takes place in very large basins, where if the basin were filled to the height required to cover all the land, owing to the slope of the land there would be a considerable difference of level between the water at the downstream end of the basin and that at the upstream end of the next basin below. This would need a high thick bank to withstand the head, and so to reduce this and at the same time cover the higher land a novel procedure is adopted. When the time arrives for emptying the basin the level at the upper end is quickly raised and lowered again, and after a suitable interval, found by experience, emptying is begun at the bottom end. The result of this is that a wave travels down the basin covering the high land at the upper end and yet not exceeding the proper limit at the lower end.

This short description gives some idea of the complicated arrangements required to carry out basin irrigation satisfactorily, and these have become more difficult in recent times owing to the existence in the basins of little islands of cotton, irrigated in the low season by pumping from wells, the picking of which delays the normal dates for filling the basins. As soon as the water has been escaped off the land the various crops are sown by scattering the seed broadcast in October and November. Since no further watering will take place there is no need to arrange the land in compartments or to provide ditches.

Certain portions in the basin area are at too high a level to be covered with the rest of the land. On these, flood crops, mainly millet, are sown in August and watered by lift from the flood canals. The principal winter crops grown on basin land are wheat, beans, berseem or Egyptian clover, lentils, barley, fenugreek (Arabic *helba*) and chick peas. These crops mature and are harvested in March or April, after which the land lies fallow until the height of the next flood.

The old arrangements of basin irrigation are changing owing to the great increase of summer cultivation from wells by means of pumps, which practically amounts to perennial irrigation. In Assiut province 70 per cent. and in Girga 50 per cent. of the basin area is now cultivated in this way, the principal crop being cotton. The cotton crop is picked in August and September and this delays the filling of the basins. Whereas in the old system forty days were taken for filling, and there was then a delay of twenty

days before emptying began, which took another twenty days
to complete, where cotton is grown the whole process will now
be completed in thirty days. It is claimed that under the new
conditions the pure basin land is not saturated and the cereal
crops are not so good as formerly.

The growth of crops from watering from wells must have

FIG. 2. Shadoof.

been one of the early developments which led to perennial irrigation on a large scale. It is probable, as was said previously,
that the earliest beginnings would be prompted by the use of
the water which remained in depressions after the flood had
drained off the land. The first crude methods would presently
lead to simple mechanical contrivances for raising the water.

Of these appliances the shadoof is probably the earliest and is pictured on the walls of a tomb in Thebes, dating from about 1250 B.C.

The shadoof consists of a long arm pivoted between two posts, the longer portion of which carries a bucket hanging by a long stick or a rope, and the shorter a weight made of a stone or a ball of mud. (See Fig. 2.) The worker pulls the bucket down until it dips into the water, and then assisted by the counter-weight lifts up the full bucket and pours its contents into the

Fig. 3. Archimedean screw.

irrigation ditch. He will take a lot of trouble to get his counter-weight exactly right and will add or take away dabs of mud until he is satisfied. Sometimes two or even three shadoofs are arranged one above another when the water is a long way below the surface of the ground. When there is only a single lift a shadoof worker can irrigate about a quarter of an acre a day, but it is hard monotonous work in the hot sun of summer. The Egyptian peasant, however, does not mind hard monotonous work and can often be heard singing, or when several are at work together they encourage each other with a chant in which the leader sings a few words and the remainder answer, and this is repeated over and over again.

43

Other common lifting appliances are the Archimedean screw and the saqia, both of which are much later than the shadoof and were introduced by the Greeks. The Archimedean screw (see Fig. 3) is a wooden cylinder with a helix inside and an axis at both ends, of which the upper axis is prolonged by a crank. This contrivance is mounted on two posts at an angle of about 30 degrees to the horizontal with its bottom end dipping into a shallow watercourse. One or two men, usually sitting with their legs in the water, turn the crank and the water is lifted on

FIG. 4. Saqia.

to the field. The screw is only used for small lifts and two men working in relays can water three-quarters of an acre a day. The practice of spending hours in the water is not good in a country where bilharzia is common. The saqia has two forms, of which the earliest is a vertical wheel carrying a number of pots on its rim which dip into the water as the wheel turns and empty themselves into a trough leading to a field channel as the pots reach the top of the wheel (see Fig. 4). The wheel has another parallel wheel on its axis, which carries wooden cogs on its rim. Into these mesh the cogs of a horizontal wheel, and this wheel is turned by a cow or buffalo or camel attached to it by a shaft.

The animal walks round and round the axis of the wheel turning it as it goes. Sometimes it seems to be unattended, but often a small boy or girl is in charge and rides on the shaft. Where the water is too far below the axis of the wheel the pots are hung on an endless rope which passes over the vertical wheel. Another pattern used when the lift is small and known as a " Tambusha " consists of a wheel with compartments round its rim instead of pots, which fill when they are at the bottom and empty when they reach the top of the wheel. Wheels of this kind are sometimes turned by an engine. The area which can be watered by a saqia depends of course on the depth to the water and varies from one to five acres per day with a single animal. In some parts of Egypt saqias work with relays of animals and the drone of the wooden gears going on continuously is a pleasant sleepy sound. Sometimes where there is a big lift from the river surface to land level two saqias may work in conjunction, one above the other. With the larger land-owners pumps have superseded these ancient lifting machines, and the usual installation consists of an engine and a pump drawing from a pipe of 6 to 10 inches diameter, or several pipes, sunk to a depth of from 60 to 180 feet. The crops grown by lift irrigation in the basins are cotton and cereals.

Irrigation from wells has always been looked upon as a useful addition, but not as a substitute for irrigation from the river. It is not always possible, as in the northern Delta, and along the west coast where water from any depth is saline and useless for irrigation. The continued use of a water containing much dissolved salts, unless there is good drainage and the land is occasionally washed, will result in the accumulation of salts in the ground so that ultimately crops will not grow. In Upper Egypt the subsoil water is usually good, but it must not be forgotten that it comes from the Nile, and is not a supply in addition to what comes into Egypt by the river. Pumped water has one important advantage, and that is that it is not usually wasted by giving more than is needed by the crops.

With the basin system of irrigation there is little risk of the land deteriorating since it is washed each year, receives a thin layer perhaps a millimetre thick of fresh soil, and remains fallow for half the year during which it cracks deeply and gets thoroughly

45

aerated. It is a strong belief amongst cultivators that the silt itself has considerable fertilizing value, but it is hard to separate the effect of the silt from the other effects of the basin system of irrigation, and it is a subject about which there has been much controversy. There is no doubt, however, that the system as a whole is very effective, since it has continued to produce crops on the same land for thousands of years.

3. PERENNIAL IRRIGATION. HISTORICAL

Four-fifths of Egypt is now converted to perennial irrigation and this is distinguished from irrigation by flooding by the fact that much smaller quantities of water are run on to the land at regular intervals of two or three weeks throughout the year. This must have been practised in very early times by lifting appliances working from pools, wells, or from the river, but only began to develop on a large scale by canals in the time of Mohammed Ali Pasha, Viceroy of Egypt. Linant de Bellefonds Pasha, a Belgian engineer who was Minister of Public Works in those days and was responsible for some of the schemes, has left an account of irrigation in Egypt as it was in the early part of the nineteenth century, from which much of interest about the country can be gathered.

Before this time each village managed its own irrigation and dug canals and made banks for the watering of its own land, regardless of the welfare of its neighbours. The result was that there were continual disputes which led to fights and even to pitched battles between different districts about questions of watering their lands. Quarrels still take place about water, but they are much smaller affairs and usually occur between neighbours who draw from the same field ditch.

Mohammed Ali Pasha began in 1816 to improve river banks and dig large canals in order to control the river and enable some irrigation to take place at the low stage for the cultivation in a large way of the cotton plant, introduced by Jumel and Maho. Linant's map of a little later date is interesting as showing the waterways before they were much affected by the attempt to improve them. It shows a network of canals none of them straight, in which in many cases it is impossible to guess which way the water flowed. Nearly all of these were no doubt natural

46

canals, possibly improved by clearance of the silt which would be bound to deposit in them, as it still does in many canals to-day. To be able to irrigate in the summer it was necessary to dig canals which were deep enough at their heads to take in water from the low river. They ran away northwards at a lesser slope than the land, so that as they went further and further from the river the water was nearer and nearer to land level, which it presently reached. When this occurred or rather when the water was a little higher than the land, it was possible to irrigate, as it could be made to flow on to the land under the action of gravity. The large amount of earth dug out in making the channel was piled up to form high banks, and so in its lower part the canal could flow above land level. A great part of the length of these seifi (summer) canals as they were called would be taken in bringing the water to where it could begin to irrigate. The irrigated areas therefore were right away in the north towards the marshes fringing the lakes Mariut, Borollos and Menzala. One canal which may be mentioned had its offtake from the Nile in Cairo where the new British Cathedral now stands. This offtake and the part of the canal in the city was filled up many years ago before I arrived in Egypt, and the present High Courts were built partly on the site of this old canal. The lack of homogeneity between the undisturbed ground and that which had been filled in led to unequal settlement of the building and cracks appeared in its walls causing perturbation in responsible circles. However, after a time the movement ceased and its effects were repaired. When the Cathedral was designed, mindful of the experience of the High Courts, the building was set back a little from the river so as to avoid the channel of the old canal, and a very solid concrete raft was laid down to form the foundations. This was quite successful and the heavy building has only sunk a normal amount, and that evenly, so all has gone as was expected.

The old canal, following the course of a still older canal not far from the eastern edge of the Delta, ultimately arrived at the Wadi Tumilat, the narrow strip of cultivation shut in by desert to north and south, which runs from the Delta to the Suez Canal. This strip of Nile alluvium was no doubt deposited when the wadi formed an escape for some of the flood water from the Nile. It has had its ups and downs as is shown by the traces of old canals which were visible a century ago, but which have to a considerable extent been obliterated by the digging of the present Ismailia Canal, at the time when the Suez Canal was made. There are several records of the existence of a previous canal from the Nile to the Red Sea, but apparently its existence was not continuous and it probably got filled with sand between Kassassin and the Bitter Lake. The canal from the Nile to the Red Sea must have existed when Queen Hatshepsut's expedition to Punt sailed along it some 3,400 years ago. Another canal which joined the old Pelusiac branch of the Nile to the Red Sea was begun by Necho about 600 B.C. and completed by Ptolemy II somewhere about 250 B.C. This canal according to Linant had the effect of joining Lake Menzala, and consequently the Mediterranean, to the Red Sea, but the statements of ancient writers on which he bases himself are naturally obscure.

From this it is easy to see how the idea of a canal joining the Mediterranean to the Red Sea arose from time to time through the Middle Ages, and became more definite in the time of Napoleon Bonaparte's expedition to Egypt, leading to the survey of the Isthmus. Owing, however, to a mistake in the levelling, the Red Sea was thought to be at a considerably higher level than the Mediterranean, though it is actually at about the same level, so the idea of a canal was given up. Later the error of the levelling was demonstrated by Linant and other engineers. Ferdinand de Lesseps, who was not an engineer but a diplomat later laid a plan for a canal before the Viceroy, Said Pasha, who determined to carry it out. The Suez Canal, which is 100 miles long, was finished in 1869, and the present Ismailia Canal which followed somewhat the line of previous canals from Cairo to Suez, and brought fresh water from the Nile, was finished a few years earlier.

Judging by the dense clay soil of the lowest part of the Wadi Tumilat on the south side, this was at one time a marsh with no exit or drainage. In modern times it has resisted attempts to reclaim it, and part of it to the south of the village of Tel-el-Kebir has for more than twenty-five years produced some of the best duck-shooting in Egypt. This has been enjoyed by many residents and also by British officers serving in Egypt. The shoot was for many years managed by some friends and myself, and when it was finally taken over by His Majesty King Farouk, he very graciously invited all the old members to continue to shoot at Tel-el-Kebir as his guests, and some of us are still enjoying this hospitality. The Wadi Tumilat and the Delta near its entrance are the old land of Goshen, given by Pharaoh to Jacob and his descendants, from which later the Exodus took place. Much time and scholarship have been spent in trying to trace the route of the Exodus and various theories have been put forward. It seems likely that the sea which was crossed was one of the salt lakes, Timsah, or the Bitter Lakes, which had been piled up by a strong wind exposing the bed of the lake, over which the Hebrews crossed. The subject is interesting, but as Lucas says,[1] only a few of the halting places of the Israelites can ever be identified, since they were not places of any size with buildings which might be discovered by digging, and so we leave it to the scholars who have studied the question.

Previous to the digging of the Suez Canal the Bitter Lakes were a salt marsh of a treacherous nature which was liable to engulf anything which ventured on it. Linant mentions that one of his camels, which was tempted to walk across this white crust by the sight of herbage in the distance, disappeared as if ice had suddenly broken beneath its feet, but this is perhaps an exaggeration.

After this digression we return to irrigation. The perennial system could not expand very far with the long canals gaining slowly in level on the land, which have already been described. One of the difficulties with these canals was the great amount of labour required to clear them of the silt deposited in flood, so that their beds would be low enough to admit water at the low time of the year. This was done by forced unpaid labour, the Corvee, which had probably existed from the time of the Pyramids, but inflicted great hardship on the population. A labourer had to give sixty days' work at a place distant from his village, without counting the time of getting to and from the work. Very often this meant the movement of his whole family with him. During the time of the projects of Mohammed Ali Pasha it was estimated that at least 400,000 labourers were

[1] *The Route of the Exodus.* A. Lucas. Published by Ed. Arnold, London.

continuously employed and twice as many members of their families were required to feed them and keep them at work. In the early days of these projects there was no organization for their design and study as a whole, and the governor of a province, pushed by the sheikhs of a number of villages, would apply to the Viceroy for a canal, explaining its need and value. With no proper study and co-ordination many projects turned out to be useless. The Mahmoudieh Canal from the Rosetta Branch of the river to Alexandria which employed a force of 320,000 men, was dug without any survey or levelling of the line. Each sheikh brought his gang of men, and each was given a section of the canal, in which they dug more or less in the required direction, with the result that the sections did not always meet and had to be joined up by bends. The corvee inflicted hardships and disturbed the life of the population, but the work done, unlike that of building the pyramids, was for the general good of the country. The use of the corvee of unpaid labour was given up in favour of a voluntary system of paid labourers in about 1890. In the case of a high flood and consequent danger of a breach in the Nile bank people are still compelled to serve as watchmen until the danger is over, but they are paid, though their labour is not given very willingly.

The great burden on the country imposed by the attempts at perennial irrigation with an inadequate system led Linant to propose the building of a barrage at the head of the Delta, and this was accepted by the Viceroy, who suggested the use of the stone in the Pyramids. The demolition of the Pyramids was repugnant to Linant who managed to show that this would be a more expensive way of obtaining stone than by quarrying. However, interest in the project lapsed until a new scheme for a barrage was proposed to the Viceroy by M. Mougel, who had come out to construct a dock at Alexandria. This scheme was accepted in 1843 and work began under Mougel.

It will be convenient at this point to describe a barrage, which is a species of dam built across the river in order to be able to raise the level upstream so that when the river is low, water can still flow into canals dug to a reasonable depth. A barrage differs from a dam since its function is not to form a storage reservoir, but merely to raise the level of the river behind it so as to divert some of the water into the canals whose entrances are above the barrage. It must be capable of allowing most of the discharge of the river in flood to pass through it, and consists of a broad platform of masonry or concrete stretching across the river with its upper surface at approximately the level of the river

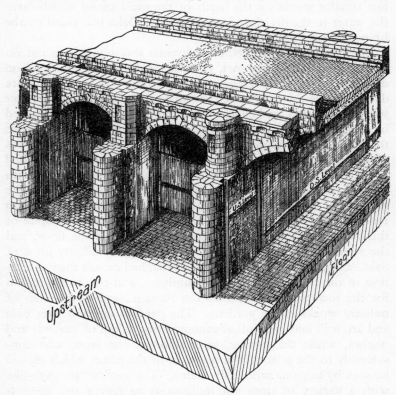

FIG. 5. Muhammad Ali Barrage.

bed (see Fig. 5, p. 51). On the platform stands a heavy masonry bridge with arched openings several yards wide between its solid piers. These openings can be closed by iron sluice gates which slide up and down in grooves, and which are raised or lowered by a travelling crane so as to keep the river upstream at the required level to fill the canals. Water can flow between or beneath the two regulating gates under the head of water

E 2

above. Plate II shows the new Edfina Barrage near the mouth of the Rosetta Branch, the latest work on the Nile. The original Delta Barrage and the new Muhammad Ali Barrage are built just below where the river divides into its two branches, and each consist of barrages across the river branches, with three similar but smaller works on the heads of the main canals which carry the water to the divisions into which the Delta is divided by the branches (see Fig. 6, p. 55).

The barrage on the Damietta branch was built first, and no special difficulties were met, as most of the work was done on dry ground. The barrage on the Rosetta branch was more difficult since the lime concrete had to be laid in running water so that much was washed away, and the difficulties were increased by the impatience of the Viceroy to get the work finished, with the result that the foundation was not good. While the work was going on Mohammed Ali Pasha died in 1848 and was succeeded by Abbas Pasha. Five years later Abbas, being dissatisfied with the progress of the work, dismissed Mougel and handed the work over to Mazhar Bey. At the same time a commission reported that the concrete floor was in a bad state. In spite of this, work was continued without making good the floor, and the whole work was completed by 1861. The military ideas of Said Pasha, who succeeded Abbas Pasha, had caused the fortification of the Barrage and its surroundings, and this is the reason for the towers and turrets on the Barrage, and other relics of military works in the gardens. The gardens are of a later date and are well laid out, full advantage being taken of mounds and ditches, while the towers, seen amongst the trees, add considerably to the attractive appearance of the place, which should be seen by any one who visits Cairo. The gardens are park-like with a variety of trees not indigenous to Egypt and there is usually a fine show of flowers.

The original object of the barrage was to raise the head of the water upstream in the summer by $3\frac{1}{2}$ metres, but when in 1863 the head was raised by from 1 to $1\frac{1}{2}$ metres, cracks appeared in the Rosetta Barrage, and a few years later part of it moved some inches downstream. The structure was described in one of the many reports written about it as a very sick man, but in spite of reports by a number of eminent engineers on the means to cure its defects, nothing was done until Sir Colin Scott-Moncrieff was put in charge of Irrigation and Public Works in 1883. An investigation was then made and it was decided to carry on perennial irrigation on the lines accepted by Mohammed Ali, with a Barrage and regulators on the canals, instead of pumping, which had been proposed as an alternative. It was also decided to repair the Barrage, and this was ultimately effected by thickening and lengthening the floor. It was not until 1890 that the repairs were finished and the Barrage was reported capable of holding a head of 4 metres (13 feet) of water. It was a fine piece of work, in which unexpected difficulties were continually being met and overcome by the skill and energy of those British engineers who had been brought by Scott-Moncrieff from India. It was the first and greatest step in the conversion of Lower Egypt to perennial irrigation.

The Barrage still needed careful attention and various measures were taken to improve it, but it could never be used without certain restrictions on the allowable head. As cultivation extended these were inconvenient and ultimately new Barrages were built across the river branches a short distance downstream of the old Barrage the work being very fortunately completed in 1939 before the war made the execution of large works impossible. The consulting engineers were Messrs. Coode, Wilson, Mitchell and Vaughan-Lee and the contractors Messrs. Mac-Donald, Gibbs & Co., while the resident engineer was Mohammed Kamel Nabeeh Bey (now Pasha), who on becoming Under-Secretary of State was succeeded by Mohammed Cararah Bey. The original Barrage having done useful work for fifty years still remains as a road bridge and a pleasing piece of architecture.

It is said that Napoleon when in Egypt foresaw the construction of a barrage at the head of the Delta, to control the division of water between the two river branches, so that either could at will be made high by turning all the water into it. However, much more than this is now done, since for half the year all the water is turned into canals, and no water flows into either branch.

Previous to the arrival of the British engineers in 1884, a commencement had been made on the improvement of the network of canals in the Delta, and during the time of Ismail

Pasha the Ibrahimia canal had been dug to water Middle Egypt. A great impetus was given to the cultivation of cotton by the American Civil War, when high prices were obtained for Egyptian cotton, the effect of which is shown by the increase of the crops between 1860 and 1864 from 600,000 to 2,000,000 kantars.[1] All this cultivation was watered by the natural supply of the river, which falls to its lowest in the middle of the season of cotton cultivation. From 1884 the improvement of the irrigation system was pushed forward vigorously and a study of measures for the increase of perennial irrigation was carried out by Sir W. Willcocks. The most important of his proposals was the construction of a dam at the Aswan Cataract, and this was later built on the designs of Sir Benjamin Baker, the consulting engineer for this work and for the Forth Bridge. The dam was a remarkable work and in 1902, when it was finished, was one of the great engineering works of the world. It enabled some of the water in the time of plenty to be stored and used later when the supply was low. After this the work of converting the basins to perennial irrigation went ahead and more barrages were built and canals were dug. At the same time the salt and marshy lands of the northern Delta began to be drained and made fit for cultivation, but even at the end of the nineteenth century the country towards the lakes was sparsely inhabited and parts were only accessible on foot or on a donkey. Until fifteen years or so ago there was magnificent snipe shooting in winter in these marsh lands, but drainage and reclamation have obliterated many of their haunts. It is good for an irrigation man to be a keen shot because he becomes interested in many places which need his attention, but it is his unfortunate duty to destroy those very spots where he can best enjoy his sport.

4. WORKING OF PERENNIAL IRRIGATION

By the beginning of the twentieth century the canal system had been remodelled and in its main features was as it is to-day, with three large canals beginning at the Delta Barrage and feeding the western, central and eastern divisions of the Delta, while the Ibrahimia Canal taking off the Nile behind the new barrage at Assiut feeds Middle Egypt. The lay-out of the canals is shown

---

[1] A kantar is approximately 99 lb.

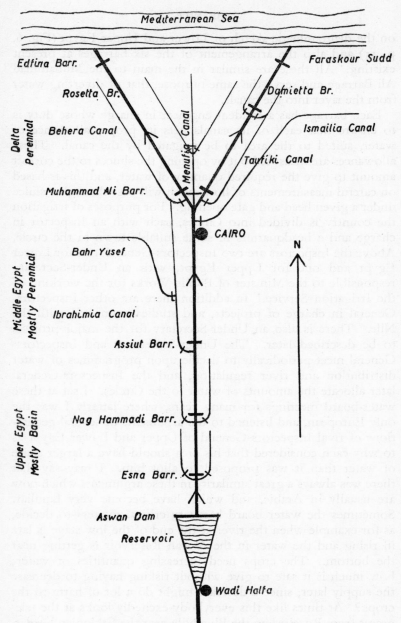

FIG. 6. Diagram of the irrigation system.

on the diagrammatic sketch of Lower and Upper Egypt (Fig. 6, p. 55) and also the arrangement of the six barrages at present existing. All these are similar in the main to the Muhammad Ali Barrage and serve the same purpose, that of diverting water from the river into the canals.

Each barrage has a resident engineer in charge whose duty is to ensure that each of its canals gets its proper allowance of water, suited to the area to be irrigated by the canal. These allowances are measured out by opening the sluices to the correct amount to give the required quantity of water, and this is based on careful measurements of how much will pass through a sluice under a given head and gate opening. For purposes of irrigation the country is divided into Circles, each with an Inspector in charge and a headquarters in some suitable town in the circle. Above the Inspectors are two Inspectors-General, one for Lower Egypt and one for Upper Egypt, with an Under-Secretary responsible to the Minister of Public Works for the working of the Irrigation Service. In addition there are other Inspectors-General in charge of projects, and studies connected with the Nile. There is also an Under-Secretary for the major projects to be described later. The Under-Secretaries and Inspectors-General meet periodically to decide upon programmes of water distribution and river regulation, and the Inspectors-General later allocate the amounts of water to the Circles. I sat at these water-board meetings for many years, where latterly I was the only European, and listened to the arguments of several generations of rival Inspectors-General of Upper and Lower Egypt as to why each considered that his area should have a larger share of water than it was proposed to allot him. I may say that there was always a great similarity in these arguments which now are usually in Arabic, and which have become very familiar. Sometimes the water board has very critical matters to decide, as for example when the river at the end of the low stage is late in rising and the water in the Aswan Reservoir is getting near the bottom. The crops need increasing quantities of water; how much is it safe to give without risking having to decrease the supply later, since a decrease might do a lot of harm to the crops? At times like this everybody excitedly looks at the telegrams from Roseires on the Blue Nile near the Ethiopian border,

III.   A LARGE CANAL IN THE CENTRE OF THE DELTA.   THE BAHR SHIBIN WITH
SAQIAS ON THE LEFT

IV.   HOEING YOUNG COTTON PLANTS IN THE DELTA

and from Khashm el Girba on the Atbara. At both of these places the river can rise and fall very quickly and irrigation officials anxiously look for a rise, and when it comes hope that it will be maintained. In the early days soon after the re-occupation of the Sudan, when Khashm el Girba was right in the wilds, one morning the telegram giving the state of the river had a note at the bottom saying " Office surrounded by lions and tigers. Send help." Some official telegraphed back " There are no tigers in the Sudan," which did not shake the telegraphist, who merely replied " Delete tigers." The main canals have regulators at intervals depending on their slopes and the positions of the branch canals. A regulator is similar to a barrage, but as the canals are much narrower than the river it has fewer openings. Its object is the same, namely to hold up the level of the main canal so that water can enter the branch canals at a suitable level to enable them to distribute it. Sometimes as many as four branch canals take off the main canal above the same regulator. Branch canals do not irrigate directly the land alongside them, but deliver water to smaller canals known as distributaries, which in turn deliver it to permanent irrigation ditches, known in Arabic as " misqa." Where a branch canal takes off the main canal there is a masonry or brickwork regulator with sluices like the regulator on the main canal, and similarly on the distributaries. On all these canals head-regulators by their sluices control the amount of water going down them. A distributary waters from 1,000 to 10,000 feddans (acres), and for the country as a whole a misqa waters on the average 25 or 30 feddans. A misqa is supplied by a pipe through the bank of the distributary and may serve many holdings. The pipe may be closed by an iron door or merely by a lump of clay, and its size depends on the area to be served, thus a 30-feddan misqa would require a 6 inch pipe. In the old-established perennial area of the Delta there are big misqas up to a mile long serving hundreds of feddans and scores of peasants, who share in its water and the cost of its maintenance in proportions fixed by ancient custom. On one of its firm grassy banks would run the footpath which provides a right of way for men and animals passing daily from village to field and back. From the misqa water goes into the field ditches or furrows, which are temporary and are made with a plough or hoe for the purpose of one crop only, and never contain more water than one man can distribute. Some crops like cotton or sugar-cane are planted in rows with furrows between, and water is run into these from the field ditches by the simple means of cutting the bank of the ditch with a hoe and blocking the ditch below the cut with the resulting earth until the section is watered. The blockage is then removed and the cut in the bank closed so that the water can pass down the ditch to the next section. If the crop is planted on the flat, " berseem " (clover) or wheat for example, the field is divided into rectangular compartments by a network of little banks, and each of these compartments is filled to a depth of 3 or 4 inches from a field ditch. The skill with which a fellah will lay out his field ditches having regard to the small variations of level which exist, variations imperceptible to the ordinary eye, has to be seen to be believed, and yet the same man is incapable of hanging a picture level. I saw this skill for detecting small differences of level when I was engaged on an experiment on the effect of sub-soil water on the growth of cotton. The experimental field had to be divided into plots of equal size, and arrangements made for watering it and measuring the water as it went on to the plots. A headman was borrowed from a State Domains farm to supervise the agricultural operations, and I watched him lay out his ditches for watering each plot. In some cases the ditch seemed to be a little complicated in its course, and the headman explained to me that this was to arrange for the watering of some plots which were higher than others. To me the field looked as level as the floor of a room and an instrument would have been needed to detect any difference. When the first watering took place I was watching with considerable interest to see the results and there was no doubt that the headman's judgment had been right every time.

The efficiency of a canal system is measured by the area irrigated by a given quantity of water, and is expressed by a figure, generally called the Water Duty, which in Egypt represents the average number of cubic metres per day supplied for each feddan of crop grown. From the end of July, when summer fallow is planted with maize, the whole area is under crop and irrigation is at its heaviest. Fortunately this season corresponds to that of the Nile flood and the only limits of supply are the carrying capacity of canals and the danger of overcharging the drainage system with wasted water. To provide an element of elasticity the distributaries are run intermittently, high enough to command all the misqas for a period of from five to ten days according to local demand, then closed altogether for the remainder of the fifteen days supposed to elapse between waterings at this season. The periods are arranged in such a way that the draw on the main canals is nearly uniform and they run continuously at or near their full capacity. Until thirty years ago this was generally limited to 25 cubic metres per day for every feddan served, but now in most cases the water duty is 30 in Lower Egypt and 35 in Middle Egypt. This increase is due to the policy of trying to meet demands for high levels to give easy irrigation during flood, and to the great extension of the drainage system.

After October demand falls off rapidly as the weather gets cooler. Winter crops, cereals, beans, berseem, cover practically the whole area but require irrigation less frequently. During the whole month of January canals are closed for the clearance of silt from their beds, and the repair of regulators and bridges. Harvesting of various winter crops proceeds from March to June and at the same time summer crops, mainly cotton and rice, are being planted on about half the gross area, following fallow or a catch crop such as berseem, the remainder being left fallow after cereals (see Plates IV and V). At a date varying from year to year, but generally in February or March, the natural flow of the falling river drops below the total irrigation demand and has to be supplemented by the release of stored water. At the same time various restrictions on the use of water come into force.

To meet the variation from year to year in the natural summer supply as forecast in March, demand can be varied by limiting the canals from which rice may be irrigated, thus indirectly restricting the area under this crop, which takes about two and a half times as much water as an equal area of cotton. Rice grows standing in about 10 centimetres of water which must be changed at frequent intervals, so that even if only 5 per cent. of the area on a canal be planted with rice it cannot be closed for more than five days at a time and its overhead losses are continuous. The heavy irrigation of fallow land, preparatory to its cultivation under maize, is postponed until the rising flood is reported from the up river gauging stations and the date of its arrival in Egypt is known, thus fixing the period over which the remaining stored water must be spread. The standing crops have first claim on it and the balance is allotted to the flooding of fallow for the maize crop. Maize sown in early July yields a heavier crop than that sown a month later on the natural rise of the river.

Economy in the use of water is arrived at by the imposition of what are known as Summer Rotations. All the perennial canals in Egypt (except those giving water for rice) are divided into three sections, of which lists are circulated to every village. A timetable is published giving first claim on the water to each section of canals in rotation for a fixed period which is generally six days. Care is taken to equalize the area served in each section by the distributaries dependent on each major canal, so that the share of the latter may be a constant percentage of the total available supply. The main canal discharge is similarly divided between its branches in portion to the area they serve in each section. The concentration of water on one-third of the smaller canals enables them to be run high enough to command the misqa heads, while reducing loss by seepage and evaporation from the other two-thirds which are closed. Thus every cultivator should have a chance to water his crop once in eighteen days, and more frequently in dry or sandy districts, where the fixed rotation periods are shorter. The recent heightening of the Aswan Dam and the building of the Gebel Aulia Dam have increased the amount of summer water available, thus increasing the area of perennial cultivation, improving the lot of the cultivator, and lessening the difficulties of the irrigation official in its distribution.

In low years even now distribution of a short water supply is difficult, and it was more difficult in the early years of this century with only the small Aswan Reservoir. At this time one of my friends was in charge of a circle while the inspector was away ill. He had only been a few years in the country but made up by energy what he lacked in experience. Riding round his district on his horse to see that distribution of water was going properly, he came one day to a short canal which served the lands of two

villages, a large one near the head and a small one near the tail.
As he rode along this he found that the people of the first village
had cut the bank in a number of places, and had pulled out the
pipes which feed the field ditches and ensure that not more than
the proper amount of water can be taken. Irrigation was proceeding copiously and merrily through the cuts. A little lower
down at the boundary between the villages he found that the
canal was closed by a well-made bank which prevented any
water going to the lower village, and at the same time held up a
good head of water for the irrigation above. My friend called
up the Sheikhs of the lower village and told them to remove the
block, but they were afraid. So after saying what he thought of
them he returned to his headquarters and called on the Mudir
(Governor of the province), who was afterwards Prime Minister,
and explained what had happened and what he proposed to do
if the Mudir would provide some armed police. The Mudir
agreed and the sluice-gate at the head of the canal was screwed
down so that no water at all could enter. The police guard
camped at the regulator and ensured that the gate remained
closed. In a day or two the village sent a deputation to say that
the crops were suffering, and were told that the sluice would not
be opened until the block was removed, the breaches in the bank
were closed, and all pipes put back at their proper levels. Moreover the persons who had cut the bank were to be delivered up
to be prosecuted under the Canals Act. The delegates retired
to consider the proposition, and after a day or so of delay
returned to say that all had been put right and that the delin-
quents were outside. These were three or four miserable-
looking individuals who were duly sentenced to imprisonment.
They of course were not the actual instigators, who were probably the sheikhs of the village, but as the convicted persons no
doubt received considerable bribes to persuade them to come
forward, justice did eventually punish the right people and helped
the poor.

For ten years my family and I lived in the country outside
Cairo where we had about one and a half acres of garden.
Joining us were two similar houses and gardens and the holdings
of fellaheen from a neighbouring village. These were watered
from a misqa a few hundred yards long taking off the distributary

not far from its offtake on the main canal of our area. Both
the distributary and the main canal had roads on their banks,
which were the usual earth roads, kept in order by scraping to
fill up holes, and watering to consolidate them. A man has a
section and does his work with a bucket and a fass, the universal
agricultural tool of Egypt. Our distributary would run for
several days at a high enough level in our section to water all the
holdings dependent on it. On our misqa were the ditches to
our garden, to the two neighbouring ones, and to several plots
belonging to fellaheen, and our turn for water came about third.
When the people above us on the ditch had finished watering,
our gardener turned the water into a pipe which brought it into
our garden. Here there was a system of little ditches and pipes
under garden paths which allowed all the plots and the lawn to
be watered conveniently. The gardener would be busy for
some hours directing the water into the various plots, going
about with his fass cutting the banks of ditches, and stopping
pipes with earth and bits of board until the whole had its due
allowance. Then our entry pipe was shut off and water passed
on to the next garden. Occasionally the misqa had to be cleared
of grass and weeds which had grown on its sides, or of silt
which had gradually deposited. This was done as a joint affair
by the gardeners of the three houses and the fellahin. During
September the watering of roses was stopped in order to give
them a rest from flowering which had gone on practically all
the year, and during January there was no water because of the
canal closure for repairs. Occasionally our gardener com-
plained of the neighbouring gardeners or the fellahin, but the
disputes were usually easily settled.

Living in the country as we did was very interesting and
peaceful away from the noises of Cairo. On a hot day one
could always find a cool spot under a tree, and in winter it was
rare that one could not sit in the sun sheltered from the wind.
There were usually birds to be observed, and during the winter
we saw many of the common English birds, or at any rate their
cousins, while in spring and autumn interesting migrants stayed
a little in the many trees which grew in the gardens round us.
Trees are not very numerous in Egypt and the clump round us
is very conspicuous. A good many, however, have been planted

since the first war when their value as fuel was impressed on many people who previously thought they were harmful to the crops. As we were away from a village it was necessary to have a night watchman, and ours was a tall imposing figure of partly Bedawin descent. We suspected that he was the chief of the thieves of the district, and had the rest terrorized, for nothing of importance was ever stolen from us, though a saddle disappeared from the next-door house. Musa accused the servants of this but I suspected that he only did this because of some quarrel between them. He was certainly guilty of trying to cause trouble for our own servants by accusations of stealing drink from the house, in proof of which he showed me a part-filled bottle of whisky hidden in a hedge. As, however, the whisky was not any brand of which I had ever heard, and did not smell like the produce of Scotland, I knew that it had never been my property, and threatened Musa with severe treatment from the police if ever he tried any further tricks.

In Egypt there is an extensive and somewhat complicated system of artificial drainage, second only to irrigation in its importance to agriculture. Experience has proved that even the best land tends to deteriorate under perennial irrigation by free flow, unless provided with drainage ditches to carry off surplus water. Where the soil contains much salt, as in the Northern Delta, the effect of capillarity must be counteracted by the percolation of water downwards and sideways into ditches deep enough and near enough to collect it. In those districts well-farmed estates are intersected by a network of drains 25 to 55 yards apart and from 2 feet 6 to 4 feet deep, which may occupy anything up to 10 per cent. of the cultivable area. The public drains dug and maintained by Government form a network similar to that of the irrigation canal system, and are designed to provide an outfall low enough to give at least 5 feet depth of drainage in the fields of those owners who keep their collector drains sufficiently deep and clean. At the present time in some parts of the Delta the drains are being deepened to give 8 feet depth of drainage with the object of improving land which has deteriorated. The smallest branch drains generally run parallel to and midway between distributary canals. They discharge into large branches which in turn join the big main drains flowing down the shallow valleys between the ridges formed by old branches of the Nile in the Delta, on which the main irrigation canals are placed.

Experiments are being made on a large scale with pipe drainage. The pipes are about a foot long and 2 inches internal diameter and are made of porous concrete. They are laid in trenches, the joints being surrounded by broken brick, and the trenches are then filled in. Something like 18,000 acres have been drained and by the end of 1951 the area will reach 50,000 acres. The pioneer of this system in Egypt is Mr. G. H. Dempster. Its advantages over open field drains are that no land is wasted, the system maintains its efficiency with much less work, and there is less waste of water.

When the water slope of main and branch drains is allowed for it is found that very little land lying below the contour of 3·50 metres (12 feet) above sea-level can be given complete drainage by gravitation, and generally the water of a branch serving land most of which lies below this contour, is lifted into the main drain by electrically-driven pumps served by power lines stretching right across the Delta.

The level of Lake Mariut, near Alexandria, is lowered by pumps to about 10 feet below sea-level, and so allows the low-lying land surrounding the lake, of which some is below sea-level, to drain into it. Not all of this drainage has to be pumped as some disappears by evaporation. The effect of the drainage of the marshy areas in the north is very striking to one who knew the country before it was drained. Then there were large areas of grassy marsh and others covered with a bright red weed, most of which were of little use except for the grazing of cattle on the fringes, and for cover for duck and snipe. Now many of these areas are covered with flourishing crops, population has pushed out into the waste and the snipe are confined to the much smaller areas still unreclaimed.

The drainage system of Middle Egypt differs from that of the Delta in that there are many more small public drains. When the basins were converted to perennial irrigation about thirty years ago the engineers had an almost clean sheet to work on and laid out their network of alternate canals and drains only 500 yards apart, so as to render access to them easier for the small landowners. There is only one main drain, the Muhit, which is about 220 miles long from its source near Deirut to its mouth on the Rosetta Branch at Khatatba. A drop of water would, however, have small chance of making the whole journey because at six points on its course alternative outfalls to the Nile or Bahr Yusef are provided, one or other of which will be low enough to receive the water of the drain except during about two months at the end of the flood, when pumping is resorted to. The Fayum drains into Lake Karun.

It is only in the twentieth century that the importance of drainage has been fully realized in Egypt. For thousands of years the basin system of irrigation was practised, which with its annual flooding and season of fallow did not lead to deterioration of the land. Consequently it took the farmers a long time to realize that the continual watering employed in the perennial system could only go on if there was efficient drainage to allow the water to percolate through the soil, and prevent the accumulation of salt by evaporation of the water in the top layers of the soil.

The provision of water and its distribution until it arrives at the misqa is the business of the Government, which has therefore to construct and maintain in good order dams, barrages, regulators and canals, as well as to organize the programme of distribution. This work is in the hands of the Irrigation Department of the Ministry of Public Works, whose headquarters is in Cairo. Here policy is decided as to major projects and developments, the programme of water distribution in accordance with the state of the river, and the shares to be allotted to the Circles. A Circle of Irrigation is a large district under the administration of an inspector with a staff of engineers. There are four Circles in Lower Egypt and six in Middle and Upper Egypt, and each is divided into smaller districts under the charge of district engineers. There is no water rate and irrigation is paid for out of the land tax, which is levied on all cultivated land, at a rate which varies with the value of the land, and is reassessed at fairly long intervals of time.

5. THE ASWAN DAM AND WATER MEASUREMENT

A great deal has already been said about the Aswan Dam but a little more is needed to complete the description. The shape of the dam is shown in Fig. 1 (p. 29), which shows the sluice ways through the dam. These can be closed by massive iron gates weighing up to 30 tons, which slide in grooves and are drawn up into the wells shown in the sketch by means of winches. The sluices also serve the purpose of measuring the flow of the river, and this is measurement on the grand scale, instituted by Sir Murdoch MacDonald and based on the most fundamental method of measuring liquid, that of the pint pot. The pot in this case is a granite tank below the dam into which 22,000 tons of water from a sluice can be poured, and at its quickest the pot is filled in about three minutes. It is a grand and impressive experiment (see Plate VI). There are two sizes of sluice and it is a set of the smaller which can discharge into the tank. A small sluice, however, is as high as a room and wide enough to take a 6-foot-6 bedstead. The iron gate which closes it weighs 15 tons and withstands a force of 130 tons when the reservoir is full. When all is ready for the experiment the engineer in charge gives a signal, the crane operator slips in his clutch and the massive gate is rapidly lifted until the sluice is full open. A magnificent jet of 100 tons of water a second is now pouring into the tank with a roar, while the water circulates round and round the tank, forming a wide vortex. In three minutes the tank is full, and the signal to close the gate is given; the clutch is released and the gate falls of its own weight with a thud on to the sill of the sluice. All these operations are timed with a stop watch, but the 20,000 tons of water in the tank will go on revolving for an hour or two before its surface becomes flat enough to measure the quantity. The quantity and the time taken give the volume passing in a second through a single sluice, and multiplying this by the number of sluices open we get the discharge of the river. It is not quite as simple as this, however, for there are different kinds of sluice (which have been compared), and some refinements and corrections must be made before the discharge is accurately known, but this is the principle of it. The accuracy of the measurement is remarkable, and as far as I know Aswan is the only place in the world where such large volumes of water are measured directly in a measuring tank. They have been of fundamental importance in the measurement of the flow of the Nile, and in the development of the use

V. THRESHING AT THE FARM OF YUSEF SIMAIKA BEY. THE EQUIVALENT OF
TREADING OUT THE CORN

VI. ASWAN DAM. MEASUREMENT OF THE DISCHARGE OF A SLUICE WITH THE
TANK. BEFORE SECOND HEIGHTENING

of hydraulic models as instruments of research. In 1918 when the resident engineer, the late David Watt, and I began experiments with a model of an Aswan sluice, it was known that in the case of a ship a scale model could be used to predict the behaviour of the prototype and to find the resistance of the water to its motion. Osborne Reynolds also had made a model of the estuary of the Mersey to study the effect on it of tides, but the relation between the discharge through a sluice and its model had never been investigated experimentally. The accurate tank measurements provided excellent material for comparisons between prototype and model, so we made hundreds of experiments on models of different scales. In these experiments everything was to scale. The sluice was a close copy of the original, it was mounted in a wooden dam which was a copy of a portion of the actual dam, and the level of the water behind the model corresponded with the level behind the real dam. It was found that the discharge of the model was the same fraction of the prototype discharge as would have been predicted by theory— a very satisfactory result. Since then models have been used to predict the discharge through the sluices of other dams and barrages. Notable instances on the Nile are the Gebel Aulia Dam on the White Nile, the Sennar Dam on the Blue Nile, and the head regulator on the Gezira Canal, which takes off the river above the Sennar Dam. The Sudan's share of Blue Nile water goes into the Gezira Canal, while Egypt's share passes through the Sennar Dam and down the river. The measurement of these shares depends entirely on experiments made with models in Egypt. Since the original experiments of Watt and myself on models of Aswan and Sennar sluices the method has become regular practice in Egypt for use in the design of regulating works on the Nile or on canals, and a large laboratory has recently been built for this work in the gardens of the Muhammad Ali Barrage.

At the present time work has begun on a project for putting the Aswan Dam to a new use, that of producing hydro-electric power. I suppose that everyone who has stood on the dam and seen the wonderful rush of water through the sluices below and on either side of him must have thought what a lot of energy is going to waste here. Why can't it be used? The history of

F 2

projects to make use of the energy goes back to the first war, and there have been at least six schemes since that time, with a good deal of discussion and dispute as to the best kind of installation and the best way of using the power. After this lengthy period of gestation, it is good to think that labour has begun

FIG. 6a. Carrying a heavy Theodolite down the Great Pyramid.

and one may soon expect an addition to the great works for the utilization of the Nile.

Egypt is a country providing many examples of massive masonry construction and for interest we may compare the Aswan Dam with another colossal building, the Great Pyramid. The dam contains about one and a half million cubic metres of masonry and the Pyramid about two and a half million. The

Pyramid therefore surpasses the dam in volume, but not in its services to Egypt, which at any rate in modern times are limited to acting as a triangulation point and as an attraction to tourists, unless one includes the inspiration it supplies to Pyramid cranks.

In my early days in Egypt I occasionally worked on triangulation, and on one occasion had to observe from the top of the Great Pyramid on to points on the Mokattam Hills opposite, and also on to a point on the top of one of the towers of the Delta Barrage. This involved climbing the Pyramid at dawn and again in the afternoon with a heavy theodolite, so as to observe while the sun was low and there was not much shimmer or unsteadiness of the atmosphere (see Fig. 6A, p. 68). Precise survey work can only be done in countries like Egypt for two or three hours morning and evening. These ascents went on for three days and were a little toilsome, for although the large stones of which the pyramid is built form a sort of stairway, yet each of the steps is as high as a table. There is, however, plenty of room on the top. Following the pyramid I went to the barrage, where my triangulation point was on the top of a high and narrow turret. This was reached by climbing up a ladder on the outside of the turret, which had a parapet about a foot high round its top. When the theodolite was set up, its tripod filled the whole top of the turret inside the parapet, so one had to observe by standing on the parapet, with a considerable drop below one. One's attention was rather divided between trying to make good observations and not to step over the edge or accidentally disturb the legs of the tripod and so have to begin the observations again, which one felt would have been a major catastrophe.

The problems connected with forecasting, storing and distributing the Nile water have hardly been mentioned but they will be discussed at some length later in Chapter XV and following chapters.

Chapter Four

THE MAIN NILE IN THE NORTHERN SUDAN

1. GENERAL

THE Sudan is by far the largest political unit in the Nile Basin, and the most thinly populated, with an area equal to half that of Europe. It stretches from Wadi Halfa, approximately in latitude 22° N., to Nimule almost due south of Halfa in latitude 3° 40′ N., a total distance of 1,800 miles as the aeroplane flies, and it has a maximum width of 950 miles. These are long distances and an area of over a million square miles is included within its boundaries, of which most of that north of Khartoum in latitude 15° is desert except a narrow strip along the Nile. The population (1949) is estimated at about 7½ million of which about 420,000 are concentrated in the five largest towns, Khartoum and Omdurman and their environs, El Obeid, Wad Medani and Atbara. Apart from the deserts, large areas even where there is a reasonable rainfall, have very few permanent inhabitants, for the reason that in the dry season water for drinking is scarce.

North of Khartoum there is a settled but scanty population along the river cultivating small patches by means of saqias, and a nomadic population owning camels, donkeys, sheep and goats. In places pumps have been installed on the river and there are also basins in Dongola province which are inundated during the flood. From Abu Hamed or Dongola almost to Cairo less than 1 inch of rain falls in a year, and the country is frequently rainless. The rainfall increases as one goes southwards and south of Khartoum rain crops begin to be grown. In the Gezira, the land between the Blue and White Niles, an area of 900,000 acres is cultivated by irrigation from the Sennar Dam. Further south the country is covered with thorn bush, grass, or thin forest, thick forest and big trees existing only in the extreme south on the higher ground.

The northern part of the Sudan has many rocky hills rising out of the plain, while south of Khartoum the country is flat plain with only occasional hills. This plain continues to the Ethiopian Highlands on the east, the Lake Plateau and the slopes up to the Nile-Congo divide on the south, while on the west it extends to the highland of Jebel Marra, the Nuba Mountains and the slopes of the watershed between the Nile and Lake Chad Basins. The highest mountains in the Sudan lie in the high-lands limiting the plain; Kinyeti about 10,460 feet in the Imatong Mountains in the south, and Jebel Marra about 10,130 feet in the west being the highest peaks. This plain, which covers the greater part of the Sudan, is crossed by all tributaries of the Nile of any importance. Only one, the Bahr el Ghazal or river of gazelles, so called by early Arab traders because of the amount of game to be seen near it, is entirely within the Sudan, but owing to swamps its contribution to the main stream is insignificant. Most of the Sobat is in the Sudan, but the greater part of its water comes from Ethiopia. The two main streams, the Blue and White Niles, and the important tributary the Atbara, all flow through the Sudan but derive their supplies from outside the boundaries of the country.

From the Egyptian boundary south to roughly latitude 12° N., the people are Moslems and speak Arabic and are commonly called Arabs, though they are of mixed descent. South of this latitude more primitive people are found who may be generally described as negroid, but this racial group again covers many different tribes. The northern people are brown, but owing to mixing, all shades up to black exist, while the southern people are mostly black, and from them arises the name Sudan—the land of the blacks—applied by early Arabic-speaking people. The negroid peoples have their own languages, tribal customs and religions, and there is a very great diversity particularly in language. Slave raiding, wars and migrations have led in some regions to a considerable mixing of peoples so that in a very small area one may find representatives of many different tribes. Particularly is this the case along the Ethiopian border between the Blue Nile and the Baro. The negroids are cultivators and herdsmen, and cattle play a very important part in the lives of Nuers, Dinkas and Shilluks living on the southern parts of the plain. In addition most of the people who live near water depend to some extent on fishing.

71

The Sudan is one of the hot regions of the world and at a number of places in Upper Egypt and the northern Sudan temperatures of 120° F. or more have been recorded, while the average maximum from Wadi Halfa to Khartoum is more than 40° C. (104° F.) for several of the months from April to October. The Central and Southern Sudan are also hot, but at most places the monthly average maximum does not reach 40° C. The hottest months in the Southern Sudan are from January to March after which the onset of the rainy season produces cooler weather.

Residents in hot countries are apt to talk about 120° F., as if it were a common occurrence. Actually it is not common, though thermometers not exposed under standard conditions, in which they are shielded from direct radiation in a properly ventilated white screen, may register much higher temperatures than those defined by meteorologists as air temperatures in the shade. During the war of 1914–18 very high temperatures were recorded by some military observer at Ismailia, which actually is not a very hot place. One of my friends who was sceptical asked me to look at the installation, as I was then in charge of meteorology in Egypt and the Sudan. The screen proved to be a wooden box of the sort commonly used to contain two four-gallon tins of paraffin. It had no proper ventilation or double roof and was in a small courtyard closely surrounded by buildings. I reported that if their object was to record really high temperatures there was only one more thing which could be done and that was to paint the box black.

2. THE MAIN NILE IN THE SUDAN

When I joined the Survey of Egypt in 1906 parties were working on the Nile between Halfa and Khartoum making surveys with the object of finding possible sites for a dam as an alternative to raising the Aswan Dam. With the conditions of that time, however, it was decided that heightening Aswan was the better choice. Following this decision a party travelled up from Mombasa to Lake Victoria, levelled between Lakes Victoria and Albert and then travelled down the Nile, a very considerable journey in those days. Their accounts of the journey gave me the wish to see something of the Nile Basin, large areas of which were still almost unknown. In 1909 when engaged on the magnetic survey of Egypt I went up to Wadi Halfa and had my first peep through the door into the Sudan before returning northwards.

It was then only ten years after the re-opening of the Sudan, and the Nile from Halfa to Khartoum was associated with the wars with the Mahdi and Khalifa, the expedition sent to relieve General Gordon and Khartoum, and the later one under Lord Kitchener to reconquer the Sudan. In both of these latter cases the main struggle was to overcome the natural conditions of the country, the fierce heat and the numerous rocks and rapids of the river, all making travel and transport extremely difficult. Over the whole distance the river bank is never far from the desert, and often the desert is the river bank. For the first quarter of the distance of 930 miles as the river flows there is only cultivation in small patches right on the river's edge watered by saqias, and for the first 100 miles, known as the "Batn-el-Hagar" or belly of rocks, the river is a succession of rocks and rapids impossible to navigate except at the top of the flood and then only with extreme difficulty even for small boats.

On ordinary maps five cataracts are marked between Wadi Halfa and Khartoum, but at none of them is there any well-marked and considerable fall at one spot; rather are they in the nature of a series of rapids. Besides the named cataracts there are many other places where small rapids exist and rocks beset the channel (see Plate VII). The rapids themselves are caused by bars of hard rock crossing the course of the river, which are more slowly eroded than the neighbouring rocks and so form sills or steps. At the Second Cataract there are several reefs of a mixed nature, the erosion of which has led to the formation of many channels and islands over a length of about eight miles. At low stage most of the channels are dry or very shallow, while in flood the river submerges many of the rocks and islands. A writer [1] at the time of the expedition to relieve General Gordon says of the cataracts at low Nile

" these rapids are wild and desolate archipelagos . . . while the river bank on either side presents a broken series of precipitous and often

---

[1] James Grant, in Cassell's *History of the War in the Soudan.*

73

inaccessible cliffs and ragged spurs. Their sombre and gloomy appearance is heightened by the colour of the rock, which, between high and low water mark is usually of a jet hue, in many parts polished to such an extent by the long action of the water that it has the appearance of being carefully black-leaded."

As far as Kerma, about 250 miles from Halfa, there is no continuous navigation, although after the Batn-el-Hagar the river is not so thickly beset with obstructions. In the Batn-el-Hagar for 100 miles south of Halfa there are, owing to the narrow rocky valley, only isolated patches of cultivation where silt has accumulated in bays in the hills and saqias lift the water. From Kerma to Merowe and Karima, where the Fourth Cataract begins, there is a navigable stretch with a fair amount of cultivation on both banks. It is in this reach that, in addition to saqias on the river bank, there are also pumps and some basin irrigation, and a regular service of steamers. Following this is a stretch of about seventy miles to the head of Shirri island, which includes the Fourth Cataract and is not navigable except just at the top of the flood. It is proposed to build a dam at the Fourth Cataract partly to protect Egypt from high floods, and partly to store some water from the tail end of the flood for use in Egypt in the following low season (see Plate VIII). In fact the dam would be used in much the same manner as the Aswan Dam, but its reservoir would be larger, and would stretch as far as Abu Hamed. From Abu Hamed to Khartoum there are still obstacles to navigation but they are fewer and there are long stretches of easily navigable water. Between Abu Hamed and Berber there is the Fifth Cataract and two or three other rapids, but all can be passed at high Nile. A major feature between Dongola and Berber is the big S-bend, in the middle of which, from Abu Hamed to Korti and Debba, the river flows south-westwards for about 170 miles. Along the Nile the word "bahri" which comes from "bahr" a river, is used for north, so north is really the way the river flows, and consequently downstream of Abu Hamed the points of the compass are twisted round until the north becomes south-west. The same occurs at Qena in Upper Egypt where for some distance the Nile flows a little south of west and the two villages of Abu Manna which lie on

VII. RAPID AT AKASHA IN THE BATN EL HAGAR

VIII. FOURTH CATARACT. ONE OF THE POSSIBLE DAM SITES

an east-west line are named South Abu Manna and North Abu Manna.

One of the curses of the river-side between the Third and Fourth Cataracts is a small fly called locally " nimitti." This occurs in most years at the season when the river is low, in such vast numbers as to appear like a cloud of smoke overlying the river, and extending into the desert on either side. It is said that sometimes the cloud is so dense that it can be felt by swinging the arms. The fly is *simulium griseicollis* and is of the family known as buffalo gnats. It is a small pale-coloured fly which bites birds and donkeys, and to a lesser extent men. It causes great annoyance by crawling over the skin and getting into eyes, nose and ears. The remedy is to stay indoors or, if out of doors, to wear a veil, a procedure which the temperature may make very uncomfortable. The people of the country sometimes protect themselves against the fly by carrying pieces of smouldering rope or cow-dung. The fly breeds in slow-flowing water principally on mud-banks. It is not known to carry any disease like its relative, *simulium damnosum*, which will be mentioned again later. This latter fly is found also in places on the Main Nile from Khartoum to Halfa. An account of the simulium flies in the Sudan, from which the above is taken, will be found in a paper by D. J. Lewis in the *Transactions of the Royal Entomological Society*, London, Vol. 99, December, 1948.

From Abu Hamed southwards cultivation increases and so does the natural vegetation of grass and thorny acacia bushes which often extend for some distance from the river. Above Berber is the mouth of the Atbara which brings down much silt in flood and has a strong current, with the result that there are many sand-banks in the main stream below the junction, which move about and make navigation difficult when the river is low. From Atbara to Khartoum there is a fair amount of cultivation along the river, some of it dependent on pumps. At Zeidab upstream of Atbara there is an experimental farm which has existed for many years where cotton was tried out on a reasonable sized area before embarking on large scale cotton-growing in the Sudan. The history of cotton-growing in the Sudan, showing as it does the difficulties which had to be overcome before any appreciable return was possible, might well be studied by those who think quick returns can be got out of Africa. The town of Atbara on the mouth of the river has superseded Wadi Halfa as railway headquarters, and the amalgamation of provinces north of Khartoum into one with headquarters at El Damer near Atbara, has lessened the importance which Halfa had as the headquarters of a province.

Between Atbara and Khartoum navigation is difficult near Sabaloka Gorge, sometimes called the Sixth Cataract, where the river has cut through some hills for a distance of eight miles (see Plate IX). Why it should have cut through the middle instead of going round is a puzzle to the ordinary observer. When the river is low, rocks and rapids obstruct navigation for some miles downstream and upstream of the gorge. These, however, are the last obstruction for hundreds of miles beyond Khartoum. In Halfa and Dongola provinces the people are similar to the Berberines between Aswan and Halfa, and like them speak Nubian dialects, though they speak Arabic as well; and some of them are seen in Egypt working as servants or in the Camel Corps. In Berber, the southern province, the people are mainly Arab though with a negro admixture and they speak only Arabic.

There is a sufficient rainfall here to make life away from the Nile possible and many of the people are partly nomadic, with flocks of sheep and goats for which there is grazing inland for part of the year. The nomadic people between the Nile and the Red Sea from the extreme south of Egypt to the Atbara are known as Beja and are of a different origin to Nubians or Arabs. They are distinguished by " Fuzzy " hair, speak a language of their own and are thought to be descendants of the earliest invaders of the Nile Valley.[1]

Until recent times the route up the Nile was the only one to the Southern Sudan and the countries beyond. In Ancient Egypt it was the route for such trade with the south as existed, and there was always the difficulty that there was no continuous route by water. The distance was shortened by the use of the desert track from Korosko in Nubia to Abu Hamed, which cut out the bad stretch of river from the Second to beyond the Fourth Cataract. The only water in the 230 miles of this desert journey

[1] See G. W. Murray, *Sons of Ishmael*. Routledge.

is the brackish water at Murrat Wells, which can, however, be drunk by camels. The journey in the cool season was not unpleasant, but in the summer it was very severe both for man and beast, and Sir Samuel Baker, who traversed it in May, 1861, has given an account in which he describes the hardships of travel in hot weather with a limited water supply, which in turn, was considerably reduced by evaporation through the skins in which it was contained.

Modern resources have lessened the difficulties of desert travel and the camel has been replaced by the motor truck, but the traveller still cannot avoid strong winds and high temperatures. One of the most unpleasant nights of my life was spent in the Batn-el-Hagar in an old building constructed of loose stone. With a very high temperature and a strong wind filling the air, even inside the building, with sand, the atmosphere was so oppressive that at times during the night one wondered for a moment whether one could endure.

A canal from Abu Hamed to Korosko or down the Wadi Alaqi was suggested several times in the past and it is said that a survey was made in the time of Mohammed Ali Pasha. The levels, however, make it impracticable since on either of the above lines the land rises several hundred feet above the level of the river at Abu Hamed, and a canal would involve many miles of tunnel as an alternative to a very deep rock cutting. Others, the first of whom was Sir Samuel Baker, have suggested a series of dams to hold up water and drown the rocks and rapids, the dams having also the advantages of storing water for irrigation and producing power.

As we have mentioned, the first of these, the Aswan Dam, was built fifty years ago and a second is likely to be built for irrigation and flood protection. It will also produce power and will assist navigation over a short reach. The requirements of water storage for irrigation, however, are not entirely compatible either with those for the generation of power or for the improvement of navigation. Moreover to build a dam requires the fulfilment of various conditions, in particular there must be sound rock for foundation, and even in the cataracts this does not exist everywhere. However, let us get an idea of the amount of work involved in dams to make the cataracts navigable, and this can be done by considering the difference in the level of the river between Abu Hamed and Wadi Halfa. When this is compared with the height of the water held up by the Aswan Dam it appears that six dams each of about the size of the Aswan Dam would be required to drown the cataracts. Obviously this scheme is also impracticable and the only solution would appear to be a series of locks, accompanied by blasting away rocks in places where they obstruct the fairway. However a flight over the Batn-el-Hagar, where at every mile or two obstacles appear, will show the colossal nature of any such scheme and suggests that safe navigation from Wadi Halfa to Abu Hamed is never likely to be provided.

It was these formidable obstacles that the ships and boats of the Anglo-Egyptian relief expedition of 1884 were compelled to traverse. Great preparations were made for this difficult piece of navigation and several hundred boats, each complete with equipment and stores, were sent out from England. To take charge of them a number of Canadian Voyageurs and Iroquois Indians were recruited, as well as a contingent from the Royal Navy. There were, in addition, several paddle steamers, and all these craft were hauled up through the cataracts against strong currents by gangs of men, of whom thousands were assembled for the work. The passage was not achieved without accidents due to ships and boats striking rocks. Actually the flotilla started to navigate the cataracts just as the river was beginning to fall, and so encountered far more difficulties than they would have if they had started a month or more earlier on a rising river. Many boats were wrecked and stores went to the bottom of the Nile. After incredible labours the expedition reached Korti about thirty miles downstream of Merowe and from there a column struck across the desert to Metemma opposite Shendi, thus cutting out the big bend of the river round by Abu Hamed. Waiting at Metemma were several steamers sent by Gordon— one of which, the *Bordein*, is still preserved—and in two of these a party left on January 24th, 1885, for Khartoum arriving on the 28th, only to find that the town had been captured by large forces two days before and Gordon and many of the inhabitants had been killed. There was nothing for the party to do except return. The responsibility for the failure of the expedition to relieve Khartoum must rest on Mr. Gladstone and his Government, who delayed and decided only then under the pressure of public opinion, to send an expedition when it was already too late. Finally, after many labours and disappointments, the whole expedition was withdrawn to the frontier at Halfa, and for thirteen years barbarism closed the Sudan to outside influences.

Six months after the death of Gordon the Mahdi died. He was succeeded by one of his lieutenants the Khalifa Abdullahi, who attempted to carry out the Mahdi's plan to invade Egypt and extend Dervish rule. The invasion of Egypt was delayed owing to Ethiopian attacks and troubles in the Western Sudan, but by 1889 the Ethiopians had been defeated and the Sudanese rebels crushed. British forces had been withdrawn and the defence of the frontier which was at Wadi Halfa was left to the Egyptian Army commanded principally by British officers. In that year Wad-el-Negumi, one of the ablest generals of the Khalifa, pushed past Wadi Halfa on the west bank of the Nile with a powerful force. He was met at Toshka fifty miles north of Wadi Halfa by the Egyptian army which consisted partly of Sudanese and partly of Egyptians under the Sirdar, Sir Francis Grenfell. The Khalifa's forces were completely defeated and many, including Wad-el-Negumi, were killed. This brought to an end the Mahdi's scheme of world conquest. There were, however, further raids on Egyptian territory, one of which reached Beris, a village in the south of Kharga Oasis, and there was continual fighting round the Sudan borders and with tribes in the Sudan. In 1896 the decision was made to reconquer the Sudan and the operation was carried out by a mixed British and Egyptian force under the Sirdar, Lord Kitchener. The railway was pushed southward from Halfa across the desert to Abu Hamed and then on to Khartoum, and at the same time supplies were brought up by the river route. In April, 1898, one of the Khalifa's Emirs was defeated with very heavy losses at the battle of Atbara, and in September a battle was fought at Omdurman on the west of the Nile a few miles north of Khartoum. Here died twenty-seven British and twenty-nine Egyptians, while the bodies of more than 10,000 dervishes were counted. This was practically the end of Mahdism, though the Khalifa himself escaped and some of his Emirs still commanded forces in other parts of the Sudan. These forces were finally defeated, and many, including the Khalifa and his principal Emirs were killed at Um Debreikat in November, 1899. The history of these times can be read in such contemporary accounts as Cassell's *War in the Sudan*, *Fire and Sword in the Sudan* by Slatin Pasha, various lives of Gordon, and Mr. Winston Churchill's *River War*.

The development of communications southwards from Wadi Halfa was first studied on the instructions of the Khedive Ismail Pasha, who asked Sir John Fowler to report on the matter. Surveys were made for a railway line from Halfa to Khartoum and on to Suakin on the Red Sea, with a branch from the Dongola bend to El Fasher. Only a short portion of this was built at the time. At the beginning of 1897 the present line from Halfa across the desert to Abu Hamed was begun, thus cutting off a large bend of the river, and was carried out at the phenomenal rate of nearly a mile a day. This was done to make possible Lord Kitchener's campaign, and the railway ultimately reached the Nile opposite Khartoum by the end of 1899. The railway system has since been continued up the Blue Nile to Sennar and then westwards across the Gezira and White Nile to El Obeid. A line goes from Atbara, now railway headquarters, to Port Sudan and Suakin, and another from Sennar to Kassala and then due north to join the line from Atbara. At the present time motor transport is used all over the Sudan, though in the Southern Plains it is mostly confined to the dry season.

Mr. Waller and I have recently travelled by car from Khartoum to Wadi Halfa keeping as near the river as possible. The track is usually on the desert outside any cultivation, and sometimes goes well inland to avoid broken ground and sand close to the river. In parts there are great sheets of sand, and it is advisable to travel at a good pace to avoid sinking in and sticking. Large tyres and plenty of clearance on the car are important. For the last 200 miles the country is rough and broken and consists largely of rocky hills and ravines. In this region the road is nearly always away from the river and has been cleared of rocks, though the sandy beds of the ravines still present possibilities of trouble. It is possible with a suitable car, such as a land-rover or jeep, to make side excursions and to see the river at various points in the Batn-el-Hagar. The scenery along the river though grim is attractive in the low time of the year, when blue water and an occasional palm grove form a contrast to the black or reddish hills which often descend steeply to the river. But from March onwards the traveller may think that delight in the scenery is offset by the terrific heat.

Chapter Five

THE BLUE NILE AND ATBARA IN THE CENTRAL SUDAN

1. THE BLUE NILE AND IRRIGATION

THE Central Sudan may be considered as beginning in the latitude of Khartoum and extending south for 450 miles to the Sobat river on the one side and the Bahr el Ghazal on the other. The greater part of it is a clay plain, which covers the country between the White and Blue Niles and continues eastwards to the foothills of Ethiopia. Darfur and part of Kordofan on the west of the Nile are sandy country known as " goz." The Central Sudan is inhabited in the north by people of mixed Arab and negro descent many of whom are nomadic, owning herds of camels and sheep, for which the rainfall of 8 to 20 inches provides grazing and enables crops to be raised. Along the rivers are people of similar origin but more settled habits, cultivating along the margin of the river by the use of water raised by saqias and pumps. In addition to these small areas cultivated by water drawn directly from the rivers, there is the large area of 900,000 acres cultivated from the Sennar reservoir on the Blue Nile (now being increased to 1,000,000). This is a good example of a successful co-operative enterprise carried out in tropical Africa. It was based on experimental work by the Sudan Plantation Syndicate at several farms of some thousands of acres each, watered by pumps from the Nile.

The possibility of irrigating a considerable area of the Gezira, the country in the angle formed by the Blue and White Niles, by means of a dam on the Blue Nile had been suggested by Sir Wm. Garstin and Mr. C. E. Dupuis as early as 1904. In 1919 the Sudan Government came to an agreement with the Syndicate to develop land on a large scale in the Gezira. The Government would build the dam and the main canal system, while the Syndicate would be responsible for agricultural and business operations. The land to start with was in part owned by the Government and in part by native owners. It was obvious

IX. NORTHERN END OF SABALOKA GORGE

X. IN THE SUDAN GEZIRA. PLANTS AND PICKED COTTON

that the scheme must be administered as a whole and so the Government took control of native-owned lands by paying a rent and giving the owners the right to take up tenancies as cultivators of thirty or forty acre plots. The profits from the most important crop, long-staple cotton, were to be divided between the Government, the Syndicate and the tenants, while food and other crops went to the tenants. Thus the tenants were not mere labourers and had a definite interest in the scheme (see Plate X). The Sennar Dam was finished in 1925 and irrigation of the Gezira began in the same year. In spite of trials of the Egyptian type of cotton extending over twenty years, there were difficulties to be overcome to make irrigation on a large scale successful, and Egyptian practice could not be adopted without modification. The impermeable nature of the soil, pests, and danger of malaria all introduced difficulties. However, the scheme had virgin ground to work on and was not hampered in its lay-out by any existing works or old established practices. This was a great advantage and from the beginning procedure was based on careful measurement of water, for which measuring devices were installed at the beginning. Distribution of water is scientifically controlled from its entry through the head sluices of the Main Canal at Sennar down to its delivery to individual holdings, with the result that the available water is made to serve the maximum area. During flood the Blue Nile carries more water than can be used by Egypt and the Sudan, but by January it is usually getting tight. From the time when there ceases to be surplus water, under the terms of the Nile Waters Agreement of 1929 the Sudan can take no more water from the river, whose natural flow must be passed on to Egypt.[1]

The Sennar Dam serves a double purpose; it allows the river level to be raised so that the water can flow into the Main Gezira Canal, and it also stores water above this level which is used later when the natural flow of the river must be passed on to Egypt. The irrigation season begins in the Gezira at the middle of July, by which time there is usually sufficient water both for Egypt and the Sudan. Up to this time the river has been flowing

---

[1] A full account of irrigation in the Sudan is given by W. N. Allan and R. J. Smith in *Agriculture in the Sudan*. Edited by Tothill. Oxford University Press. A very valuable book.

G 2

freely through the sluices of the Sennar Dam which are then partially closed until the level rises to a point which allows the proper discharge to pass down the Canal. This is restricted to a maximum of 14½ mlpd. (millions cubic metres per day) from July 31st to November 30th, and 13·8 mlpd. in December. In November, when the crest of the flood has passed, the level behind the dam is raised to full reservoir level. This stored water remains until the date in January when the natural supply falls short of the combined requirements of Egypt and the Sudan, and after which the Sudan must draw only on the supply stored in the reservoir. These complicated arrangements depend on careful measurements of the flow in the Blue Nile and in the Main Canal. As already mentioned (p. 67) the sluices are used as water-meters and the calibration of these depends on model experiments done by myself and others, and ultimately on the tank measurements at Aswan. It may be said that these agree closely with the current-meter measurements made regularly at Sennar.

The Gezira Scheme and the project for a dam on the White Nile at Gebel Aulia were the subject of violent irresponsible attacks extending from 1917 to 1921. Fantastic accusations were made against those responsible for the projects, which, had they been true, would have meant that the majority of the senior officials of the Egyptian Irrigation Service and Physical Department were either directly dishonest or concealing the dishonesty of others, or were merely incompetent. This alone was bad enough, but the statement that Egypt was to be robbed of water for the benefit of a syndicate in the Sudan, was the means of implanting fear in Egypt for the safety of its water supply and distrust of the British Government, traces of which still remain. The accusations, fantastic as they were, led to the appointment first of a Committee of well-known engineers in London to examine the matter. This Committee reported in favour of the projects and rejected the accusations. This, however did not silence the accusers and the matter was re-examined in Cairo by a second commission, whose members had been chosen by the Governments of the United States and India and by Cambridge University. The report of this commission was also against those who made the charges, but again did not silence them, and the matter was finally brought to an end by a prosecu-

tion in the British Consular Court in which one of the accusers
was found guilty of criminal libel and sedition. The final judgment has been delivered by the projects themselves. The Gezira
Scheme has been successful and the partition of water between
Egypt and the Sudan has gone on for twenty-five years with no
disputes or difficulties. The Gebel Aulia Dam was built and has
been working very usefully for thirteen years, without producing
any of the misfortunes predicted by the prophets of evil.

The contrast between the uncultivated Gezira south of Khartoum with its barren ground and scattered bushes, and the fields
of cotton and food crops which begin forty miles upstream, is as
striking as the transition from desert to cultivation in Egypt,
and bears witness, if any were needed, to the importance of
extending the use of Nile water to its maximum.

An interesting relic of the Nile Projects controversy occurred,
about three years after its finish, when I called to make the
acquaintance of a new Minister of Public Works. When the
Minister, a lawyer, was appointed I was on the Nile in
Uganda and there received a letter from my deputy saying
that the new Minister was making transfers of heads of
departments, and that if I did not return quickly I might find that
I had been made head of the Zoo or the Opera House, both of
which were then departments of the Public Works. I returned
immediately and went to report my arrival and make the acquaintance of the Minister. As I took my leave after some pleasant
conversation in French about scientific work, law and the relations between them, he said " Well, Dr. Hurst, I have always
heard that you were a man of great ability, and I trust that Egypt
will have the benefit of your ability as well as the gentlemen of
the Sudan Syndicate." As I had then spent twenty years in the
service of the Egyptian Government, and the Sudan Plantations
Syndicate was only a name to me, I thought this did not show
much knowledge of my activities. However I did not attach
much importance to the remark and never heard any more of it,
and I may say that my relations with this Minister and with his
successors have always been pleasant. The agreement with the
Syndicate has now expired and their interest and responsibilities
have reverted to the Sudan Government.

Pump irrigation has already been mentioned. It is practised

mainly on the Main Nile and White Nile under licence from the Sudan Government for each pump. Many schemes, including the largest which covers more than 8,000 feddans, are owned by the Government and cultivated by tenants, while some fairly large privately owned schemes are also cultivated by tenants. There are in addition co-operative schemes. In these latter all co-operators first take half their crops; working expenses, cost of maintenance of pumps and any other machinery, interest and repayment of capital, are then taken out of the other half, the remainder being shared among the co-operators. There are also small schemes which are worked by their owners.

Basin irrigation is practised on the Main Nile in Shendi and Dongola districts. The basins in the Sudan are of much more recent origin and have not reached the same even surface and full cultivation as in Egypt. This is due to the fact that they have not developed those deep layers of silt which exist in Egypt. They depend for flooding entirely on the height of the Nile and consequently the area which can be cultivated varies very much from good to bad years. It may be more than 100,000 feddans in a high year and not much more than 10,000 in a low year.

At the present time the Gezira and also the country to the east of the Blue Nile and along the Atbara are being examined to classify their soils and see what areas are potentially cultivable.

In addition to cultivation from the Nile there is also some on the Khor Gash and the Khor Baraka,[1] two torrents which come down from Eritrea in the rainy season, but do not belong to the Nile system, and gradually disappear on the plain. These both flow between July and September in a series of spates and bring down large quantities of silt, the deposit of which has formed deltas. The Gash is controlled by regulators and canals and an area of 40,000 to 60,000 feddans is cultivated each year, this being roughly from one-third to one half of the area commanded by the canals, the remainder being left unwatered. The main crops are cotton and dura (maize or millet). The Baraka is a similar torrent to the Gash, but is more irregular. It is not regulated owing to the high cost and doubtful success of any scheme. The crops are planted on the naturally flooded area which varies from year to year both in its position and acreage.

[1] A Khor is a water course, but it may only occasionally carry water.

Rain crops of maize and millet are grown from Khartoum southwards. The limit of this cultivation is further north on the eastern edge of the Sudan owing to the slightly heavier rainfall caused by the presence of the Ethiopian Highlands. Rain cultivation in these regions of scanty rainfall is precarious, and accounts for the necessity of increasing cultivation by irrigation to give a more stable agriculture.

The Atbara and the tributaries of the Blue Nile, the Rahad and Dinder, come from the high country of Ethiopia and are torrential streams carrying in flood large quantities of water but are later reduced to pools in the sands of their beds. The eastern boundary of the Sudan from Kassala to the Blue Nile lies in the plain, and the mountains of Eritrea and Ethiopia are usually a long way off until the boundary approaches the Blue Nile. Southwards from Sennar, Kassala, and Kosti on the White Nile a good deal of the country is covered with bush and small trees, though further south there are areas of open grass plain.

In former times Sennar and Kassala lay on the route of the Moslem pilgrimage from Darfur and West Africa to Mecca. The pilgrimage was a gradual drift across Africa, taking several years because of the need of working for the means of life on the way. The result is that small communities of people from Darfur and the Moslem countries further west have settled in the Eastern Sudan. In 1913 I travelled up the Blue Nile to Roseires in the dry season by camel, and owing to one of the camels throwing its load and bolting into the bush I camped a few miles from Maiurno, a village of West African settlers. My camel men and servants gave the camel up for lost as they said the people of the village were sorcerers and could transform themselves into hyaenas. This reputation for sorcery must have been widespread, as a British official told me that the Sheikh of Maiurno had the power to wish away mosquitoes and that he had seen him do it. As, however, this official thought the moon regularly influenced the rains, in spite of the evidence of the figures collected under his own supervision, I did not attach undue importance to his account. The belief that certain people can transform themselves into animals is widespread in the Sudan and Central Africa. The animals most commonly chosen in the Sudan are

87

hyaenas and crocodiles, but further south lions and leopards are occasionally " were " animals.

My Egyptian servants had strong beliefs in the magical powers of people in the Sudan and these probably dated back, with other strong dislikes, to the time when criminals and conscripts were sent to the Sudan, from which many failed to return. When I lost a knife it was attributed to a Sudanese guide who had left us a few days before. I pointed out that the man was not with us when the knife was lost, and that it had probably been left behind at the previous camp. The reply to this was that the guide had no doubt wanted the knife and consequently put a spell on it so that it went to him.

From Sennar to the Ethiopian boundary the Blue Nile passes through wooded country, the trees being at first small thorny acacias, but further south larger and more varied. A common tree is the baobab (called tebeldi in the Sudan) which is of considerable girth and has a soft inside. In some parts of the Sudan the tree is hollowed out and, during the rains, is used as a water cistern. The river trough is about 400 yards wide and is filled in flood, which is at its maximum in August after which it falls away. By March it has dropped about 25 feet and shrunk to a small stream about half its flood width, winding about in the sands of its bed. In flood it can be navigated by steamers as far as two or three miles beyond Roseires, after which it is obstructed by the Ganis or Damazin Rapids, sometimes called the Roseires Cataract.

Jessen of the McMillan expedition in 1903 managed to get a steam launch through the Ganis rapids. This was in June while the river was still low, and the journey was accomplished with the greatest difficulty and danger from the stream, the rocks and the powerful eddies, strong enough to be described as whirlpools. The journey was finally brought to a complete stop by the rapids at Famaka and Fazogli not far from the present frontier of the Sudan (see Plate XI).

At Roseires there is a river gauge which is one of the most important in the Nile system, since it is the southernmost gauge on the Blue Nile and gives the first warning of its rise. In June and July its readings, which are telegraphed daily to Cairo and Khartoum, are watched with the closest attention because of the

XI. LOOKING UP THE BLUE NILE TO GEBEL FAZOGLI NEAR THE ETHIOPIAN BORDER

XII. THE ATBARA. KHASHM EL GIRBA GORGE AND RIVER GAUGE SET IN THE ROCKS

delicate regulation necessary on the Aswan Dam to enable the reservoir supply to hold out until the arrival of Blue Nile water provides enough, and to spare, for Egypt and the Sudan.

The scenery along the river south of Roseires with the occasional rocky hills and in the distance the mountains of Ethiopia, is delightful. There are many ravines down which torrents rush in the rains, but which are otherwise dry. In the sands of these dry beds gold is found and small quantities are washed out by the natives. One old woman whom I came across had two tiny specks as the result of half a day's work. The gold of the Fazogli district has been known for more than a century, and an attempt was made by Mohammed Ali Pasha to develop gold-mining, but it was unsuccessful. Apparently the gold though widely distributed has never been found in a concentration worth exploiting.

The country all along the boundary from the Blue Nile to the Baro is very pleasant and the usual road lies amongst outlying hills with the higher mountains behind. There is a Government post at Kurmuk within a mile of the boundary. When I was there in 1939 most goods were cheaper in the Sudan than in Ethiopia, and even Brazilian coffee was cheaper in Kurmuk than coffee grown over the border. Parties of Ethiopians were to be seen who had come down with mules and donkeys to buy what they needed. As these purchases had to be smuggled into Ethiopia, the party would split up and return by bush paths, thus avoiding the Italian posts.

Owing to slave raiding in former times the people along the border are very mixed and speak many different languages. People living on neighbouring hills, and many of the villages are in the hills, sometimes speak different languages and if one asks a man to what tribe he belongs he usually gives the name of his village or the near-by hills. The same is true on the other side of the boundary, and the boundary does not separate different peoples. In the nineteen twenties slave-trading and smuggling of arms in Kurmuk district was well organized, the principals being an important chief with an Arab name, who ruled the Ethiopian district over the border, and his wife who lived in the Sudan. When the traffic was discovered vigorous police action put an end to it. Many slaves were freed and the lady was imprisoned.

North of Sennar the Blue Nile receives two tributaries, the Rahad and the Dinder, both coming from Ethiopia. The Dinder in flood carries as much water as one of the big canals in Egypt and the Rahad has about one-third of the discharge of the Dinder. They carry a useful discharge for only about four months of the year and are dry except for pools for about half the year.

2. THE ATBARA

The Atbara is similar in its habits to the Rahad and Dinder, but carries a much bigger discharge for a rather longer season. Nearly all its water comes from Ethiopia, and it rises and falls rapidly like the Blue Nile. It is important during the flood, and in 1903 a gauge was cut on the rocks of the gorge at Khashm-el-Girba, so that advance knowledge of the state of the river could be sent to Egypt (see Plate XII). The Atbara enters the Sudan near Gallabat and is joined lower down by the Salam and Setit. The largest tributary of the Atbara is the Setit or Takkaze and it has a basin double the area of that of the Atbara itself, so that it might claim to be really the main stream. Unfortunately no discharges of the tributaries of the Atbara have so far been measured so we do not know their relative importance. For most of its course in the Sudan the Atbara is well below the general level of the plain. From the boundary for half of its course it is bordered by country known as " Karab " from an Arabic word meaning bad (Plate XIII). Between the plain and the river the ground is very much eroded and cut up by gullies formed by water running off the plains after rain. It is similar in origin to the " bad lands " of the Western United States, and occurs also, on the Blue Nile, though it is there less striking.

Sir Samuel Baker spent some time on the Atbara in 1861, hunting and exploring the river. Here he made the acquaintance of some of those Hamran Arabs who were accustomed to hunt elephants and other game on horseback with swords, a most exciting and dangerous business. He found game plentiful and the country up the Setit delightful. The country is still delightful, but the increased population has made the game very much more scarce. In *The Nile Tributaries of Abyssinia*,[1] Baker has a good

[1] London, 1867.

XIII. BROKEN COUNTRY ("KARAB") ALONG THE ATBARA NEAR THE JUNCTION WITH BAHR ES SALAM. VILLAGE AND RIVER IN THE DISTANCE.

XIV. ISLANDS IN LAKE TANA NEAR THE OUTLET. BOAT (TANKWA) MADE OF PAPYRUS STALKS.

(Photo. by G. W. Grabham)

deal to say of the importance of developing irrigation from the Nile by means of dams, and suggests a beginning with a dam at Aswan followed by others in the Cataracts. He also suggested a dam on the Atbara which would irrigate the country between Goz Regeb on the Atbara and Berber on the Nile. Baker's views were very much in advance of his time, and so far as I know he was the first to see the tremendous possibilities in the complete control of the Nile, a condition we have not yet achieved but, if political difficulties can be overcome, still hope for.

Chapter Six

THE BLUE NILE AND ATBARA IN
ETHIOPIA

1. THE BLUE NILE

A SHORT distance beyond the Sudan border, the Blue Nile emerges from the mountains of Ethiopia in which the Blue Nile, Atbara and their tributaries all rise at heights of from 6,000 to 10,000 feet above sea-level. The reputed source of the Blue Nile, for example, is a little spring from which a stream, the little Abbai, flows down to lake Tana, of which it is the principal tributary. The spring is holy and is in charge of the priests of a neighbouring church, and only by them may water be drawn from it. It is a place of pilgrimage and is believed to have curative powers. The Ethiopians also believe that the Abbai is the stream Gihon, referred to in the book of Genesis as the one of those flowing from the Garden of Eden, " that compasseth the whole land of Ethiopia." The first European to see it was Pedro Paez a Portuguese Jesuit who visited it in 1613 and wrote an account which was quoted by various later writers who described the travels of the Jesuits in Ethiopia. James Bruce travelled in Ethiopia round about 1770 and became so much *persona grata* with the king and nobles that he was made Governor of the district which includes the source of the Abbai. While visiting the spring he observed an occultation of one of Jupiter's satellites, from which he calculated its longitude, and found a value only differing by about 20 minutes of arc from its position on present-day maps. Considering the means at his disposal, this was a creditable effort. He entered Ethiopia from Massawa, and travelled up to Gondar, the capital, and then spent some time travelling round Lake Tana and the head waters of the Blue Nile, after which he made his way from Gondar to the Blue Nile at Sennar and so down the river to Cairo.

For the greater part of its course from Lake Tana to the Sudan plain the Blue Nile is in a canyon, and in places is 4,000 feet below the level of the land above, so that it is two days' difficult travel to cross the canyon from one side to the other. All its tributaries are likewise in deep ravines. As far as is known nobody has succeeded in following the river throughout its course in Ethiopia, though Jessen of the McMillan expedition in 1905 followed it closely for about two-fifths of the distance from the Sudan boundary to Lake Tana. His was a very trying journey through extremely difficult country. The lower levels of the valley are not inhabited, the people living on the high ground away from the river. Consequently there are rarely tracks actually along the river, and the country is in fact often so broken that no track could possibly be made near the river except by tremendous engineering works. Any tracks going in the same direction as the river climb up and down every time a tributary is encountered, and many detours inland must be made. The regular tracks of the country go down to the river only where there are fords. Jessen having followed the Blue Nile as closely as was possible got nearly as far as the Bir, a north bank tributary in a precipitous ravine. Supplies were almost exhausted and the donkeys were in poor condition owing to scarcity of grass at the end of the dry season, while Jessen and his companion Scott had worn out their boots with the continual climbing over rocks, and were suffering from sore feet. At this point they were met by soldiers who insisted on taking the party many miles from the river to the headquarters of the powerful Ras who ruled the district. Here they were allowed to continue their journey and the party, having obtained some necessaries and mules, marched south-east to the Blue Nile which they forded some distance above the spot where they had left it, and from there made their way to Addis Ababa. McMillan had previously attempted to come down the Blue Nile in steel boats, but had been wrecked almost at the start and Jessen's mission was to report on the navigability of the river lower down. He had no difficulty in concluding that rocks and rapids made it impossible. Jessen's journey is described by him in *McMillan's Expeditions*.[1] Fifteen years later I was asked by Mr. C. F. Rey (later Sir Charles) if I would join him in another expedition to come down the Blue Nile in boats. By this time special steels were available of much greater strength and he thought it would

[1] London, 1906.

be possible to get boats which would stand the battering which they would get in the cataracts. However, before anything definite was arranged Rey became Resident Commissioner for Bechuanaland.

The valley from the termination of Jessen's exploration up to Lake Tana has been travelled along its top by Major R. E. Cheesman, the river being approached wherever possible, and an account of his explorations will be found in his book *Lake Tana and the Blue Nile*.[1] The canyon has a total length of about 300 miles and finally runs out on to the plateau about 20 miles below Lake Tana. At the head of the canyon the river drops 150 feet at the falls of Tis Esat, which according to Cheesman are amongst the most beautiful in the world. Just below the Falls the ravine narrows to a width of a few feet and is spanned by an old bridge dating from soon after the time of the Portuguese in Ethiopia. About fifty miles below the lake is another bridge which is ascribed to the Portuguese, but has been repaired in recent times. During the reign of Menelik an Italian was employed to build a bridge near the southernmost point on the great bend of the Blue Nile. The abutments were built in good masonry, and it is said that the iron girders were ordered from Italy and were delivered at Jibuti on the Red Sea. Somewhere between Jibuti and Addis Ababa they disappeared without trace from the train. Stranger still a second set was ordered and the story says that they also vanished on the journey between the port and the capital, so that to this day the bridge remains unfinished and almost forgotten. A suggestion which I have heard to account for the loss is that the Ras of Gojam did not wish his country to be accessible to the Central Government and arranged for the girders to be stolen and buried, so I suggest to some adventurous person that a search with a mine detector be made round about the places where the train stayed for the night on its journey from the coast. A bridge has, however, recently been built at Shafartak where the road from Addis Ababa to Gojam used to cross the Blue Nile by a ford.

Below the Tis Esat Falls the valley gradually gets deeper, as do the valleys of the tributaries, but in places there are villages with cultivation on the flat land high above the river. It is

[1] Macmillan. London, 1936.

XV.   FALLS OF TIS ESAT ON THE BLUE NILE BELOW LAKE TANA
(Photo by J. R. Herbert)

XVI.   SUDAN GOVERNMENT STEAMER AND BARGES ON THE WHITE NILE.
SHILLUKS IN THE FOREGROUND

noteworthy that many of the tributary streams are tiny compared with the enormous gorges which they occupy, and the Blue Nile itself is only 120 to 150 yards wide. In places there are fords where it is shallow in the dry season, in ordinary years probably from March to June, and where it can be crossed by wading. When the rains set in every ravine contains a stream bringing its quota to the Blue Nile, and many are too deep to be crossed, so that travelling during the rains is extremely difficult. The catchment areas of many of these streams are not very large but the steep and rocky nature of the country ensures that a good proportion of the rainfall finds its way into the rivers. There are several considerable tributaries, besides the numerous small ones, which enter the Blue Nile between Lake Tana and the Sudan boundary. The largest is the Didessa coming from the south and draining a large area, which is not, however, as mountainous as the catchment of the main stream. Unfortunately practically nothing is known of the hydrology of the Didessa, though the lower half of its course has been traversed. It is in a deep valley and the country is mountainous and thickly wooded, intersected by rivers in deep ravines.

Since the war air routes into Ethiopia have been developed and no doubt during and since the war much of the Blue Nile basin has been seen from the air. Ethiopian air lines now operate from Addis Ababa with flights to Lake Tana, Gondar, Gambeila, Harrar and other places. Lake Tana was reconnoitred from the air by the Sudan Irrigation Department during the very high flood of 1946 with a view to the possibility that the maximum level of the lake might be fixed.

2. LAKE TANA AND THE SURROUNDING COUNTRY

Between the falls of Tis Esat and Lake Tana the valley is flat and several miles wide and on this stretch there is a succession of small rapids and cataracts. (See Plates XIV and XV). The Blue Nile leaves the lake by a series of cataracts which are impressive when the lake is high but the flow is much reduced at low stage. The total quantity flowing out of the lake is only about one-fourteenth of the supply of the Blue Nile, but it is important since it is free of silt and, by building a small dam at the outlet of the lake, it could be used as a reservoir to increase the flow of the Blue Nile when at its lowest, and perhaps to contain some reserve for emergencies.

Lake Tana lies at about 6,000 feet above the sea, and at what one may call roughly a middle level of the highlands of Ethiopia. About half of the high country of Ethiopia and Eritrea lies at a higher level than the lake and reaches its highest point in a peak of the Simien Mountains to the north-east of the lake, which rises to 15,000 feet or a little lower than Mont Blanc. There are several other peaks rising out of the plateau to more than 13,000 feet, on which snow occasionally falls, but it is not permanent and cannot be said to contribute appreciably to the Nile flood. The plateau country is not flat, for a great deal of it is hilly with grassy downs, swampy valleys and scattered trees. Occasionally rocky peaks, some of which are of volcanic origin, rise out of it to considerable heights. The Simien Mountains in particular are an enormous rocky mass covering a considerable area. Major H. C. Maydon who spent some time amongst them hunting the walia ibex has given a graphic description in the *Lonsdale Book on Big-game Shooting in Africa*.[1] From the north the mass looks like a huge elevated plateau with a few outstanding peaks and a continuous line of precipices. Its lower slopes are cut into numerous deep ravines draining to the Takkaze or Setit, which flows round the eastern and northern sides of the mass down to the Atbara. On these high mountains although it is usually warm in the day-time when the sun shines, it is bitterly cold at night. Like other high mountains of Africa they have their special vegetation of giant lobelias and tree heaths which grow densely in the ravines. The feature for the hunter is the tremendous precipices with often no way down for miles, and where the game when shot often finishes with a crash a thousand feet below.

In general the plateau is not thickly wooded though forest is often found on the slopes of the river valleys. In the rainy season the whole country is covered with tall grass. Malaria and horse-sickness prevail in the low country except during the dry months December to April, and the plateau round Lake Tana is malarious during and following the rainy season, but the higher levels 7,000 feet or more, are free from malaria and horse-sickness

[1] Seeley, Service & Co. London, 1932.

96

throughout the year. The country within the Ethiopian border varies greatly in altitude and is generally divided into three zones. First: low land below 6,000 feet, which includes the river valleys and the parts of the plain at the foot of the escarpment within the border. In the valleys the climate is hot and oppressive as well as malarious, while the climate of the plain is similar to that of the neighbouring parts of the Sudan, of which Gambeila may be taken as typical. Second: the plateau lying between 6,000 and 8,000 feet. The greater part of the Nile basin in Ethiopia is included in this area, which contains most of the population. The plateau has a pleasant climate in the dry season with warm days and cold nights, when a fire is welcome. At the beginning of the dry season the air is clear, but by December dust haze occurs and this is intensified when the grass is burnt towards the end of the dry season. In the rainy season the mornings are usually sunny, but by mid-day it becomes clouded over and thunderstorms occur in the afternoon. At the height of the rainy season rain falls about three days out of four, but its incidence varies greatly with locality, the maximum being reached usually about the beginning of August. Many people are killed and many houses destroyed by lightning in the frequent thunderstorms of the rainy season. Third: the high country above 8,000 feet. The higher parts of this area are cold and have a heavy rainfall. At these levels malaria and horse-sickness are rare at any time of the year.

The dry season lasts from October to February and the rainy season from March to September. In the dry season the wind is generally from the north and north-east, while in the rainy season it is from the south-west over practically all of Ethiopia in the Nile Basin. This current brings moisture which almost certainly comes from the South Atlantic Ocean. This theory was first put forward forty years ago by Mr. J. I. Craig, then in the Egyptian Survey Department, and all evidence since collected goes to confirm it (see Chapter XV). Further climatic data will be found in Chapter XI. The broken nature of large areas of Ethiopia and the absence of made roads makes travel difficult even in the dry season. In the rainy season the streams are swollen, and their banks are often muddy, everything is damp and even the local people avoid travelling if possible. The advent of motor transport and the building of main roads has eliminated some of the difficulties of travel, but all-weather roads and bridges over streams are costly in upkeep, and away from the few main roads conditions are much as they used to be, and transport is still by pack animals. Lake Tana was first examined by Mr. C. E. Dupuis of the Egyptian Irrigation Service in 1903, as a part of the reconnaissance of the Upper Nile begun by Sir Wm. Garstin. This was followed in 1915 by another party consisting of Mr. A Burton Buckley and Mr. O. L. Prowde from Egypt, and Col. H. D. Pearson from the Sudan. Arising out of this the Tana Mission from the Egyptian Ministry of Public Works went up to the lake, and from 1920–24 its various members made a hydrological survey of the lake and its outlet in order that a project for controlling the lake by a dam might be drawn up.[1] The project was further studied at the request of the Ethiopian Government in 1933–35—by engineers of the J. G. White Corporation of New York. Such a project forms an important link in the chain of projects proposed by myself and my colleagues in Vol. VII of the *Nile Basin*,[2] which will be described in Chapter XVII.

Lake Tana has an area of about 1,200 square miles and as far as its depth has been sounded is fairly shallow. Its water is soft and without taste or smell, and is, in bulk, a greenish colour and somewhat turbid. The natives travel on the lake in boats made of bundles of papyrus stems called tankwas. The lake contains some fish but not, as far as is known, Nile perch or tiger fish. There are no crocodiles, and the hippopotamus was at one time abundant but is now almost extinct. Cheesman heard rumours that a fish as large as a man lived in the lake, but although he offered a reward he was unable to obtain a specimen or any remains of such a fish.

From time to time in the last thirty years attention in Egypt has been directed to Lake Tana and the Blue Nile and strange and erroneous statements have been made. It has been asserted that

[1] *Report on a Mission to Lake Tana*, by G. W. Grabham and R. P. Black, Ministry of Public Works, Egypt. The Tana Mission consisted of G. W. Grabham and R. P. Black, followed by J. R. Herbert and Dr. J. P. Mitchell, and then H. G. Bambridge and Dr. R. B. Black.
[2] *The Conservation of the Nile Water*, by Hurst, Black and Simaika. Physical Department, Ministry of Public Works, Egypt.

the Blue Nile could be diverted into the Red Sea or elsewhere away from Egypt, so turning that country into a desert. This nonsense revives a mediæval idea that on the occasion of a famine in Egypt the Ethiopians had diverted the Nile. The ruler of Egypt therefore sent an ambassador to the king of Ethiopia with many presents to beg him to allow the Nile to return to its course. The same idea was used very much later by an Ethiopian ruler as a threat to Egypt, and all that need be said, however, is that such a diversion is no more possible than it is to divert the Rhine into the Adriatic.

3. THE PEOPLE OF ETHIOPIA

Many different peoples are to be found within the confines of Ethiopia and it is said that seventy different languages are spoken.[1] Perhaps about one-third of the people belong to those who are commonly called Abyssinians or Ethiopians. These are the Amhara and are mostly to be found in the northern provinces. They are the ruling race of the country, from which most of the emperors and kings have been drawn, and which provides the rases or provincial rulers and most of the officials. They are a Semitic people from across the Red Sea, possibly from the Yemen, but have some admixture of the various peoples which they have conquered. They are Christians and the emperors claim descent from King Solomon, who is said to have had a son, Menelik I, by the Queen of Sheba who was Ethiopian. At some early date they adopted the Jewish religion but were converted to Christianity about the fourth century, and later many monks came from Egypt and Syria. The Abuna or Archbishop always came from Egypt and was a Coptic bishop chosen by the Coptic Patriarch, but in the present year (1951) an Ethiopian was chosen and consecrated in Cairo. Religion plays an important part in the life of the Amhara, as indicated by the many churches and religious festivals. The priests are the educated class of the country, but in recent years, however, many young non-clerical men have been educated in Europe. Amharic is the official language but the services of the Church are conducted in Geez, the classical Ethiopic.

In the sixteenth century the country was invaded by Moham-

[1] See C. F. Rey. *Real Abyssinia*. London, 1935.

H 2

medans and many Ethiopians were converted to Islam; their
descendants remain Moslem to this day living peaceably in their
own villages alongside their Christian neighbours. Of the
remaining population a large proportion are Galla, who first
appeared as raiders from the south-east about 400 years ago,
and over-ran a good deal of the country. They were gradually
subdued by various " kings " and finally pacified by Menelik.
They inhabit the southern and western parts of the country and
are less advanced than the Amhara. Their origin is probably
Hamitic and their tradition is that they came from across the
water, which indicates that they are of Arabian origin.

In addition to the Amhara and Galla there are the many tribes
of negro people known as Shankala, who live in the low country
at the foot of the escarpment. They are similar to the people
over the border in the Sudan and like them, because of the raids
made upon them time and time again, have become very much
split up and mixed. They have however left their traces on the
people of the high country through the large numbers who were
brought in as slaves.

Other inhabitants of the plateau are the Guragies who are
cultivators speaking a language of their own, but go to the towns
to act as labourers in the dry season after the harvest. They seem
to occupy the position of the Saidi (Upper Egyptian) labourer in
Egypt. In the low and arid or desert country to the east are the
Danakil people and south of them the Somalis, both of which
are almost entirely nomadic and herdsmen dependent on sheep,
goats and camels.

The principal occupations of the country are agriculture and
stock-breeding. The stock comprises large quantities of the
usual African type of humped cattle, sheep and goats. Mules,
ponies and donkeys are plentiful and are the usual means of
transport. Owing to an abundant rainfall crops can be produced
without irrigation, and maize, wheat, millet and barley are grown,
as well as several kinds of vegetables. Coffee is also grown in
quantity, but tobacco is not grown, as Ethiopians do not smoke.
Honey is an important product, as from it a sort of wine called
tej is made, and this with a beer brewed from barley, and araki, a
spirit distilled from tej, are necessities at any feast. Raw meat is
a favourite dish and large quantities of chillies, and sauces made

from them, are eaten with this and other foods. The members of the Tana Mission on one occasion entertained an important Ras to lunch. Amongst the accessories on the table was a very hot sauce which excited the curiosity of the Ras who asked what it was. When he was told that it was a particularly hot sauce he poured out a wineglass full and told one of his retainers to drink it off. The man took it at a gulp, his face became red, his eyes bulged and it looked as if he would die of apoplexy. However, his discomfiture gradually passed off and the Ras tried a little of it. After recovering he said truly it was hot and must have been distilled from fire.

4. THE ATBARA

I have already said that the Atbara and its tributaries, with the exception of a few small streams which come from Eritrea, rise in Ethiopia. The stream which is called the Atbara rises not far from Gondar to the north of Lake Tana, but this river and its tributaries occupy only three-tenths of the basin above the confluence of the Setit or Takkaze with the Atbara, while the Setit occupies the remaining seven-tenths. The Setit rises to the east of Lake Tana and has a course of several hundred miles from its most remote source to its confluence with the Atbara. The hydrology of these Ethiopian tributaries has not been studied.

Most of Eritrea is outside the Nile Basin. It is much more arid than Ethiopia and both its principal rivers, the Gash and the Baraka which are muddy torrents for a few months and dry for the rest of the year, spread out on the Sudan plains and disappear.

Chapter Seven

THE WHITE NILE AND THE CENTRAL SUDAN

UNTIL towards the end of the nineteenth century the White Nile was the only route to the Great Lakes and the country on either side was difficult of access. It is still a main route and the only one for heavy goods to and from the Southern Sudan. From the Sobat mouth to its junction with the Blue Nile it is a slow-flowing stream with an average width of 400 yards, though much wider in places and often with more than one channel. The journey to Juba, 100 miles from the Uganda border, can be made very comfortably on the steamers of the Sudan Government, and from the top deck one gets a good view of the river and its banks. These are at first not very interesting and rather arid, but south of Kosti the country becomes more wooded. Hippopotamuses and crocodiles are common, and occasional antelopes can be seen. There are elephant in places and buffalo but the latter are not often seen from the steamer. The White Nile abounds with waterfowl, storks, cranes, ibis, small waders, and in the winter large quantities of pintail, teal and other duck.

At Renk on the east bank the mixed Arab population begins to give place to the Dinka people, and on the west from Kaka southwards there are the Shilluk who are also to be found on the east bank round Malakal (see Plate XVI). These two tribes, and the Nuer who inhabit both banks of the Sobat, belong to the Nilotic group of people. They are tall and long-limbed and live on the grass plains and the edges of the swamps of the Sudd. The Nilotes are all cattle-owning people but cultivate maize, millet and some vegetables, and those living near rivers fish and hunt the hippopotamus. The men of all these tribes may wear a skin or a strip of cloth but are usually naked; all carry spears. The young girls wear only a few beads, but the married women wear aprons fore and aft made of skins. Sometimes the young man about to be married must provide skins for the bride, and when my wife and I were in the Western Bahr-el-

Ghazal we were asked to give the son of a Dinka chief a lift to the Bahr-el-Arab in our truck in order that he might kill an antelope and get its skin. The young man wore a collar of beads in rows extending from his throat on to his shoulders and chest and carried a spear. He was useful in collecting a crowd to push the truck across the sandy bed of the Lol river. Finally when we arrived at Safaha on the Bahr-el-Arab, he begged, as time was short, that I would shoot a cob for him. I did this and got for him the materials for the bridal dress. We were told that, after some sort of tanning, the skins were chewed by the women until they became softened like suede.

The language and customs of the Nuer and Dinka are closely related and they must be of the same origin, though it is not known when they divided. The Shilluks are distinguished by their style of hair-dressing, in which by means of a mixture of ingredients the hair is worked into a sort of felt of such various shapes as cockscombs, haloes, knobs or saucers. A line of Shilluk villages extends along the left bank of the White Nile from Kaka to Lake No. The principal is Kodok on the White Nile, formerly called Fashoda, and which will be remembered in connection with the Marchand expedition.

In the eighteen-nineties the French and other European nations were colonizing Africa, and French colonial expansion was directed towards the Nile. As a result of this by 1896 the French crossed the Nile-Congo Divide into the Bahr-el-Ghazal Basin and established themselves at Tembura and Deim Zubeir. An expedition to take possession of the White Nile was planned and Captain Marchand came out from France with the necessary equipment including two small gun-boats and some barges. All this equipment came up the Congo and continued up a tributary to the highest navigable point. From there a road 100 miles long was cut through forest to a point on the Sueh river which goes down to the Bahr-el-Ghazal. The making of this road and the transport of stores along it was a great undertaking and was made possible only by the labours of hundreds of natives. The navigation of the Sueh river is not continuous but Marchand was able to pass down it into the Jur, which is now regularly navigated during flood but also has its difficulties. From here he was able to establish a number of posts in the basin of the

Bahr-el-Ghazal, that is the Nile, and to write that he held an all-powerful position. This was not done without opposition and great hardship including shortage of food. In spite of this and several attacks by the Dervishes he managed to reach Kodok by July, 1898, where he was again attacked by Dervishes. They were beaten off and he was awaiting a second attack in September when Lord Kitchener and an Anglo-Egyptian expedition arrived immediately after the battle of Omdurman. After much negotiation between Great Britain and France, which aroused some feeling, Kodok was evacuated by Marchand and his party by the end of the year.

Twenty-five miles south of Khartoum at Gebel Aulia a dam 3·1 miles long has been built across the White Nile to form a reservoir which extends beyond Renk, and has a length of 300 miles. The dam was suggested by the fact that when the Blue Nile rises in flood it ponds up the waters of the White Nile forming a natural reservoir. The dam makes use of this ponding, and its sluices are regulated so as to hold back the White Nile when the Blue Nile falls, and also to increase the amount of water over that which would naturally be held back. The reservoir is filled during and after the Blue Nile flood and its water is used in Egypt from February to May, after which the Aswan supply is drawn upon. The project at its beginning was the subject of much ignorant criticism which caused the size of the projected reservoir to be reduced, and had political effects which delayed construction for ten years. None of these criticisms has been justified in the working of the reservoir which has gone on successfully for fourteen years, with considerable benefits to Egypt and none of the plagues which were forecast for the Sudan. The water in a reservoir in a hot dry climate is always subject to considerable loss by evaporation, and sometimes by soakage into the ground. The White Nile Valley is wide and shallow so that both these methods of loss are greater than on the Aswan Reservoir which has a more favourable shape. A reasonable allowance was made for these losses on the basis of knowledge then existing, and experience of the working shows that the estimate was a generous one for the actual losses by evaporation and soakage have been less than was assumed.

About 500 miles from Khartoum and downstream of the Sobat

mouth is Malakal the headquarters of the Upper Nile Province
and also of the Egyptian Irrigation Service in the Southern Sudan.
From the point of view of Nile studies and projects it is an
important place, since the measurements of the discharge of the
southern tributaries and their levels, as well as surveys for projects on the Upper Nile, are directed from Malakal.

Chapter Eight

THE UPPER WHITE NILE AND SOUTHERN SUDAN

I. GENERAL

THE junction of the White Nile and Sobat, like the junction of the Blue and White Niles, is an important point in the Nile regime. Like the Blue Nile the Sobat has, in flood, a large volume, but falls very low in the dry season; it also draws the greater part of its waters from the Ethiopian Highlands. The White Nile above the Sobat mouth runs for some distance from west to east when it debouches from the great swamps. Its main stream is the Bahr-el-Jebel (river of the mountains), which has in the swamps however many side channels, one of which, the Bahr-el-Zeraf (river of giraffes), separates from the Jebel and joins the White Nile not far above the Sobat mouth. At Lake No the Bahr-el-Jebel is joined by the Bahr-el-Ghazal (river of gazelles) from the west, and the combination is then called the White Nile. The Bahr-el-Ghazal is the outflow from a large swamp area, into which many streams rising on the Nile-Congo Divide pour their waters. In this swamp they are almost entirely evaporated or transpired by the vegetation, and their final contribution to the White Nile supply is trivial.

The rainfall of the Southern Sudan varies from 800 to 1,200 millimetres (32 to 48 in.) per annum over most of the area, but it is heavier in the south of the Bahr-el-Ghazal province, on the undulating country towards the Nile-Congo Divide. December, January and February are almost rainless, while from March the rainfall increases to a maximum in July and August, after which it lessens. At the height of the rains large areas of the plain are under water, and the clayey nature of the soil and the tall grass which springs up, make travelling difficult. In general the wide-spreading plain alternates between open grass and bush, or thin savannah forest composed of small trees which give very little shade. A common tree is the heglig (*balanites ægyptiaca*) which bears a fruit which looks like a plum but con-

106

sists of a large stone covered with a thin layer of slightly acid but pleasant pulp. The Sudan produces very little wild fruit, and not many timbers of first class utility. The larger trees are found on the slopes of the hill country fringing the Sudan, and in the Bahr-el-Ghazal on the ironstone country which rises towards the Nile-Congo Divide. The wood of many of these trees is hard and difficult to work, though the African mahogany, a magnificent tree, is used for many purposes. When the grass on the plains has dried it is burnt by the natives and soon afterwards fresh green grass begins to appear. This grass burning is detrimental to good tree growth.

After the rains are over the plains dry up, and away from the rivers the lack of drinking water is a major difficulty, and prevents full use being made of large areas of otherwise good grazing. Much work has been done by the Government in the last few years in providing water by digging wells or by creating small reservoirs (hafirs) by throwing up earth banks across some of the shallow depressions which cross the plain and are drainage lines. Until motor transport came into common use the only means of travel, except on the navigable rivers, was with donkeys, mules or porters, and was a matter of great difficulty over the clay plain except in the dry season. In the dry season it was important to know where water could be found and whether any food for men and animals was obtainable along the route, for if food is not obtainable there is a definite limit to which the country can be penetrated by porters or pack animals. Consequently the plain to the east of the Bahr-el-Jebel was not well known and to-day there are still areas which have not been traversed by Europeans and are not populated. The country from Gemeiza on the Bahr-el-Jebel to Jebel Kathangor (or Kasangor) is practically an unknown area, and is probably waterless for part of the year.

The most important features of the Nile are the large swamps on the Bahr-el-Jebel and Bahr-el-Ghazal. The area of swamp depends on the height of the rivers and on the local rainfall, so that its extent is usually greatest towards the end of the rainy season in September and October and shrinks as the rivers fall and the heavy evaporation and plant transpiration of the dry season set in. In seasons of heavy rainfall and high flood much of the plains may be under water, as in 1917–18 and 1932 when the plain east of the Jebel was almost completely flooded until well into the dry season. In addition to the area which is flooded only in the rainy season and at high river levels, and which is ordinary grass land at other times, there is the permanent swamp in which papyrus, reeds and other aquatic plants flourish, and which require swampy conditions for the greater part of the year. The different kinds of vegetation are clearly distinguished from the air and the Air Survey Maps of the Bahr-el-Jebel indicate the limits of the permanent swamp. In very low years however much of even the permanent swamp dries up. Such was the case from 1921 to 1923 when the drying of the swamps forced large herds of elephants on to the edge of the river. The permanent swamp along the Bahr-el-Jebel has a length of about 350 miles, ignoring small bends of the river, its area on the Air Survey Maps is about 3,200 square miles, and its average width about 9 miles.

Conditions are different in the case of the Bahr-el-Ghazal, since the swamps are formed by the rivers which run off the slopes of the Nile-Congo Divide, spreading out when they reach the plain. All these rivers are torrential and dry for part of the year, so that some of what is swamp in the rains is ordinary grassland at other times of the year. The area has not been surveyed from the air and since mapping from the ground must be done mainly in the dry season, native report has often to be relied upon for accounts of the nature of the country in the rains, though naturally the experience of the observer enables him to some extent to check these reports. As the country is more fully explored the tendency is to reduce the areas marked swamp. The area of swamp in the Ghazal Basin is about 5,600 square miles, but this was not measured on the most recent maps and is in part conjectural.

2. THE SOBAT

The Sobat is formed by two main branches, the Baro and the Pibor, of which the Baro produces the greater quantity of water. All of the Baro and a good part of the Pibor water comes from Ethiopia, though the Pibor receives some water from drainage of the plain. In years of heavy rain on the mountains which form the fringe of the Sudan in the south—the Acholi, Imatong,

XVII. THE BARO IN FLOOD. ANUAK VILLAGE IN ETHIOPIAN TERRITORY

XVIII. A SUDD OF FLOATING GRASS (UM SOOF) FORMING ON THE PIBOR. THE
RIVER WAS COMPLETELY BLOCKED HIGHER UP IN 1922

Dongotona, usually grouped together as Imatong—some of the water which runs off them by torrential streams may make its way over the plain into the southern tributaries of the Pibor. From the high country to the east and south numerous streams flow down into the plain. In their upper courses they are mountain torrents carrying large volumes of water in flood but many of them become a trickle in the dry season, and are dry in the plains. The largest is the Baro, which is a perennial stream (see Plate XVII), but neither the Baro, Pibor, or the main stream of the Sobat is navigable in the dry season by anything much larger than a canoe. Until cars became commonly used in the Sudan canoes were the ordinary means of communication in the dry season between Gambeila on the Baro, Akobo on the Pibor and the White Nile. The Sobat and Pibor to Akobo are navigable for steamers from June to December, but navigation to Gambeila usually ceases about the middle of October. The Pibor and its tributaries are liable to be blocked by vegetation in flood time (see Plate XVIII).

In the dry season roads exist between the principal places in the Southern Sudan, but the length of time during which those in the plain are usable by motor traffic depends on the incidence of the rains and the importance of the road. A road in the plain is constructed by clearing it of bush and trees and putting a grader over it to smooth it. A more important road will have ditches on either side and be embanked over low and marshy ground, with bridges over streams. Most of the plain is a grey or blackish clay called " cotton soil," which is most tiring to walk over when wet because of the amount which clings to one's boots. When dry the soil cracks deeply and the grass grows in knobby tufts, which make it very rough going.

I recently made a round tour of the eastern plain with my colleague H. G. Bambridge and Mrs. Bambridge. Bambridge is the Egyptian Government's Inspector of Irrigation in the Southern Sudan, whose business is the collection of information about the tributaries of the Nile, their flow, levels, special surveys and anything necessary in connection with the great projects for the utilisation of Nile water. He has been on work of this nature for the last thirty years and a better and more instructive companion could not be found.

Our journey was started at the end of February, 1950, when we set out from Malakal with men and cars to make a round of 1,000 miles. Going south and then nearly due east we got to the station of Akobo on the Pibor, having passed through alternations of thin bush, scattered trees and open plain, and crossed shallow depressions which were the drainage lines, and in which there were occasionally pools. As far as could be seen the country was dead flat, although actually it has a very slight slope of a few inches to the mile towards the north. Akobo is the headquarters of a large district whose affairs are regulated by a District Commissioner. It contains, besides the District Commissioner's house, office and government buildings, a mission, some traders and a number of native houses made of poles and grass, and is similar to many other government posts. A District Commissioner, having a large district to attend to, is kept busy with a multitude of duties. He must tour his district, which in the dry season he can now do by car, where formerly he walked or rode, but even now in the rainy season he must walk or ride to places away from the river. He must see that the roads and bridges are kept in order, build and repair rest houses, and teach the people to do various constructive jobs. He is usually keen on the development of the resources of the district, the planting of gardens, the trial of new crops, and in cattle-country, in dairy work and the improvement of the stock. In addition he is responsible for the preservation of order and supervision of courts held by the native chiefs. From these courts there is appeal to an assembly of chiefs and elders, and finally to a court of appeal consisting of chiefs and elders on which the District Commissioner sits. This court is summoned by the District Commissioner, who appoints a date and place of meeting, the date being indicated by sending to each member a string with knots on it, one of which is to be untied each day. These officials in remote places lead hard lives, but are keen and will talk for hours about their districts and the people. Much information has been collected by them on native languages and customs, the natural history and the physical features of their districts, some of which has been published in the periodical *Sudan Notes and Records*.

From Akobo we continued south to Pibor Post and went to

see the junction of the Veveno and Lotilla, head streams of the Pibor, which at this time of the year consisted of pools from which herds of cattle drink and in which fish are trapped. The Veveno and Lotilla, like many other khors or channels, start as numbers of shallow depressions a few inches deep which collect the drainage of the country in the rains and join together to form larger channels. There was a project at one time to lessen the losses in the Bahr-el-Jebel Swamps by digging a channel from a spot near Gemeiza on the Jebel to the Veveno, enlarging the Veveno and improving the Pibor, and finally bringing the water into the White Nile via the Sobat. The project was considered by a Committee of the Ministry of Public Works, but was not accepted.

We continued our journey from Pibor Post across to Pachalla on the Akobo River, which is here the boundary between the Sudan and Ethiopia, since Ethiopia has a large salient between the Baro and the Akobo projecting 140 miles into the plain. The people of this salient are negroid and have no racial connection with the peoples of the Ethiopian Highlands. Going south we soon passed through country in which game was plentiful, to the Boma Plateau where it projects into the plain. With some difficulty, and not without damage to a car, we climbed a very rough and rocky mountain road to the police post on the slopes of Nyelichu nearly 6,000 feet high. To the east we looked towards the high country of Ethiopia and to the west out over the plain with outlying hills and Jebel Kasangor in the distance. In this south-eastern corner of the plain there occur great migrations of antelope which move in almost solid masses. We saw large numbers of cob, but we were too early to witness the migration. We also saw several herds of eland, which are found in the Sudan only in this area. We were interested to see these animals, standing nearly 6 feet at the shoulder, jump over bushes as high as themselves.

When we left Boma for Kathangor (or Kasangor), an isolated mass apparently of volcanic origin, a strong hot wind was blowing which did not improve the desolate appearance of the plain, on which the only trees are pole-like grey-looking acacias scattered at intervals of 100 yards or so. The plain was waterless but round Kathangor it is obviously swampy in the rains due to the Lotilliet coming from the Didinga mountains to the south, and the Kuron coming from Ethiopia. We saw no channel round Kathangor but sixty miles south the Khor Lotilliet or Lokalyan is 140 yards wide and looks as if it might occasionally have a stream 4 or 5 feet deep, and the natives indicated by signs water above a man's head. It obviously spreads out and forms a swamp in the rains. At the time of our visit it was dry and people were watering cattle from pits dug in the sandy bed, and in which the water was about 6 feet down. The holes were protected by a barrier of thorns and girls were using gourds to fill small wooden troughs from which the animals drank in turn.

The Lotilliet is similar to other streams which we crossed on our way from Kapoeta to Juba, and which come off the Southern mountains. Some of these are considerable torrents where they leave the mountains, but flow into unknown country and as far as is known spread out and disappear as definite watercourses. What becomes of their water is a question on which investigations by the Sudan Government are just starting. The Kinyeti which flows past the Government station of Torit is the only stream which flows all the year round. One of the problems to be solved is why the hydrology of the plains east of the Bahr-el-Jebel is different from that of the Bahr-el-Ghazal to the west.

Travelling west from Kapoeta, the road goes up and down along the foot of the mountains and in and out amongst others. It was made more difficult for Bambridge who was driving, by the fact that on leaving the Boma a large stone had been thrown up and broken the foot-brake lever making the brake useless. The mountains are steep, sometimes with rocky pinnacles and sometimes with large domes of igneous rock making a great contrast with the monotonous plain. The highest mountain in the Sudan, Kinyeti 10,460 feet, lies in the Imatong to the southeast of Torit, and there are several peaks above 8,000 feet in the whole group of mountains along the Uganda frontier. These can be climbed, but it usually necessitates quite an expedition which takes one into delightful country with a very different vegetation from that of the plains, as the high plateaux are usually well wooded.

Before Torit we stayed at a rest-house at the foot of a great dome of rock near a small village. The rest-house was of the usual type with a thatched roof carried by a ridge pole on two forked uprights well set in the ground, with rafters cut from the bush and resting on mud walls. We climbed up the hill some distance to see the water supply of the village which consisted of several pools in the rock. An intelligent Sudanese, who was a student on holiday, told me that the village was formerly on the top of the rock as a protection against enemies, but with the abolition of slave raiding and the establishment by the Government of peaceful conditions, they were able to live at the foot of the mountain near to their fields.

Torit is a fairly important place, the headquarters of a District Commissioner and also of the Equatorial Battalion of the Sudan Defence Force, while medical research on tropical diseases is carried on there by the Rockefeller Institution. At Juba, the headquarters of Equatoria Province, there is a Diesel ferry across the Bahr-el-Jebel for cars and passengers, while roads go westwards to the Bahr-el-Ghazal and Belgian Congo, southwards to Uganda and northwards to Mongalla, Bor and Malakal. It is the largest town in the Southern Sudan and has an aerodrome on which several routes converge.

Before we leave the Sobat, the Machar Marsh should be mentioned. The Machar Marsh, an area lying to the north of the junction of the Baro and Pibor, is unsurveyed and very little known, and covers an area of about 2,500 square miles marked as swamp on the maps. At the present time its exploration is being attempted by the Jonglei Team, with the object that the area might be improved and developed to provide grazing to replace some of that which will be lost when the proposed extensive schemes of water conservation on the Nile are working. The swamp is fed by spills from the Baro and by several torrents which come from Ethiopia between the Blue Nile and the Baro, of which the principal is the Khor Yabus. There is an outlet from the swamp by the Khor Adar which joins the White Nile near Melut, but the flow along this is generally small. It is estimated that the water which flows annually into the swamp and disappears, apart from the rain falling on it, is about three-quarters of what is stored in the Aswan Reservoir. The fringes of the swamp are inhabited by cattle-owning people.

3. THE BAHR-EL-JEBEL AND BAHR-EL-ZERAF

Sudan Government steamers call at Malakal and there is a regular service as far as Juba on the Bahr-el-Jebel. A journey on one of these steamers will give one a good idea of the Sudd Region and the swamps. A short distance above Malakal one passes the Sobat mouth and in flood time there is a sharp line of separation between the silty water of the Sobat and the clear darker-looking water from the Bahr-el-Jebel, just as there is between the waters of the Blue and White Niles at their junction. Some twenty-seven miles above the Sobat is the mouth of the Bahr-el-Zeraf, which derives its water from the Bahr-el-Jebel a long way to the south. In the last century it was sometimes connected with the Jebel through small channels and sometimes drew its water by flow through the swamp. About 180 miles from the Zeraf mouth the Jebel and Zeraf are separated from each other by two of three miles of swamp, but below this point the rivers separate leaving, except for fringes of swamp, hard ground between them. Across this narrow neck of swamp two channels known as the Cuts were dredged in 1910 and 1913.

Above the Cuts the channel is known as the Upper Zeraf. Previous to the construction of the Cuts it was sometimes possible to find a way from the Zeraf to the Jebel, but the way was probably more often blocked than open. In 1871 Sir Samuel Baker managed by incredible labours to cut a way for his steamers and reach the Jebel some distance north of Ghaba Shambe. At one point the cutting had the effect of draining the marsh and so left his ships stranded. He escaped from this predicament by building a dam of clay and timber behind his ships, and thus held up sufficient water to float them again. The work of making a channel through mud and masses of vegetation with hand tools—knives, swords and spades—plagued by mosquitoes, biting flies and leeches, and subject to malaria, the origin and cure of which was then unknown was truly colossal. Baker's channel was cleared by dredgers in 1911 but closed up again after some years and has remained closed ever since. In 1922 when Mr. F. Newhouse, Mr. G. Middleton and I went into the Upper Zeraf in the *Walad*, a small shallow draft steamer, we, after passing through some lagoons, very shortly came to a wall of vegetation through which there was no passage.

It was thought at the time that the making of the Cuts would increase the amount of water reaching the tail of the swamps. It is not possible to say whether this was the case or no, owing to the small amount of information available previous to their construction, but it is true that the discharge through the Cuts prevents the Zeraf from falling as low in the dry season as it otherwise would. There is also the advantage that as the Cuts are navigable they give an alternative way to the south which is shorter by fifty miles than the route via the Bahr-el-Jebel.

From a short distance upstream of the Sobat mouth the White Nile is flowing from west to east and on its north bank there is a gradually widening strip of swamp, until at Lake No the Bahr-el-Jebel coming from the south joins the Bahr-el-Ghazal coming from the west. This may be said to be the beginning of the Sudd Region, so called from the blocks (Arabic *sudd*) of vegetation which used to choke the Jebel and Ghazal. The appearance of the Bahr-el-Jebel for 300 miles south does not change very much. From the lower deck of the steamer all that can be seen is a channel which winds about between walls of vegetation 12 feet or so high, with occasionally an entrance to a lagoon. From the top deck, from which the reis (captain) and helmsman navigate the ship there is a view over a wide flat expanse of vegetation broken by occasional lagoons and side channels, or trees on the higher ground several miles away. There are a few places where patches of dry ground come down to the river, as at Adok, and in some cases on the west bank advantage has been taken of these to make roads inland to the drier ground outside the permanent swamp. An important road starts from Ghaba Shambe at the head of a large lagoon and is one of the means of entry to the Bahr-el-Ghazal province. There are several systems of side channels which in some cases are navigable right through. An important one is the Atem system on the east of the Jebel where the swamps reach their maximum width of about twelve miles. This takes off the river about twenty miles north of Bor and winds about in swamps with lagoons and side channels until it reaches the dry ground bounding the swamp at Jonglei.

Jonglei has been mentioned several times previously, but like many another place shown on the map of the Sudan, it consists only of a few huts (see Plate XX). Its importance is that it was chosen by the late Mr. A. D. Butcher as the starting place for a projected canal to convey water directly to a point on the White Nile between the Zeraf and the Sobat mouths. The effect of this would be to carry about half the discharge of the Jebel with only small losses such as normally occur in canals. By this abstraction the quantity flowing in the Jebel would be so reduced as to prevent it overflowing into swamps and being wasted. The final effect would be the saving of large quantities of water, and in addition the canal would form an important link in the chain of projects proposed by my colleagues and myself for the future conservation of the Nile.

The Atem finally returns to the Jebel a short distance south of Ghaba Shambe. It is a puzzling stream to navigate owing to the network of channels which change from time to time, sometimes one and sometimes another branch offering the easiest navigation. Sudanese who navigate the steamers make no use of maps and seem to rely on memory and an ability to judge from its appearance where the deeper water lies. This memory for channels is astounding when one considers that the reis of an irrigation inspection steamer navigates, at different times, all the tributaries of the White Nile, and in doing so traverses several thousand miles of waterway.

Of the plants which grow so luxuriantly in the Sudd region, papyrus appears to be the commonest. It always roots in the bank and never grows from the bottom in deep water, though it may stretch out from the bank for a little distance as a sort of raft. It grows in clumps of long stalks with feathery heads reaching a height of 12 or 14 feet. This is the plant which lines the Bahr-el-Jebel from Lake No to somewhere about Kenisa. South of this stretch it is still plentiful but tall reeds (*phragmitis communis*, Arabic, boos), begin to be common on the river bank, which gets higher relative to the water as one goes south. This greater distance from the water is more favourable to reeds, as their roots can penetrate deeper than those of papyrus. Another common plant is *vossia cuspidata* (Arabic, um soof) which is a kind of grass rooted to the bank and sending out shoots several yards long, which float on the water and send up leaves 3 or 4 feet long. The distance it extends into the stream depends on the water's velocity, and many streams are fringed with this

XIX.   FISHING IN THE KHOR YABUS.   GARMOOT (CATFISH) IN THE NET

XX.   HAMED SULEIMAN PASHA, UNDER-SECRETARY, AND DR. MOHAMMED AMIN
BEY, INSPECTOR-GENERAL, EGYPTIAN PUBLIC WORKS, AT JONGLEI, WITH A GAUGE
OBSERVER AND LOCAL DINKAS

plant. The water lettuce (*pistia stratiotes*), which floats on the water and accumulates in places sheltered from the wind, is also common. Sometimes the wind breaks up the accumulations and the water surface becomes almost covered with these attractive little plants. I have seen this on several occasions and once in particular on the White Nile near Melut. Dr. Lawrence Balls and I once saw the water lettuce growing in a ditch near Damietta. He, a distinguished botanist with a wide knowledge of Egypt, had never seen the plant in Egypt before, and I who had done a good deal of paddling about in swamp in Egypt after snipe, thought it was confined to the Upper Nile, so it looked as if we had made a discovery. However, on looking up a list of plants found in drains and canals in Egypt, we discovered that it was noted as occurring in a small area near Damietta. The study of plant distribution must present many curious problems, but this seems rather striking; why should pistia occur in a very tiny area of northern Egypt when its next place of occurrence is 2,000 miles away as the river flows?

The study of swamp vegetation is important and has been the object of missions from the Fuad I University of Cairo.[1] It will easily be realized that when it is proposed to undertake large works which will alter the regime of the river over hundreds of miles, in a country which is dominated by vegetation, a knowledge of the habits of that vegetation is extremely important. In its passage through the swamps the Jebel loses about half its water, and this loss cannot be accounted for by ordinary evaporation. It is known from many experiments in other parts of the world that vegetation with free access to water, transpires more than would be evaporated from an equal surface of open water. Experiments were made with tanks planted with papyrus and placed in the papyrus near the Bahr-el-Jebel. At first the papyrus was never as flourishing in the tank as outside it, and transpiration was not as great as would be expected from experiments elsewhere. On the advice of the botanist, however, the method of planting and culture of the papyrus was altered, with the result that it now grows more vigorously and transpires an amount more nearly approaching what would be expected. The mystery

[1] *Report on a Botanical Excursion to the Sudd Region*, by Dr. Ahmed Mohammed Migahid, Fuad I University Press. Cairo, 1948.

of where the water goes has consequently now been largely removed.

Population is scanty along the Bahr-el-Jebel until one gets south of Kenisa as there is very little dry ground for them to live on. Where there is dry land one may see and smell now and then a camp of fishermen or hippo hunters. In the dry time of the year from Bor southwards, where the bank is above water level and there are large areas of grazing, the people bring their cattle down and make camps on the river bank. In the evening and early morning one can see the cattle all tied up to pegs and quantities of smoke arising from fires which are lighted to keep off the insects. The people too are often covered with some of the wood ashes in which they have slept. This gives a man an odd appearance when, completely grey with ashes from head to foot, he has waded into the water to have a morning drink.

In the papyrus swamp one can occasionally see from the top deck of the steamer, the backs of elephants with white egrets perched upon them. In a dry season when the papyrus has been burnt Mrs. Gray's antelope will probably be encountered some-where between Lake No and Bor. It is peculiar to the swamps of the Southern Sudan and the old males are very handsome animals, their colouring being nearly black with a white patch on the neck and withers. The situtunga, also a swamp animal, is rarely seen. I have, however, twice seen a specimen when going up the Bahr-el-Ghazal river in a steamer. Once, on rounding a bend, we came suddenly on one standing in shallow swamp, and we had a good view before he moved a few paces into deep water and submerged himself completely, that being the last we saw of him. South of Bor the swamp gradually narrows and the dry ground is higher and usually covered with thin forest. There is here more chance of seeing game than in the papyrus country; elephants, sometimes in numbers, will almost certainly be seen.

Previous to the re-occupation of the Sudan, the Jebel, Zeraf and Ghazal were frequently blocked by masses of vegetable matter for months or even years at a time, and one of the first pieces of work undertaken by the British was the clearing of blocks on the Bahr-el-Jebel. The blocks are formed by strong winds, which are frequent at the beginning and end of the rainy season, and which break loose masses of papyrus and um soof which float down the river. These masses can be quite large, and a friend of mine once saw a waterbuck travelling on one. Thus large areas of vegetation may be moving together and sometimes are held up at sharp bends or narrow places. The section of the river is decreased and the velocity of the water thus increased, so that masses of plants carrying earth on their roots are sucked down under the floating barrier, and finally the whole river is blocked by a mass which keeps increasing and consolidating under the pressure of the water rising behind. The blocks ultimately become so solid that even elephants can cross them, and they may reach a mile or two in length. The water eventually finds another channel, but sometimes blocks burst, either owing to increasing pressure or to strong winds. In the Sudd-cutting operations of 1900–1 five steamers and a large gang of Dervish prisoners were employed. Explosives were tried without success, and the most successful method was to attack a block from the down-stream side, cutting it into rectangular pieces and hauling these out by means of a steamer. The pieces were then allowed to float away downstream. Altogether nineteen blocks were removed from the eighty miles of river south from Lake No, and it was arduous work under trying conditions. It will be realized that when a steamer was shut in on the upstream side of the block there was little that could be done to cut a way through. Since 1900 blocks have occasionally formed, but to-day the regular navigation of the river usually prevents them from forming. Blocks still occur in less frequented rivers like the Pibor, and Cut 2 (the northern one) has been blocked several times (see Plate XVIII).

By the time Mongalla is reached the swamp has decreased in width considerably and hills begin to be visible to the south. Mongalla was formerly the headquarters of the Equatorial Province, while Rejaf was the centre of trade and beginning of the road to the Congo. For many years now trade and Government have been centred at Juba, and Rejaf has lapsed into unimportance, while the only importance of Mongalla is that it is a river-gauging station. Here the discharge is measured by stretching a wire rope across the river as a means of holding the observation boat in place. When not in use the rope lies on the bottom of the river and is hauled tight above the surface when needed. There is usually not much river traffic, but if a steamer or boat happened to appear while work was in progress the rope was lowered. It once happened that the observer, after finishing observations, and no doubt absorbed in his calculations, forgot to see that the rope was lowered to the bed, and it was left above the water. After dark a motor boat came down the river, struck the wire and was upset. The owner, however, clung to the rope and shouted for help, and the watchman in charge of the rope, hearing the shout, thought a steamer must be coming and promptly lowered the wire into the water. Very fortunately the occupants of the launch managed to get ashore without serious hurt from what was a dangerous situation, for apart from the risk of drowning, crocodiles are plentiful hereabouts.

A short distance south of Juba the flat plain comes to an end and the river is in a well-defined valley, with its course here and there obstructed by rapids. There is no navigation for 120 miles but there is a good all-weather road some distance to the east of the river. The road goes up to Nimule on the Uganda border, where it joins the network of good roads in Uganda. This portion of the journey is done by motor transport, and a regular service connects the Sudan Government steamers with the steamers of the Kenya-Uganda Railways which steam from Nimule to Butiaba on Lake Albert.

The Nile from Khartoum to Juba receives very little water from rainfall on the plains, and in its course through the swamps its losses are heavy. South of Juba, however, the main volume from Lake Albert is increased by flow from torrential streams coming from the hilly country which is the beginning of the high land of East and Central Africa. These torrents carry water from April to November mostly in spates, when they rise rapidly and fall again. There are only a few streams of any size, but in exceptional years the torrents between Lake Albert and Mongalla have, for a month or two, contributed more water than came from the lake. The main streams are the Kit and the Aswa on the eastern side, over which there are now good bridges. When I first went up to Uganda in 1924 the road was only a track cleared of trees and stones, and one travelled on foot with porters and crossed the streams by wading, which cause no difficulty in the dry season when there is no depth of water. In the rainy season, however, one might be kept for days waiting for spates to subside. It was necessary to take precautions against sleeping sickness which then existed in parts of the Southern Sudan and Uganda. One of the precautions was to use porters from Rejaf for half the journey and then to send them back. The next day another lot appeared from the south and the journey was continued with the new porters. Sleeping sickness has now practically disappeared from this area and creates no difficulty for the traveller, whereas in 1924 permits were required and travelling, except on business, was not encouraged.

Travelling on foot with porters was very pleasant once the porters had been collected and the initial arrangements made. The baggage was packed in 50-lb. loads, and, in the Sudan and East Africa, is carried on the head. Loads at the beginning of the journey were laid out in line, and the porters lined up under charge of a Sudanese policeman. At the word each went for a load and there was a rush for what looked like small loads. The disappointment of those who got them and finding that in spite of their looks their weights were normal, was amusing to watch. Once the loads were allotted, however, there was no more bother as each porter took the same load every day. When travelling with porters a few medicines were a necessary item of equipment, and nearly every day a little time would be spent examining porters or villagers who were sick or had a fancy for a medicine for other reasons. To those whom I thought were not really sick I usually gave Epsom salts, quinine powder and castor oil mixed up in a mug with water, which I insisted should be drunk without heel taps. More than one patient came to me the following day to testify to the power of the medicine.

An average day's march for a porter is 15 miles, and resthouses on the old Rejaf-Nimule road were arranged at suitable distances accordingly. At one of the rest-houses I met a party with a professional hunter, and whilst I was there a young man arrived who said that he was walking from the Cape to Cairo for some sort of wager. The young man was full of confidence, and, having informed us that he was a civil engineer and given us some information about the dam at Sennar, which, however, was completely erroneous, he proceeded to say that a march of only 15 miles a day was just ridiculous, and he himself thought nothing of 20. The hunter replied that the young man did not carry a 50-lb. load on his head, and the 15-mile average was based on practical experience of what porters could reasonably be expected to do day after day. The next morning, to avoid confusion, I let the other two parties get away first. I was just finishing my breakfast when the young man returned to say that his porters had thrown down their loads and bolted, and could I help him to get some more. I called up my policeman and the local chief and asked them what could be done. The chief was reluctant to provide any of his own people because he had heard that this man was continually pushing his porters to hurry and to do more than they were able. I explained this to the young man who did not know any African language, and finally persuaded the chief to produce some more porters. When this was done the young man asked me to " Tell these porters I have a pistol and shall shoot them if they run away," to which I replied that the Sudan Government would certainly hang him if he did, and advised him to be a little easier on the natives if he wanted to finish his journey. I never heard where he got to finally. Travelling with porters is now largely a thing of the past except where motor transport cannot be used.

Between Rejaf and Nimule the country is covered with thin forest and one gets an occasional view of hills and distant mountains. The Bahr-el-Jebel is in a narrow valley all the way with hilly country on either side. Near the mouth of the Aswa River there is a point where some years ago a block of vegetation formed and consolidated like those which formerly occurred lower down in the swamps. The block became so solid that people and even elephants crossed the river on it. It lasted for some years and then broke up and may possibly recur from time to time.

At Nimule the river takes a sharp bend and changes character, becoming, in Uganda, a wide slow-flowing stream fringed with swamp and navigable for steamers into Lake Albert and to the Murchison Falls. At Nimule there is a small rapid and about four miles below are the magnificent Fola Rapids, where the whole river is narrowed to about 25 yards (see Plate XXI). We suggested in Volume VII of The Nile Basin that a

XXI.   THE WHOLE STREAM OF THE BAHR EL JEBEL AT THE FOLA RAPIDS BELOW
NIMULE

XXII.   SABRY EL KORDI PASHA WITH NILE PERCH CAUGHT NEAR MESHRA EL REK,
BAHR EL GHAZAL

large reservoir for Century Storage should be made in Lake Albert by means of a dam at Nimule. This would store water from years of plenty for use in lean ones, and would directly benefit Egypt. The site is the best from the point of view of both conservation and control of the river, but the fact that it would flood a large area in Uganda is an obstacle. The governments concerned have agreed to the construction of a dam at the outlet of the Nile from Lake Victoria, and preliminary work has begun. This dam will provide power for Uganda and a big reservoir for Egypt, but without a dam to control Lake Albert the reservoir will be of very little use to Egypt. Uganda is prepared to agree to a small dam at a site near the lake, but so far agreement has not been concluded and the matter is still under discussion.

4. THE BAHR-EL-GHAZAL

The Bahr-el-Ghazal joins the Bahr-el-Jebel through Lake No, which is a large lagoon extending westwards for seven miles. The water which passes out into the Jebel is the insignificant remainder of a rainfall of about a metre on a catchment nearly as large as France, the rest being evaporated or transpired by swamp vegetation. The Ghazal is formed by a number of streams rising on the Nile-Congo Divide, of which the largest are the Jur and the Lol, but only the Jur is continuous with the Bahr-el-Ghazal; all the others end in the swamp on the lower course of the river. The Bahr-el-Arab has the largest basin of any of the tributaries, but as it is the most northerly its rainfall is smaller than that on the remainder of the Ghazal basin, and owing to its small slope the northern part of the Arab basin contributes very little water. Actually drainage channels beginning on the high mountain mass of Jebel Marra are shown on maps as connecting with the Arab. It may be that occasionally after a heavy rainfall water from Jebel Marra reaches the Bahr-el-Arab, or swamps connected with it, but there can be no great quantity from this source.

Excluding the country north of the Bahr-el-Arab, the remaining area is of two kinds, the plain of the Southern Sudan in which lie the lower courses of the tributaries, and the undulating country rising to the Nile-Congo Divide, in which lie their upper courses.

On the lower courses of the tributaries and the main stream are large areas of swamp, and, as we have said, all the tributaries except the Jur, which is really the main stream, end in swamp and do not join the Ghazal directly. The Lol which for several months carries a lot of water and is nearly as large as the Jur, also ends in swamp. In September, 1930, when flying with the R.A.F. from Wau down the Jur, I was able to see a good deal of the swamp country. For some distance the Lol and Jur are only about fifteen miles apart and at that time of the year the swamps were full and much open water was visible. There seemed little doubt that the Jur and Lol were then connected through lagoons and small channels, and that a good deal of country was flooded which would later be dry grass plain. This expansion and shrinkage of inundation on the plains has already been mentioned in connection with our discussion of the country east of the Bahr-el-Jebel.

The country on the upper courses of the Bahr-el-Ghazal tributaries is forest covered, which may, for the greater part, be described as savannah forest. It is not very thick, though it contains magnificent trees. In the ravines formed by the streams near their sources, thick tropical forest exists like that in the Congo Basin, and was called by Schweinfurth, "Gallery Forest." They consist of tall trees growing on the sides and bottom of the ravine, with hanging lianas and thick undergrowth below them, and are the home of that rare forest antelope, the bongo. The country is undulating with outcrops of lateritic ironstone, and becomes more hilly near the Divide. The water parting, however, is often not a well-marked ridge but gently rounded country in which ravines have been eroded, so that the beginnings of two streams may be a few hundred yards apart, one going to the Nile and the other to the Congo.

Lower down towards the end of the undulating ironstone country the valleys become wider and shallower and the stream winds about in a flat grassy plain called locally " toich," which may be a mile or two wide and is bounded by the higher land and the trees. In flood time the river overflows this plain which becomes covered with new grass and later provides good grazing. In the dry season all the tributaries are reduced to pools or just a small flow, but water can always be obtained by digging in the sand of the bed. In the rains the tributaries rise and fall quickly with spates, but the main tributaries are considerable streams.

There are, in addition to the river, two main routes into the Bahr-el-Ghazal basin. One road leaves the Bahr-el-Jebel at Shambe and goes to Wau, the principal town and headquarters of the Bahr-el Ghazal province. This road crosses all the tributaries some distance above where they spread out into the swamp, and where they are considerable streams in the rainy season and are then usually crossed by ferries. In the dry season cars can cross the sandy beds of these streams on causeways which are built up annually. Another road to the south of this leaves the Nile at Juba for Aba in the Congo, but some twenty miles before the Congo boundary a branch goes westwards, keeping about this distance from the boundary to Tembura, and from there north to Wau. This is an all-weather road, mainly on ironstone which lends itself to road-making, and has the advantage of crossing the streams where they are small and can be easily bridged.

In July, 1930, Mohammed Sabry el Kordi Bey of the Irrigation Service (now Pasha and Under-Secretary of State), and I set off from Khartoum in the inspection steamer *Fayum* to make a reconnaissance of the Bahr-el-Ghazal basin, by river as far as Wau, which is the usual limit of navigation of the Jur, and then by car back to the Bahr-el-Jebel at Juba. We were unfortunate, as our fine new ship broke a main bearing before we got to Malakal, but Mr. S. B. Moir, Inspector of Irrigation at Malakal, sent the steamer *Kordofan* to our rescue and we were able to continue our journey. At Malakal we were fortunate in meeting an R.A.F. patrol under Wing-Commander Sholto Douglas, which had been making a reconnaissance with float-planes of some of the southern Nile tributaries. I, who had no experience of flying, was very much impressed with the accounts of where the patrol had been and what it had seen. So much so, that I persuaded the Wing-Commander to let me make a flight with them. At that time the country was far less accessible than now, and we were still in the reconnaissance stage as far as the hydrology of parts of the Upper Nile were concerned. I was anxious to see something of the swamp country from the air, so it was arranged that Flight-Lieutenant W. A. B. Bowen-Buscarlet with one of their planes, would pick me up off the steamer next morning at Lake No and give me a flight over the swamp. The plane arrived at 7.15 next morning and alighted on the water alongside the *Kordofan*. I went on board and we took off and flew up the Bahr-el-Jebel to Adok. It was most interesting and exciting to see the country from the air for the first time and recognize features one knew from travelling up and down by steamer. It was still more interesting and instructive when we left the Jebel and flew northwest to the Bahr-el-Ghazal across what was then very little known country. Papyrus, which appeared to be everywhere when one is travelling by steamer, is seen from the air not to extend very far from the lagoons and channels, and is succeeded by grass or reeds. Moreover there were far more patches of dry ground in the swamp than one had expected from the available information. Finally we reached the Bahr-el-Ghazal and flew back along it to its mouth, alighting alongside the steamer at Lake No about four hours after we had left, I having had a marvellous experience. It was clear to me that air-reconnaissance was an essential part of the study of the Nile, and that some things showed up clearly from the air which would never be discovered from the ground. I immediately started negotiations to get more flying a little later. Sabry and I continued our journey up the Bahr-el-Ghazal while Bowen-Buscarlet flew the plane back to Malakal.

The lower Ghazal is swampy, though the papyrus is smaller and less healthy than on the Jebel, and in many places dry ground and trees are close to the river. About eighty miles from its tail the Ghazal is joined by a channel which is called the Bahr-el-Arab which was sudded a short distance from its mouth. It originates in the swamp at the tail of the Lol and is probably not continuous with the stream called the Bahr-el-Arab further west which has already been mentioned. Upstream of the mouth of the Arab the country becomes more swampy and no banks are visible. It widens out into Lake Ambadi and a channel continues from there to Meshra-el-Rek. This channel has very little flow and has been dredged from time to time to keep it navigable. It was between Meshra and the mouth of the Bahr-el-Arab that Romolo Gessi, one of Gordon's officers, was, in 1888, trapped by floating vegetation and lost many of his company. From September to January he and a large number of soldiers with their wives and children were shut in. Their steamer could make no progress and, surrounded by swamp, there was no means of escape. Their food supply exhausted, scores of the wretched people died before rescuers arrived.

Meshra is on a peninsula in the swamp, connected to the dry ground to the south by a narrow strip of higher ground along which runs the road to Wau. Meshra-el-Rek, as its name implies, was originally the port for the slave trade of this region, and is still a means of entry in the dry season, served regularly by steamers. When we arrived we found the channel very shallow and we had to tie up about four miles short of Meshra as there was not enough water for our barge. Nile steamers generally travel with one or more up to five or six barges which carry stores, merchandise, and sometimes passengers. The *Kordofan* was not a very stable ship and it was usual to travel with a barge lashed alongside to increase the stability in case of strong winds, which have been known to turn ships over.

The Jur generally has enough water for navigation in July, but this year it was late in rising and several Sudan Government steamers were waiting near the mouth for the water to rise and make navigation possible. The lower part of the Jur, known as the Narrows, is very narrow and very winding and steamers are assisted by tugs. We were held up near Meshra for a week, but fortunately it was possible by pushing a small collapsible boat through the reeds to reach some dry ground where one could shoot guinea-fowl or an occasional small antelope, which were a satisfactory addition to the food supply. We also fished, and I initiated my companion, Sabry el Kordi, into the pleasant sport of spinning for Nile perch and tiger fish, both game fish, the former making good eating. Sabry's initiation was very successful, for before the week was out he hooked a 77 lb. " aigl " (perch) and brought it to the gaff after a fight of half an hour (see Plate XXII). The Nile perch reaches a great size, the largest to my knowledge being a 280 pounder caught in Lake No by the late Mr. E. W. Buckley of the Egyptian Irrigation Service. Fish of 250 lb. have been caught below the Gebel Aulia Dam. The tiger fish is much smaller than the Nile

perch, but is a very fierce fighter, whose hard mouth makes him
difficult to hook, and whose habit of leaping out of the water
and shaking himself often rids him of the hook when it appears
to have been well and truly taken. When fishing in these waters
where a large aigl may be hooked, the tackle must be stout,
but this does not give the fighting qualities of the smaller tiger
fish (" kas ") full play. On a rod and tackle, such as are used for
sea-trout, the kas gives great sport and dashes about more
fiercely than any trout. It is necessary to use a steel wire trace
for both kas and aigl, the teeth of the kas being very formidable.

The Narrows of the Jur stretch for about thirty miles as the
aeroplane flies, and the whole region is a dreary grass swamp
through which the river winds in short sharp bends with a width
for long stretches of not much more than 30 feet (see Plate
XXIII). The only features are a few lagoons and solitary trees
or clumps of trees, near which may be one or two Dinka huts.
The current is not very strong but, owing to the narrowness of
the river and the many sharp turns, an ordinary steamer can only
progress by putting out an anchor forward and hauling the ship
up to it by means of the capstan. This is very tedious and hard
work for the crew who must be continually in the water to carry
the anchor forward and move it from side to side of the river.
The alternative is to work the steamer round the bends by poling.
There is also a possibility of the steamer arresting vegetation
and getting sudded in, and for this reason it is advisable to
anchor for the night in a lagoon or side channel, lest in the
morning one finds that floating vegetation stopped by the steamer
has blocked the river.

Our men worked hard but became very tired of navigation
with poles and anchors, and chanted as they worked " Ya rabbona
tub alina men marakib " (O God deliver us from ships) (see
Plate XXIV). At one point a large crocodile in the um
soof fringing the river was disturbed by the ship and ran for
some yards on the vegetation alongside before it could sub-
merge, while the men tried to hit it with pieces of wood. After
two days of this slow travel the river began to widen and navigation was easier.

The Narrows are caused by the spilling of water higher up
which rapidly reduces the volume of the river. Thus the channel

XXIII. DINKAS IN A SWAMP ON THE JUR RIVER OFFERING A FISH IN EXCHANGE
FOR SUGAR

XXIV. NAVIGATING THE NARROWS ON THE JUR RIVER, CARRYING THE ANCHOR
FORWARD

gets narrower and shallower and in consequence the meanders become shorter. A certain amount of embanking and closing of spills beginning some distance upstream, where the banks of the river are higher, might make it possible to increase the section and reduce the sharpness of the bends and so make navigation easier. It would be advisable, however, to experiment with a model before trying any scheme on a large scale.

Above the Narrows the stream gradually gets larger though there are still plenty of spills into the swamp, and finally the country becomes forest covered and the plain ends. The Jur is then in a definite valley though it still wanders in its flood plain. It is usually navigable as far as Wau from July to October. Just above Wau two large streams the Sueh and Busseri join to form the Jur. The Sueh can be navigated in flood for about sixty miles above Wau to the Raffili Rapids, and the Busseri also is navigable for some distance. Near Wau there was formerly a headquarters of slave traders, for whom the Bahr-el-Ghazal was a good hunting ground, and it was here that Marchand established Fort Desaix when he made his adventurous journey to gain control of the Upper Nile for France.

In March, 1931, my wife and I made a journey by car from Shambe on the Bahr-el-Jebel westwards through Wau to Kafia Kingi and the Adda River, the most westerly but one of Nile tributaries, near the boundary of French Equatorial Africa. In this journey we crossed all the tributaries of the Bahr-el-Ghazal coming from the Nile-Congo Divide and also went north from Nyamlell to see the Bahr-el-Arab. At this time of the year most of the streams were dry except for occasional pools or, in some cases, a trickle of water. There was a small flow of a few cubic metres a second in the Jur at Wau. This was the largest flow and was a sharp contrast with the 500 cubic metres a second which Sabry el Kordi and I had measured in the previous August.

The Loll at Nyamlell had a wide sandy bed with a long deep pool in which Dinkas in dug-out canoes were fishing with long jointed spears which they seemed to thrust haphazard into the rather opaque water (see Plate XXV). The next day all the women and children assembled to fish the shallow end of the long pool. This was an exciting business made more amusing by the presence of visitors and the taking of photographs.

The pool was fished to the accompaniment of great shoutings and splashings by a line of people stretched across it wading forward with nets and bee-hive-shaped baskets. My wife was the subject of much curiosity and interest to the Dinka women, but conversation was limited to signs since they knew no Arabic and we knew no Dinka, except a greeting which the Chief at Nyamlell had taught us. It was in this remote region right in the centre of Africa that the District Commissioner of Raga and I discovered that we were both born in the same Leicestershire village.

The two most important tribes of the Bahr-el-Ghazal basin are the Dinkas who inhabit the plain forming the northern part of the basin, and the Azande who are found in the forest country in the south-west. There are, in addition, many smaller tribes such as the Bongo, Moro and Madi inhabiting the northern slopes of the ironstone country. The policy of the Government has been, as far as possible, to settle the people along the main roads to lessen problems of transport and administration, and to make it easier to deal with such diseases as leprosy and sleeping sickness, which occur along the southern border of the province. Leprosy and sleeping sickness are dealt with by segregation in colonies of the sufferers and their families, in which each family is provided with a hut and a piece of ground for cultivation, and are assisted until they can support themselves. Each patient comes up regularly to headquarters for treatment.

The Azande are much more advanced than the tall nilotic people of the plain, and they are good craftsmen and cultivators. They occupy parts of the Belgian Congo over the border and originally invaded the Bahr-el-Ghazal from the south. They were well organized under a powerful aristocracy of outside origin known as Avongara, these chiefs possessing absolute power. Their origin is unknown and they are said to possess a secret language which might perhaps give a clue to their ancestry if it could be discovered and studied.

An Avongara ruler looked upon his people as existing only for his pleasure, and life and death were in his hands. Evidence of this absolute despotism in the shape of mutilated people could still be seen twenty years ago. The Azande hunt game in the bush with a small breed of dogs, rather like fox-terriers, commonly

XXV.   DINKAS FISHING IN THE LOLL RIVER AT NYAMLELL

XXVI.   TROPICAL FOREST ON THE ROAD BETWEEN LAKES KIVU AND EDWARD

known to foreigners as " nyum-nyum " dogs. The name comes
from the nickname given to the tribe by outsiders, and is said
to refer to the supposed cannibal habits of the tribe. The dogs
are used to drive small buck into nets where they are speared by
the hunters who are hidden close by.

The Jurs, a smaller tribe, practise the arts of iron-smelting
and blacksmithing, making use of the widespread iron ores
and using in the furnaces charcoal made from local timber.
The blacksmith works with a hearth of clay on the ground and a
bellows in the form of a skin bag usually worked by a boy,
sometimes with his feet. The products of their labour are
mostly hoes and small tools which they trade with neighbouring
tribes.

The Southern Sudan has been prospected to some extent for
minerals, and although copper and gold have been found in
small quantities, so far nothing comparable with the mineral
wealth of Africa south of the equator has been found.

Chapter Nine

THE COUNTRY OF THE GREAT LAKES
LAKES ALBERT AND EDWARD

1. GENERAL

THERE are two river systems which form the Upper White Nile, one draining into Lake Albert and including Lakes Edward and George, and the other draining into the Victoria Nile and including Lakes Victoria and Kioga. Speaking generally these two river systems have different characteristics. The Victoria system includes a good deal of swamp and many of its streams are really swamps, while the streams of the Albert or Rift Valley system are mostly mountain streams draining the Ruwenzori Range or the escarpments of the Rift Valley, with a comparatively small area of swamp.

One of the principal features of East Africa is the Great Rift Valley which runs, with some interruptions, from Rhodesia to the Jordan Valley, the Red Sea being a part of it. Before it reaches the Nile Basin it divides into two branches, of which the western contains Lakes Tanganyika, Kivu, George and Albert and continues north along the Bahr-el-Jebel, while the eastern branch goes up through Kenya and Ethiopia and is just outside the Nile Basin. Lakes Kivu and Tanganyika are divided from the Nile Basin by the Mufumbiro Mountains, a range of volcanoes stretching across the Rift Valley and whose highest peak reaches about 14,800 feet. The drainage of the northern side of this range forms the head waters of the Albert System, while the drainage of the other side finds its way into the Lake Victoria System, and some into Lake Tanganyika which overflows to the Congo.

Between the two branches of the Rift Valley is the plateau containing Lake Victoria which has an average elevation of 4,000 feet above the sea. The plateau is not flat but is almost everywhere hilly, the hills being usually rounded and not rugged, and as a rule not very steep. Lake Victoria is a shallow depression in this plateau, the maximum depth of the Lake, as far as it has been sounded, being about 230 feet. On the north the plateau descends gradually to the Sudan Plain, and on the east slopes up towards the escarpment of the eastern Rift Valley which is approximately the boundary of the Nile Basin. Northwards the boundary on the east is a series of mountain ranges running up to the southern boundary of Ethiopia; Mount Elgon the highest of these, reaches 14,000 feet, and there are others which reach nearly 10,000 feet.

The western boundary of the Nile Basin is the escarpment of the western branch of the Rift Valley. The boundary between the Albert and Victoria systems, however, is not well-defined, as the same swamp may be the source of two streams one of which may belong to one system and the other to the other. An example is the Nkussi flowing into Lake Albert, and the Kafu flowing into the Victoria Nile, which both have their sources in a swamp on the plateau. There are at least two connections of this sort between the Victoria and Albert systems.

Lake Albert is about 110 miles long and 30 miles at its widest and has an area of about 2,100 square miles. It lies at an altitude of just over 2,000 feet above sea level. Its principal tributary is the Semliki which comes from Lake Edward and receives the drainage of the western side of Ruwenzori, the third highest mountain in Africa (16,800 feet). Lake Edward has an area of 880 square miles and lies about 1,000 feet above Lake Albert. It receives a number of tributaries of which the largest is the Ruchuru coming from the Mufumbiro mountains. Lake George is small and unimportant.

Lake Victoria is the largest freshwater lake in the Eastern Hemisphere and has an area of 27,000 square miles. It is like an inland sea since its greatest length is 200 miles and its width about 170 miles. Its average depth is about 130 feet with a maximum of 230 feet. Its principal tributary is the Kagera River whose furthest sources are in latitude 4° South near Lake Tanganyika in Belgian Territory at an altitude of about 6,500 feet. The Victoria Nile, which is the only exit, leaves the lake at Jinja over the Ripon Falls. At the Owen Falls a mile or so below the Ripon Falls a dam is being built which will provide power for the industries of Uganda, and also make Lake Victoria the largest reservoir in the world, and will be one of a chain of projects for controlling the Nile in the interests of irrigation in Egypt and the Sudan.

The Victoria Nile then flows in a gorge over a series of rapids and is not navigable for forty miles. After this stretch it is navigable as far as Kamdini, where it turns westwards towards Lake Albert. On this navigable stretch it cuts across the western end of Lake Kioga, a shallow piece of water with many swampy arms running a long way into the land. Below Kamdini there is another series of rapids finishing with the Murchison Falls from which there is a placid stretch of about twenty miles until the Victoria Nile reaches Lake Albert very near the exit of the Bahr-el-Jebel from the lake.[1]

2. THE BAHR-EL-JEBEL OR ALBERT NILE AND LAKE ALBERT

At Nimule the Bahr-el-Jebel changes its character, and also changes direction by about 120 degrees. Above Nimule the valley is usually broad and shallow, the stream is fairly wide and winds about in swamp. It slightly resembles the Bahr-el-Jebel in the swamps in the Sudan, except that the high ground is never far away and the swamp is definitely limited. The scenery has not the monotony of the Sudd region and the rising ground away from the swamp is pleasantly wooded, moreover there are always hills not very far distant.

My first journey, in 1924, along this reach, was made under somewhat uncomfortable circumstances. The usual steamer, the *Samuel Baker*, was not working and we travelled on the *Livingstone*, a launch without sufficient sleeping accommodation for the eight passengers on her, and when we stopped for the night some of us had to sleep on camp beds on shore. The arrival of the launch at Dufile soon after sunset was a signal for local festivities, and many people came from the near-by village, lit several fires, and started to dance to the beating of drums. The mosquitoes appeared in clouds and forced us to retreat to our camp beds inside mosquito nets. The natives kept up the dancing for some hours, and although it was entertaining at first, it soon grew monotonous and later, annoying, as it prevented us from sleeping. We dropped some of our company

[1] For a good account of Uganda see *Uganda,* by R. Scott and H. B. Thomas. London, 1935.

next day, and those who remained aboard appreciated the greater room in which to turn round.

One of our company was a Greek who had retired from business in Alexandria and had set out on a holiday to visit friends in Khartoum. They had suggested to him that he continued his journey up the Nile by steamer to see other friends in Rejaf. Here somebody advised him to see Africa while he was about it and make his way through Uganda to Mombasa and back to Egypt by sea. The Greeks are an adventurous people and penetrated as traders years ago to all parts of north-eastern Africa, and it must have been this spirit of adventure which led the old man to carry on. He had no camp equipment or suitable clothing and generally appeared in a black suit and bowler hat. However, various people lent him kit, and with this and a few necessaries he bought in Rejaf, he made the journey without serious mishap. Later he called upon me in Cairo to tell me of his experiences and continued to visit me from time to time for a number of years.

We saw very few villages or people along this stretch of river, and along the east bank most of the people had been removed on account of sleeping sickness. About half-way between Nimule and the lake there is a road going westwards from Rhino Camp to Arua, the headquarters of the West Nile province of Uganda. We spent the next night at Rhino Camp and I was entertained to dinner by two pioneers, Messrs. Boole and Busby, who were running motor transport along the road. It was a pleasant evening, with interesting reminiscences from Boole of his twenty years in East Africa, while the mosquitoes were kept at bay by the smoke of a wood fire to windward of the dinner table.

In the early years of this century the country west of the Bahr-el-Jebel from north of Mongalla to Lake Albert was part of the Lado Enclave and was temporarily occupied by the Congo Free State. Towards the end of the occupation there was a period when the Lado was a resort for elephant hunters from all parts of Central Africa. The adventures of some of these make interesting reading, e.g. *The Company of Adventurers*, by John Boyes.[1] A good many elephants were shot, but some of the hunters had trouble with the Belgian officials and with the

[1] Published by East Africa. London, 1928.

natives. The country west of the Bahr-el-Jebel is one of the two places in Africa where the white rhinoceros can be found and the animal is stringently protected.

About ninety miles from Nimule is Mutir, which is a possible site for a dam to regulate Lake Albert. From all points of view, except that of Uganda, the dam would be much better at Nimule and we will discuss this later. About three miles upstream of Mutir is the site of Emin Pasha's station of Wadelai. A number of streams enter the Bahr-el-Jebel between Nimule and Lake Albert but none is of much importance and their mouths are usually hidden by swamp.

Going up in a steamer it is difficult to say when one actually enters Lake Albert, as the channel begins to widen very gently and is eventually several miles wide. Perhaps Panyigoro, a tiny village with a rest-house, might be taken as the point of entry. About ten miles further on several channels form the entry to the lake of the Victoria Nile. The channels pass through a mass of swamp vegetation like that of the Sudd region, and for this reason, their courses vary with the movements of the vegetation. There was a good deal of swell when we entered the lake and our launch was tossed about to an uncomfortable degree. The size of the lake enables the strong winds which occur to raise considerable waves, so that ships of sea-going design are necessary for navigation.

The boundary between the Belgian Congo and Uganda runs down the middle of the lake, from a point on the western shore roughly opposite the mouth of the Victoria Nile, to the mouth of the Semliki River. There are two principal lake ports— Butiaba on the Uganda side and Kasenyi on the Congo side— and a few small piers. Kasenyi is the port for the Kilo gold mines about fifty miles away, to which it is joined by a motor-road which climbs up the escarpment, which here rises about 2,000 feet above the lake. Butiaba is connected with Masindi by a good road and thus with all parts of Uganda.

It was at Butiaba on my first visit that I lost my servants and baggage. I intended to stay there for a few days and whilst I was arranging matters, some officious person, thinking I was going on to catch a steamer at Masindi Port, packed all my baggage into a transport lorry, pushed the servants in, and off went the lorry. Neither of my servants, who were Egyptians, understood a word of Swahili and very little English, and were too bewildered to do anything. However, Captain Greenwood, the engineer in charge of the port, very kindly put me up and I was able to catch up with my party next day. I decided to engage a local servant immediately and fortunately found one who could speak a sort of Arabic. He belonged to a racial group called locally "Nubi," and was a descendant of one of Emin Pasha's soldiers, of whom some were Nubians.

There is very little flat land round the lake except at its north-eastern and south-western ends, and round a good part of its coast the land rises steeply from the shore. On the Congo side the top of the escarpment is 4,000 feet above the lake. The greatest depth so far found in the lake is about 140 feet. Many ravines have been cut in the hills on either side, and in the rains torrents flow down them bringing mud, so that each has a tiny delta. This formation is well defined when seen from the air, and sometimes a thread of muddy water can be seen winding into the lake and gradually diffusing. The Egyptian Mission which went up to discuss projects with Uganda took the opportunity to fly round the lake and down the Bahr-el-Jebel to Mutir.

We started from Masindi, where the airfield is small, in a chartered plane whose pilot had not been at Masindi before, and who was a little doubtful whether the plane could take off with all of us on board. He decided to experiment with the heavier half of the party, of which I was a member, and as there seemed to be no difficulty with this load, all the party emplaned and the machine took off comfortably, giving us a very interesting journey with a fine view of the Murchison Falls.

Some years ago an air-survey was made of the lake and river to Nimule and a great deal can be learned from the subsequent maps. The flat land round the lake is usually covered with bushes and trees, while the ravines are thickly wooded. On the eastern shore of the lake at Kibiro there is a hot spring and a small salt collecting industry. Salt is scarce in Uganda; in the the western part of the territory there is the source at Katwe near Lake Edward, a small source at Kibiro and one or two still smaller ones elsewhere. Before there was a motor road to Katwe, one met strings of people from the country all round, each carrying on his head a load of salt wrapped in banana leaves.

The country along the Bahr-el-Jebel and round Lake Albert is associated with Gordon and Emin Pasha. The latter is responsible for the statement that the flats round Lake Albert are impregnated with salt, a statement which was repeated by Garstin. This cannot be true, for wherever I have seen the lake shore there was no trace of salt, and tall grass, bushes and trees were growing everywhere. Our flight round the lake confirmed that this was true for the vegetation along the remainder of the coast. Where land is full of salt it is either bare or supports a few special salt resistant plants, but even these will grow only on land with a small salt content.

The lake itself has a larger amount of dissolved salts than the other lakes of the Nile basin excepting Lake Edward. This has led to the suggestion that the use of the lake as a reservoir might lead to the arrival of quantities of salt in Egypt which would be detrimental to cultivation. There is, however, no reason to suppose that this would be the case. There are, in fact, no large quantities of salt round the shores of the lake which would be dissolved by raising the water level. Actually if all the salt produced in a year in the whole of Uganda were to be dissolved into the lake, chemical analysis would be unable to detect it. In the long run the amount of salt which flows out of the lake is equal to that which comes in, and this would be true if the lake were used as a reservoir, although there might be slight seasonal changes. The main quantity of water flowing into the lake is from the Victoria Nile and this has a low content of dissolved salts, so that the outflowing water has a content of about one-third of that in the lake. On its way down to Egypt the lake water mixes with that from other tributaries, so that if its content did increase temporarily it would still be well diluted before it reached Egypt. What does cause land to deteriorate is lack of drainage, and with reasonable drainage and proper use of water much larger salt contents than those in Nile water can be used without danger. However, a detailed salt survey of the lake, its surroundings and its tributaries, is to be made so that the question may be definitely settled.

Emin Pasha was a German doctor, by name Eduard Schnitzer,

who had been in Turkey, where he changed his name to Emin (commonly transliterated Amin in Egypt). He was appointed to work with General Gordon, who was then Governor of the Equatorial Province of the Sudan, which extended from Lado, about mid-way between Mongalla and Juba, to Lake Albert. When Gordon became Governor-General, Emin was appointed Governor of the province in his place. The rise of the Mahdi cut Emin off from the north and his province was the last to remain outside the Mahdi's control. However, in 1885 he was compelled to retreat southwards to Wadelai, where he wrote describing his situation and appealing for relief. A fund was started and a relief expedition was organized under H. M. Stanley, who was assisted by a dozen Europeans, mostly British.[1]

Stanley's original intention was to start from Zanzibar and march round the south end of Lake Victoria and so north-west to Lake Albert. However, just before the start, he changed his plans at the suggestion of Leopold, King of the Belgians, in favour of a route up the Congo. This had the advantage of water transport, but meant that more than 400 miles of unknown country had to be crossed on foot, most of which subsequently turned out to be thick tropical forest. Judging by what happened, the decision to change the route was not a very happy one. There were not enough ships to carry all of the expedition, and stores and men had to be left behind. After leaving the River Aruwimi, a tributary of the Congo, at Yambuya, most of the way had to be cut through the creepers and undergrowth of the tropical rain forest, where the natives were hostile, food was scarce, and many of the porters fell sick and died. Ultimately, 170 days after leaving the ships, Stanley and a portion of the expedition reached Lake Albert, to find no trace or news of Emin.

Stanley decided to return to a spot where part of the expedition had been left, and there a camp was established, crops were grown and the members of the expedition recuperated. After some months they set out again for the lake, this time with sections of a steel boat which were to be bolted together at the lake. Just before reaching the lake they received a letter from Emin, and a few days later he himself appeared. They spent days

[1] See *In Darkest Africa*, H. M. Stanley.

in discussion and Emin seemed unable to make up his mind whether to leave the province or stay, but finally he said he would go if his people would, but not otherwise. So he was left to go round his province to induce his people to leave for the coast, while Stanley returned to try to locate his missing rear-guard.

Disaster had, however, fallen upon them. Two Englishmen were dead, one had been invalided home and only two remained, while porters were dying of disease and starvation. Stanley managed to move the camp to a healthier place where food was available, and after some time the whole party set off for the camp near the lake. Again they met every kind of difficulty— an outbreak of small-pox, hostile natives who, invisible in the forest, shot at them with poisoned arrows, cannibals who followed the party like wolves and a shortage of supplies. The reason for the hostility of the natives and the lack of supplies was that the country had been devastated by slave traders. Ultimately, in December, 1888, seven months after Stanley had parted from Emin, the party reached the camp, and were able to enjoy rest and abundant food. There was no news of Emin, however, so after his men had recovered Stanley decided to march to the lake. There he got news of Emin and heard that his troops had revolted and imprisoned both Emin and the companion who had been sent with him by Stanley, and that the Mahdists had advanced southwards. Everything was in confusion, and Emin had consequently decided to evacuate the province and return to the coast. Shortly after this news of him Emin himself arrived at the lake.

There were, however, still delays as Emin could not make up his mind to abandon his province. Finally Stanley told him that far from abandoning his province the province had abandoned him, and that he had every right to leave. The expedition, with Emin and about 600 refugees, left for Zanzibar in April, 1889, travelling by way of the Semliki Valley and Lake Edward. This was the first time that Stanley had seen Ruwenzori, which he thought must be the traditional Mountains of the Moon. Some of his party started to climb the mountain and got to a height of nearly 11,000 feet, but as they were cut off by deep clefts from the main peaks they had to abandon the climb. The expedition finally reached the coast in December, 1889, nearly three years after they had left Zanzibar to go round by the Cape to the Congo. The journey had been one of incredible hardship and had cost the lives of nearly a thousand men. Emin was a good and keen naturalist and collected a great deal of information about the country along the Upper Bahr-el-Jebel and round Lake Albert, but he seems to have lacked judgment and decision. He refused to return to Europe and took service with the German Government, but later went off on his own account into the Congo, where he was killed by Arab slave traders.

The Semliki comes into the lake at its south-west end through several channels forming a delta. The configuration of these varies and when I explored it in a canoe we were unable to find a large mouth. The river brings down sediment to form sandbanks and bars which are the haunt of water-birds and numerous crocodiles, and the lake is shallow for a long way off-shore.

At present a small industry of catching crocodiles and curing their skins is being carried out at the Semliki mouth. We made the journey in a canoe from my camp some miles to the east of the Semliki, and on the way back a strong wind blew up and made dangerous the navigation of the open lake, so we decided to land. This meant pushing the canoe through reeds and ambatch bushes, which was such hard work that we finally left the canoe and waded for about half a mile to dry land. It was late afternoon when we got ashore and the camp was some miles away, but fortunately I had as guide Mr. Bezuidenhout, a South African hunter. On the way we had to run to get out of the path of an advancing herd of elephant and finally we got to camp at about nine o'clock.

It was the end of the dry season and there was a good deal of haze, so that one rarely had a glimpse of the distant view. However, whilst we were near the lake there was some rain and the atmosphere cleared so that we could see the great mass of Ruwenzori fifty miles away. This haze is characteristic of the dry season and one may be in the neighbourhood of high mountains for weeks without getting a clear view of them. The Semliki plain is seamed with depressions which contain water in the rainy season, and are shown by air-photographs to be former channels of the river. The Semliki carries a fair quantity of water and is from 70 to 100 yards wide. It can be crossed by two ferries, the roads going round the ends of Ruwenzori to the Congo.

3. THE SEMLIKI RIVER AND LAKE EDWARD

Following the course of the Semliki the land distance from Lake Albert to Lake Edward is about 150 miles, but there is no regular road and the middle portion is thick forest which begins at the foot of the northern spur of Ruwenzori. Ruwenzori is a grand mountain and stretches for about seventy miles from north to south. I was fortunate enough two or three years ago to have magnificent views of it from a point near Butembo in the Congo, with the sun shining on the snow peaks which stood out against the blue sky. It was, of course, a distant view, but next day, as we descended the western escarpment of the Rift from Beni, we had a much closer view and could see the detail of the mountain. We saw a group of six or so high snow-covered peaks which looked to us like a ridge. They appeared to be rugged and precipitous from our position below, but the mountain has since been climbed by many parties. Natives living on the lower slopes can be employed as porters, at any rate as far as the snow line, and expeditions can be arranged from Fort Portal on the Uganda side, or from Mutwanga on the Congo side. There are comfortable hotels at both places. The high peaks, however, need experienced mountaineers. As Ruwenzori is practically on the Equator there are various zones of vegetation. On the eastern side there is savannah forest and grass on the lowest slopes, with thicker forest in the valleys, and a forest zone above. The western side is more thickly wooded than the eastern and the thick forest is continuous with the Eturi Forest in the Congo. The forest is succeeded by bamboo thickets and above these one finds Alpine types of vegetation peculiar to Central Africa, reaching up to the snow-line at about 15,000 feet.

Many streams come down from the snows, though they are mainly fed by rain on the lower slopes, but none is very large, either on the west or the east of the mountain. Those streams on the eastern side go down to Lake George and one, the Mbuku, comes down so strongly in spate that it has been said that elephants were occasionally washed away. A motor road now goes from Fort Portal and along the shore of Lake Edward round the southern end of Ruwenzori to Beni in the Congo, and all the streams are bridged. When I was first in this country in 1924, I walked along what was then a track and had to ford the larger streams. While I was at Katwe rest-house, outside the village, there was a raid by people from the Congo, but I knew nothing of it, until on my way back I met a district commissioner hastily coming down to see what the battle was about.

At Katwe there is an old crater separated from Lake Edward by a narrow ridge, and in the bottom of which is a mass of salt of various shades from mauve to heliotrope. The whole district shows traces of former volcanic activity and there are many lakes in ancient craters on the eastern side of Ruwenzori and further south. They are often beautiful, with trees growing on the steep sides of the craters down to the water's edge, the water being sometimes coloured green or blue, which may be due to copper salts in solution. Copper has been found at Kilembe in the foothills of Ruwenzori.

Lake George, which is crossed by the Equator, lies a little to the east of the road, and is a small lake fringed by papyrus, and is swampy at its northern end. It is joined to Lake Edward by the wide Kazinga channel which is usually without any perceptible flow. Lake Edward is at an altitude of about 3,000 feet, 1,000 feet above Lake Albert. On the west the escarpment descends steeply to the lake and inland the country rises to about 9,000 feet, but on the east there is a good deal of hilly but not very high ground. The deepest part of the lake is at the foot of the escarpment where 380 feet was sounded by the Worthingtons.[1] Their book contains much interesting information about the lake and its inhabitants, and discusses why there are no crocodiles in Lakes Edward and George or their tributaries, while in the Semliki River at the Lake Albert end crocodiles are numerous. There are in both Edward and Albert many varieties of fish, but only two or three kinds are common to both. The Semliki River passes in its middle course through several miles of a forest-clad gorge, and this is the obstacle which has for thousands of years prevented the fish of the two lakes from mixing. There has been a good deal of discussion of the croco-

[1] *The Inland Waters of Africa.* Macmillan. London, 1933.

dile question and about twenty years ago there was correspondence in *The Times*. Various explanations have been put forward, and the most likely seems to be the one adopted by the Worthingtons, that the rush of water in the rapids prevents the crocodile getting up the Semliki by water, while the thick forest and vegetation has proved a deterrent from a land passage. It is not that crocodiles could not make their way through some miles of tropical forest, but rather that there is no incentive for them to do so. If, however, the river banks are ever cleared the obstacle will have been removed, and crocodiles would probably make their way into Lakes Edward and George and some of their tributary streams, to the obvious detriment of the region.

About one-third of the shore of Lake Edward is in Uganda and the remainder in the Belgian Congo. This latter forms part of the Belgian National Park, a sanctuary which stretches from Lake Kivu to north of Lake Edward, in which the wild life, and there is plenty, is being preserved. When I was there with the Egyptian Mission in 1948 we saw quite a fair amount of game at both ends of Lake Edward, and Dr. Amin was able to get a good photograph of an elephant in swamp close to the exit of the Semliki from the lake. There were seven of us present, including a game guard, and the noise we made falling into holes and over each other ought to have scared him long before we got to focussing distance, but it was not until the photographs had been taken that he moved further into the swamp and out of range. My friend Bambridge and I had a pleasant hour spinning for a kind of barbel, which took a spoon well and would have given very good sport had our tackle been lighter.

A number of streams flow into Lake Edward, of which the principal is the Ruchuru whose water comes from the high country of Kigezi on the eastern side of the Rift, but its most southern source is on the northern slope of Muhavura, the most eastern of the Birunga or Mufumbiro Mountains. Other streams flow down from the country round Kabale, the principal town and headquarters of Kigezi province. The discharges of the Ruchuru, Ishasha and Ntungwe were first measured in 1926 by Captain Goldsack and myself. No canoes were available, so the work had to be done by wading, which was possible as it was near the end of the dry season. There was, however, sufficient depth of water and current to make it difficult. Hydrological information about these tributaries of Lake Edward is still scanty.

The high country round Lake Edward, both in Kigezi, Ruanda, and in the Belgian Congo, is delightful. I travelled through it first on foot with porters, and recently by car. The first time, I followed tracks which took no heed of ups and downs, and I slept in grass rest-houses or in tents. On the recent journey we travelled by car over good roads and made use of comfortable hotels, usually delightfully situated, and I suppose to some extent used by tourists. The making of roads in this mountainous country requires good planning and considerable engineering skill. For example, in the Congo the road from Ruchuru to Beni climbs 3,000 feet up the escarpment from the flats at the southern end of Lake Edward in quite a short distance. Fortunately laterite is common and is a good road-making material. Care is needed on these mountain roads as they are not very wide.

When I was at Ruchuru in 1926 we were warned against spirillum or relapsing fever, which is carried by a tick called locally " Kimbutu," and was common on the road from there to Lake Edward. The tick lives in old houses and camping places, in cracks in the walls or ground, and comes out at night. We were advised to avoid these old shelters and to pitch tents on fresh ground, as the disease can have serious effects.

On this journey Captain Goldsack and I entered Ruanda near the confluence of the Niavarongo and Ruvuvu which form the Kagera River, having walked up to Lake Victoria from Tabora on the railway from Dar es Salaam to Lake Tanganyika. Ruanda-Urundi, which had been part of German East Africa before the war of 1914–18, is now mandated territory under the Belgians. We had been told that we might have difficulty with formalities on entering the country and with facilities for travel, but the contrary was the case and Belgian officials everywhere were most helpful. When we crossed the Kagera into Ruanda we sent a messenger ahead with a letter to the chief of the nearest Belgian post, who sent a note giving us provisional permits for our rifles and permission to shoot, and regretting that he would be away collecting taxes, but placing his house and vegetable garden at our disposal. When we arrived at Kigali, the capital of Ruanda, we were received by the Resident or Governor and the whole Belgian Community, and treated with great hospitality. We made our way from Kigali north to the Mufumbiro Range and walked along to the south of this to Kisenyi at the northern end of Lake Kivu. The country of Ruanda is mountainous and a good deal of what we walked over was rather like downs with short grass and not many trees, though there are occasional clumps which act as land-marks. The valleys usually contain swamps growing papyrus and reeds, through which there is only a very small flow of water, in spite of the considerable

Muhavura   Mgahinga   Sabinio

FIG. 6b. The Mufumbiro mountains from Kisoro.

slope which often exists. Experiments are now being made to drain these swamps and cultivate the land.

The population, which is numerous, consists of an aristocratic cattle-owning class, the Watusi, and a labouring class, the Wahutu, with a few Batwa who are said to be the original inhabitants of the country. The Watusi are a tall people, usually light coloured with features resembling those of Somalis, although now mixed with some Negro blood. The cattle are of the same type as those of Western Uganda, with long massive horns. Sheep and goats are also herded, and bananas, peas, beans and sweet potatoes are cultivated.

The Mufumbiro Range is a fine chain of six volcanoes stretch-

146

ing east and west for forty miles (see Fig. 6b) and cutting right across the Rift valley, so that to the north the drainage belongs to the Nile, and to the south some flows into Lake Kivu and then, by way of the Ruzizi River, to Lake Tanganyika. The highest peak, Karisimbi, rises to 14,800 feet and all six rise to more than 10,000 feet. The two western peaks, Nyamlagira and Niragongo have been active within recent times, and when I was there in 1948 there was a red glow at night high up in the sky over Niragongo, followed a few weeks later by a considerable eruption. All along the north shore of Lake Kivu lava flows can be seen, the more recent being entirely bare, and the older beginning, as the rock is broken down by weathering, to be covered with vegetation. In 1912 lava flowed down from Nyamlagira into Lake Kivu almost cutting off a small arm at its north-west corner. Lake Kivu is a delightful lake with extremely clear water and there are now several good hotels on its shores. In 1926 there were a few officials and traders and very little else.

In Ruanda there are many Missions at which we often called and where we were hospitably received and given cheroots made of a locally grown tobacco. The Fathers were usually well-informed about their district and the people, and often curious to know why two Englishmen were wandering about the country asking questions about mountains, streams, swamps, plants, fish, game, and the habits of the people. I always explained that I was an official from Egypt, which depended on the Nile water for its life, and that my duty was to study the Nile, and I had therefore come to see its sources. One old hospitable French Father, after giving us an excellent breakfast, said " Now what is the real reason for your visit? " to which I replied that it was the study of the Nile, as I had already told him. I do not think he was convinced, as he said that all the natives thought the British intended to take over Ruanda, and that we were an advance party to spy out the land.

On this visit, although we were in the neighbourhood of the Mufumbiro for several weeks and walked from Lake Kivu to Lake Edward through a gap in the range, the weather was hazy and we rarely saw more than the bases of the mountains. Fortunately on a later visit the weather was clear and we had excel-

147

lent views of the mountains from Konaba Gap and from the frontier post between Kabale and Ruhengere, and their volcanic origin was clear from their conical shapes (see Fig. 6b). High up in the bamboo forest on these volcanoes, gorillas and chimpanzees are to be found and are strictly preserved.

Chapter Ten

THE VICTORIA NILE AND LAKE VICTORIA

TO explore the Victoria Nile we return to its mouth in Lake Albert. It is possible to go up in a large launch as far as the foot of the Murchison Falls, a distance of twenty miles (see Plate XXVII). The Falls were discovered by Sir Samuel Baker in 1864, who named them after the then President of the Royal Geographical Society. The country along this stretch of the river is a game reserve and is interesting on this account, for a large variety of game is almost certain to be seen. I have seen elephant, buffalo, lion, several varieties of antelope, wart-hog, baboons and monkeys, colobus and others, besides hippopotamuses and crocodiles, and many kinds of water fowl. At first the country is flat but the scenery improves as one approaches the Falls, and the river is in a well-defined valley. The Falls are produced by the stream falling over the edge of the escarpment —which is, however, considerably lower than it is further south— and the fall of the water is about 140 feet. One lands a mile or so downstream of the Falls and follows a narrow rocky path, which after various ups and downs brings one to the top of the escarpment. It was a hot day when I was there and we climbed up in the middle of the afternoon, and although it is not really much of a climb some of us were very glad when we got to the top. Here one can stand on a flat rock and look down into a chasm into which the river falls, takes a turn to the left and then makes its final and longest leap. The top of the chasm is a narrow gap about twenty feet wide and the water approaches it in a foaming mass by a long rapid. The chasm was bridged by H. G. Bambridge in the course of survey operations in connection with the project for a Lake Albert reservoir. He first felled a couple of suitable trees beside the fall and pushed them across the chasm, afterwards shuffling across astride one of the trees. These formed the girders of the bridge and a floor was laid upon them. A few weeks after the survey work was finished a rise of the river carried the bridge away. A day or two before we visited the fall an elephant had eaten a bush growing right on the edge of the precipice beside the fall. The fall is a barrier up which no fish can travel, and a comparison of the fish in Albert with those in Victoria and in Edward throws some light on the history of the river. The Nile perch and tiger fish which are common in Lake Albert are not found in either Victoria or Edward, though there is evidence that they were in Edward in geological times.

The reach which runs roughly east and west from Murchison Falls to Kamdini is a succession of rocks and rapids which are well seen from the air. The country on both sides of the Victoria Nile and on the east side of the Bahr-el-Jebel is a game reserve and practically uninhabited. In the past sleeping sickness was common, and many of the inhabitants died and the survivors were removed to more healthy areas.

Sir Samuel Baker in 1864 was the first to explore the Victoria Nile from Kamdini, just above the rapids of Karuma, to Lake Albert. He arrived at Karuma from the Bahr-el-Jebel at Gondokoro (nearly opposite Juba) by a roundabout route, going at the start directly east beyond Torit, and then southward through the hills, later passing near the present station of Gulu in northern Uganda. He crossed the Victoria Nile near the rapids and continued south near the river to Mruli, the head-quarters of Kamrasi the King of Unyoro, near the junction of the Kafu River with the Nile and close to the present Masindi Port. Here he was detained on one pretext or another by Kamrasi, who had an insatiable appetite for gifts and had just previously similarly plundered Speke and Grant. Finally, when porters and guides had been arranged for the journey to Lake Albert, Kamrasi having exhausted Baker's gifts said that Lady Baker must be left with him. This difficulty was overcome by Baker threatening Kamrasi with a revolver while Lady Baker made an opprobrious speech in Arabic, and so the expedition started. The route followed the Kafu River, which is one of the swampy streams usual in Uganda, and which has a number of swampy tributaries receiving the drainage of a large area. One tributary starts near Kampala at a short distance from Lake Victoria, while the Kafu itself starts in a swamp near Lake Albert, which also receives the Nkussi River from this same swamp. It

XXVII.   MURCHISON FALLS

XXVIII.   THE VICTORIA NILE WITH NAPOLEON GULF IN THE BACKGROUND, THE RIPON
FALLS AT ITS HEAD, AND (LOWEST IN THE PICTURE) THE OWEN FALLS.

(*Courtesy of the Aircraft Operating Company of Africa*)

would be impossible without actual levelling to fix the position
of the water parting. Except after heavy rains, the contribution
of the Kafu system to the Victoria Nile is negligible. Baker
reached the Lake not far from its southern end, but was told
that it extended a couple of hundred miles further south, after
which its limits were unknown. Had this been true it would
have meant that it extended at least as far as Lake Kivu. Baker
then returned by canoe along the eastern shore, back along the
Victoria Nile to Karuma, and then on to the Bahr-el-Jebel at
Nimule.

The Victoria Nile is again navigable from Kamdini into Lake
Kioga and on to Namasagali, from where there is railway communication with the main line of the Kenya and Uganda Railways
which comes from Mombasa on the coast through Nairobi to
Kampala, the commercial capital of Uganda. Namasagali, where
there is a dockyard, is the headquarters of steamer navigation to
ports round Lake Kioga, and on to Atura near Kamdini. A
good deal of cotton is grown round the lake, and it is brought
to Namasagali to be railed to Mombasa. Kioga is a shallow
lake with many swampy arms stretching up valleys in the undulating country surrounding it. Because of the undulations a
rise of the lake does not flood large areas. Some of the arms are
navigable, but others are valley swamps full of papyrus and reed
growth. Parts of the lake are covered with water lilies which,
from the air, give it a green appearance in which lanes marking
steamer tracks can be seen. The watershed between the Lake
Victoria and the Victoria Nile drainage is close to Lake Victoria,
and many swampy arms parallel to the Victoria Nile run down to
Lake Kioga and the Kafu. The map would suggest that at some
time in the past the Lake Kioga drainage system and the Victoria
Nile as far as Kamdini—with the swampy arms joining it from the
east—all drained westwards along the Kafu, and that perhaps
the Victoria Nile was due to a break through of Lake Victoria
into a valley similar to the parallel valley of the Sezibwa. The
Katonga River, which is now a similar swamp system draining
into Lake Victoria on the west, also has the appearance, from the
angles at which tributaries join, of formerly flowing westward and
through what is now the Mpanga to Lake George.

At the eastern end of Lake Kioga is the great mass of Mount

Elgon rising to about 14,200 feet and making a very conspicuous object, as it rises out of fairly flat country. Many streams come off the mountain, some come down and form valley swamps draining into Kioga, some flow into the Nzoia and so to Lake Victoria, while those from the north-eastern side join the Turkwel going to Lake Rudolf, and thus are outside the Nile Basin. In their upper courses the streams flowing into Kioga are open and swiftly flowing, but lower down they are overgrown with papyrus and there is little current. It sometimes happens in seasons of heavy rainfall that considerable quantities of water flow into Kioga.

From Namasagali to Lake Victoria there are again rapids which prevent navigation and the river is in a well-wooded valley, with but very small tributaries. The discharge site for the outflow from Lake Victoria is at Namasagali and it was there that, with great difficulty, I measured a discharge in 1926 before the establishment of a proper site. Each time I got my wire rope across the river it was dragged from its anchorage by floating vegetation. Finally, on the second day I managed by the late afternoon to get the rope properly anchored, started my measurements and carried on by the light of a lantern until I finished at about 8 p.m. There were some protests from the crew of my launch when it got dark and hippopotamuses began to snort and grunt close to the boat, but we finished the measurement quite satisfactorily and without incident. Part of the difficulty arose from the lack of canoes to keep the long stretch (370 yards) of wire rope above the water. It happened that recent rains and winds had set free a lot of swamp vegetation from the margin of Lake Kioga, and this had collected to form a block at the exit of the Victoria Nile. Consequently all the canoes were busy helping to remove the block, and none was available for my use. These blocks occur from time to time as they used to in the Sudd Region many years ago.

The river between Namasagali and Lake Victoria is infested with a small biting fly known locally as " mbwa," which belongs to the species simulium, commonly called sandflies, blackflies or buffalo gnats (see p. 75). It is the fly referred to as *simulium damnosum* and which harbours one stage of a parasitic worm which is transmitted to man by its bite. The worm causes tumours, and sometimes damages the eye to such an extent as to cause blindness. The fly lays its eggs in water and the larvæ attach themselves to stones in rapids and cataracts. It is known in various parts of tropical Africa, and occurs in some of the tributaries of the Bahr-el-Ghazal. It is thought that when the Owen Falls Dam is working, it may be possible to eliminate the fly by periodically lowering the level of the Victoria Nile, thus drying the places by the water's edge where the eggs and larvæ occur, and so destroying them.

The Victoria Nile leaves Lake Victoria over the Ripon Falls, which are formed by a narrow reef of rock crossing the river diagonally, with three openings through which the water passes and falls about 15 feet. On both sides the banks rise fairly steeply to about 150 feet above the river. The Falls are at the head of Napoleon Gulf, a long arm of the lake which gradually narrows to its head. A little distance below the Falls there is now a railway and a road bridge which make the connection easy between the small town of Jinja on the right bank and Kampala and Entebbe, the principal towns of Uganda; Kampala, the commercial centre, and Entebbe on the lake, the headquarters of the Government. A mile or so below the Ripon Falls are the Owen Falls, the site of a dam to regulate Lake Victoria and convert it into a reservoir for the benefit of irrigation in Egypt, and at the same time to enable the power produced by the fall to be used for the benefit of Uganda (see Plate XXVIII). Work has already started on the dam and power-station, and they are expected to be finished by 1953. The effect of the dam will be to raise the maximum level of the lake by rather more than 4 ft., thus converting the lake into the largest reservoir in the world, with an area of 27,000 square miles, and a usable capacity of about 100,000,000,000 tons or 80,000,000 acre-feet. An acre-foot is a unit used in America, and is the amount of water which will cover an acre a foot deep. These large figures do not convey very much unless a comparison is possible: to give some idea we may say that Lake Victoria is a little smaller than Scotland, and that to fill it to the capacity mentioned would take all the flow of the Thames for more than forty years. Until the other projects, which we will describe later, are constructed, the reservoir will be of very little use in increasing the area under irrigation, partly because of the great losses of water in the swamps of the Sudd Region, and partly because when the discharge from Victoria is increased for part of the year to meet the needs of irrigation in Egypt, a good part of the increase will have to go to raise the levels of Lake Albert and Kioga to enable an increase to continue down the Nile. The effect is that the increase would be very much flattened out and reduced by the time it reached Egypt.

The Ripon Falls were discovered in 1862 by Speke who had come from the east coast of Africa round the south and west sides of Lake Victoria. He had made a great journey and says in his journal, " The expedition has now performed its functions. I saw that old Father Nile without any doubt rises in the Victoria Nyanza." The discovery is commemorated by a plaque fixed to the rock of the ridge which causes the Falls. Speke remarks on the crocodiles and hippopotami below the Falls, and the numbers of fish leaping up in an attempt to ascend into the lake. This still happens, and I have seen the river just below the Falls thick with fish, and at every minute or two a leaping fish distinct against the background of white water.

Speke then made his way down the Victoria Nile to a point some distance south of the present Namasagali, and then went westwards to join Grant and to make their way to Kamrasi's station at the mouth of the Kafu, as we have already mentioned. From there he marched across to the Nile at Nimule and along near the river to Gondokoro where he met Sir Samuel Baker. Neither the routes of Speke nor Baker had followed the Nile from Lake Victoria to Albert and then to the Sudan. There was a gap between Nimule and Lake Albert and another between the Kafu River and a point a little distance south of Namasagali. Thus Lake Kioga was still unknown and was discovered in 1874 by Colonel Chaillé Long and was called by the Khedive Ismail Pasha, Lake Ibrahim.

Victoria is a very large lake and is, in fact, more like a sea than a lake, since from Port Bell in the north to Mwanza in the south the distance is 200 miles, and the greatest breadth from east to west is 170 miles. There are many islands in the lake and these, like its shores, are hilly and often covered with forest. The Sesse Islands in the north-west were devastated by sleeping sickness many years ago; many of the inhabitants died and the remainder were removed to the mainland. Recently people have been allowed to return as the flies no longer carry infection. The coastline is hilly and much indented, but rather less so on the west. The lake, like most African lakes, is subject to sudden storms, which, because of its large expanse, cause considerable waves to rise and render navigation by small craft dangerous. Waterspouts are occasionally seen, one of which I was lucky enough to witness, and clouds of small flies which might be mistaken for waterspouts are also common.

The lake has one large tributary, the Kagera whose most distant tributary, the Luvironza, rises about forty miles from Lake Tanganyika. The Kagera drains a large area to the west and south-west of Victoria in what used to be German East Africa. On the east side of the lake there are several streams which may carry a good deal of water after heavy rains. Swampy channels overgrown by papyrus and reeds flow into the lake but carry little water. The Katonga on the west, the remains of a large river system, has already been mentioned. There are several ports round the lake, which is regularly circumnavigated by steamers of the Kenya and Uganda Railways. The coastline is shared by Uganda on the north, Kenya on the east and Tanganyika on the south. The Kenya and Uganda Railway comes from Mombasa and touches the lake at Kisumu, Jinja, and Port Bell—the port of Kampala—while the Tanganyika Railway comes up from Dar es Salaam to Lake Tanganyika and has a branch to Mwanza at the south end of Lake Victoria. The Kavirondo Gulf leading up to Kisumu is shallow, which means that storage cannot be increased by drawing the lake down below its minimum, for navigation in the gulf would be impeded.

One of my visits to Lake Victoria, in 1926, was due to a letter from Professor Schwartz the South African geologist. He wrote to Sir Ismail Sirry Pasha, who had been Minister of Public Works for many years, telling him that there was a danger that streams which rise on the watershed between Victoria and Tanganyika and flow into the lake from the south, would eventually cut back, and Victoria would drain into Tanganyika which is at a lower level. The Minister asked me what I thought of this, and I told him that although it did not seem very probable, it would be advisable for me to go and see the country and report on the matter. He agreed, and I went out to Dar es Salaam, where I was joined by Captain Goldsack, formerly of the King's African Rifles, as assistant. I had found out that the Germans had, before the 1914–18 war, a project to take water from Smith Sound, a long inlet at the south end of Lake Victoria, over the low country which separates the lake from the land sloping down towards Lake Eyassi. The water would have been used to irrigate arid land on the Vembere Steppe for the growing of cotton. The scheme, which was not a government one, was to start on a small scale with a dam on the Manyonga River to store its flood water and irrigate a small experimental area. From this pilot project data would be obtained for a larger scheme, in which another dam would be built on the Manyonga, and hydro-electric stations at the dams would supply the power to pump the water from Lake Victoria. After passing through the turbines the water would irrigate land lower down and finally drain into Lake Eyassi. In defence of this project it was said that the abstraction from Lake Victoria of such a relatively small quantity of water as 90 tons a second could make no appreciable difference to the Nile. Previous to my own researches, material did not exist for a study of the Regime of Lake Victoria, and from the data I had gathered I was able to draw up a balance sheet for the lake. For this we equate the water which comes into the lake during a number of years, to that which goes out, and allow for any rise or fall of the lake during the period; or we may choose the period so that the lake is at the same level at the beginning and end. The water which comes in is the rainfall on the lake added to what is brought by the tributary streams. The water which goes out is that which is evaporated from the lake surface and what flows out by the Nile. It so happens that evaporation and rainfall are nearly equal, as are inflow by tributaries and outflow by the Nile, and rainfall is about five times as great as the inflow by tributaries (see Ch. XV). It is obvious from this simple statement that, since over a long period as much water flows out by the Nile as flows in by tributaries, if extra water is taken out the lake will drop until the Nile discharge plus the extra out-take is again equal to the inflow. The discharge of the Nile would therefore be lessened. Previous to my visit the project was unknown to the authorities in Dar es

Salaam, and their view was that there is so much land to be developed on the natural rainfall, that it was unlikely in the near future that the large irrigation schemes would be taken up as they would be bound to mean a large capital outlay. In any case no such scheme could be taken up without revising the Nile Waters Agreement between Great Britain and Egypt. It so happened that the country through which the projected canal would pass over the watershed, lay on my route, and the examination of this country was part of the main object of my expedition. It was fortunate that it would also give information about the German project.

Goldsack and I went by railway from Dar es Salaam to Tabora and then got a lift for about fifty miles in a construction train along the branch of the line which was then being constructed from Tabora to Mwanza on Lake Victoria. We then walked along a shallow depression up to the head of Smith Sound. A feature of the country is the occurrence of flat open grass plains known as " mbuga," which are swampy in the rains. A continuous line of mbuga runs from 4° south latitude up to the head of Smith Sound, and from the southern part of this the Uyangubu River goes to join the Manyonga. We saw the Uyangubu, about three miles above its junction with the Manyonga, in the dry season. It laid in a shallow valley, a reed swamp varying from 40 to 130 yards wide through which there was a negligible flow of water. In flood the water was said to be 4 or 6 feet deep with a slow current. The mbuga in which the Uyangubu rises was crossed further north (see Plate XXIX). Here it was a flat plain covered with grass and reeds up to 5 feet high and was 700 to 1,000 yards wide, the greater part being swamp, with water in the middle 2 feet deep, but with no perceptible flow. We continued northwards, sometimes along the edge of the mbuga, sometimes wading across it—an unpleasant business—or cutting across bays. Large portions of the plain were dry, but there was always water in the middle. At one point to windward of us the grass was on fire, a distinctly unpleasant situation to be in, with a wide expanse of dry grass across which a fire was advancing rapidly. However, by hurrying and pushing on the porters we got through with nothing more serious than eyes smarting from the smoke.

From my aneroid readings it looked as if in the sixty miles south of the head of Smith Sound there was a slight rise of the floor of the valley, of the order 60 feet, and then a fall again along the Uyangubu River. This must be accepted with reserve as 60 feet cannot be measured with any precision by an aneroid, and the question whether it is 30 feet or 90 feet would make a lot of difference to the cost of the project.

We crossed the head of Smith Sound in canoes and went westwards. The country was hilly with many outcrops of granite boulders and a good deal of cultivation. Further on it was largely covered with thin savannah forest, but there was nowhere any running water, the valley bottoms being mbuga, and either dry or containing only stagnant water. Further on in the district of Buyombe there was occasionally water running south and usually in mbugas, which, if not absorbed by swamp, would flow into Lake Tanganyika. None of these streams was of any size, and in every case they were overgrown with vegetation and showed no sign of any rapid erosion; in fact the valleys seemed to be tending to fill rather than erode.

Professor E. H. L. Schwarz in his paper called " *Matériaux pour l'Etude des Calamités* " [1] says:—

" Ordinary erosion of the rivers will in course of time open a path for the waters of Lake Victoria to flow towards Tanganyika and the Congo, but an earthquake fissure might at any moment precipitate the catastrophe. We know that in many cases the slow process of erosion has been hastened by earthquake fissure in Africa. There is no need to dwell upon this impending disaster, but it serves to show on what a hazardous basis the hydrographic system in Africa stands, and also enables one to realize what an immense disaster it would be to have this great sheet of water, 27,000 square miles in area, withdrawn from it. The Nile would stop flowing and the whole of Central Africa would be reduced to the condition of Arabia."

The area referred to is that we have already described, and from which it appears that erosion, if it is going on at all, is going on very slowly, and that it will be thousands of years before erosion by streams leads to an outflow of water from Victoria to Tanganyika. An outflow through the country to the south of Smith Sound would be easier than that supposed by Professor Schwarz, but it is unlikely unless there is a general

[1] *Société de Géographie de Genève*, Jan./Mar. 1925.

XXIX.   PORTERS CROSSING A SWAMP SOUTH OF SMITH SOUND, AN INLET FROM
LAKE VICTORIA

XXX.   CAPT. GOLDSACK SOUNDING THE NIAVARONGO RIVER

subsidence of the land to the south of the lake. There is no doubt, however, that an earthquake which produces a fissure in the right place and in the right direction, would materially assist the draining of Lake Victoria. But it is obvious that the chance of the exactly right fissure occurring is very small, and in any case no steps can be taken in advance to guard against it. Moreover the Professor's forecast that if the lake were drained away southward the whole of central Africa would become as arid as Arabia, needs very little thought to controvert it.

Goldsack and I continued round the south-west corner of the lake to Biharamulo with the object of seeing something of the Kagera River, the principal tributary of Lake Victoria and head waters of the White Nile. In the country south of the lake there had been in places, many tsetse flies, and on one occasion when I got in advance of the porters and had two hours walk back in the late afternoon, I was severely bitten, although in the morning there had been no flies along the road. The natives cultivate bees by making cylindrical hives of bark or grass and hanging them in trees. The bees are later smoked out and the gathered honey usually contains a mixture of comb, dead bees, bits of bark, straw and other rubbish; these can of course be strained out though it is a slow process.

The forest country to the south and west of Victoria was, in 1926, difficult to travel over at any pace. The paths were few and there were often long distances between places where it was possible to get food for our porters. In addition our maps were German and made before 1914, and did not represent the country as it was in 1926; roads shown on the map having often disappeared and different ones been made. Often villages had been moved and their names changed. The name of a village is frequently the name of the reigning chief and is changed when the chief dies, so that the names on our maps were often un-recognized by the local people. We found that usually the natives knew only the country for about a day's march round their villages, and it was very difficult to get any definite informa-tion, as different men gave different names to places and even to such permanent features as mountains. It meant that travelling was a haphazard affair, a case of going from village to village in the general direction of one's projected journey. There were a few roads between important centres which were practicable in the dry season for cars, but they did not happen to suit us. To-day things are completely different as the country has been opened up by all-weather motor roads.

We ultimately arrived at the Kagera River near the junction of its two main constituents—the Niavarongo and Ruvuvu—and just above the fine Bugufi Falls (see Frontispiece). These rivers lie in deep valleys and the whole country is mountainous. It was here that we crossed by canoe ferry into the Belgian mandated territory of Ruanda-Urundi as has already been mentioned. The Falls are about half a mile below the confluence, and are found where the river enters a gorge between steep hills. It narrows to some 20 yards wide at the Falls, where the water drops about 30 feet. The air round about is filled with fine spray, and the noise can be heard for some distance. Some of the near-by trees still showed the names cut on them by British troops during the East African campaign, and trenches were still visible on the hillside.

Our work was to measure the discharges of the streams so as to get some idea of their relative importance, which was then unknown, and cannot be completely settled until discharges have been measured regularly over several seasons. A few odd discharges of the Kagera, the Niavarongo and Ruvuvu had been measured previous to our visit, but our measurements formed a series along the river, and are the first certainly known to be measured by current-meters. They showed that the flow of the Kagera was much less than had been estimated by Sir Wm. Garstin, and that it does not play such an important part as was formerly thought. Of recent years regular measurements of the discharge of the Kagera near its mouth have been made by the Upper Nile division of the Egyptian Irrigation Service, and are now being continued by the Uganda Hydrological Survey, but it still has not been possible to study the hydrology of the tributaries.

Before going further we will give a general account of the Kagera system. Its basin covers the country between the southern half of Lake Victoria and the Western Rift Valley, and a line running from the south-west corner of Victoria towards Lake Tanganyika. Almost the whole of the basin is mountainous and the valleys contain streams, but the small ones are very often completely overgrown with papyrus and are more like valley swamps than streams. There are many lakes in the system and they are sometimes connected with swamp. This is particularly the case on the main stream of the Kagera where it runs northwards. One of the principal tributaries is the Mukungwa coming from the eastern end of the Mufumbiro Mountains, and rising out of two delightful mountain lakes named Ruhonda and Muleru, which one passes on the road from Kabale in Uganda to Lake Kivu. The Mukungwa runs southwards to join the Niavarongo coming from the high country south-east of Lake Kivu. The joint stream called the Niavarongo flows eastwards and is joined by the Akanyaru and then the Ruvuvu, both coming from the south. There is a good deal of swamp along the Akanyaru, and the Niavarongo flows through swamp between lakes Mugesera and Rugwero. The Ruvuvu is not a swampy stream and its most distant source, the Luvironza, rises in the highland about twenty-five miles from Lake Tanganyika. This is also the most remote source of the Nile, being, according to measurements on the best existing maps, 6,700 kilometres (4,160 miles) from the sea at Damietta. Beyond the Ruvuvu the Kagera has no tributary of any importance. Its lower course where it runs eastward to Lake Victoria is navigable for about 100 miles from its mouth.

The measurement of discharges in these remote places is difficult unless permanent sites with suitable boats and tackle can be established. Our measurements were made from dug-out canoes of varying sizes and degrees of stability, manned by natives who were not skilled boatmen and had no previous experience of the work. The Kagera and Niavarongo were fairly rapid streams bordered by papyrus, and the current made the work more difficult. Our usual procedure was to lash two canoes together to make them more stable, stretch a wire rope across the river and anchor it at both ends, so that it was clear of the water. Otherwise it would almost certainly catch the flowing debris and break loose. The wire rope is marked at intervals of 5 metres so that it serves as a measure of the width of the river. The river width is divided into fifteen or more equal parts and soundings are taken at the middle of each of these (see Figs. 13

and 14, Ch. XIV and Plate XXX). The velocity at mid-depth at each sounding point is measured with a current-meter, an instrument like an anemometer, in which the number of turns of the cups in a minute indicates the speed of the water (see also Ch. XIV).

When the flow of the stream was fairly rapid it was hard work holding on to the wire to keep the boat in place, for with two irregular shaped canoes lashed together there was usually a sideways force tending to push the boat along the wire. There were one or two places where had the boat got adrift it would have been distinctly unpleasant, particularly at the spot where we had the Kagera Fall two or three hundred yards below us. Apart from falls and rapids there were always crocodiles handy to keep one alert against being upset in the water. Goldsack had an unpleasant experience. We had finished our measurement on the Niavarongo near its confluence with the Akanyaru (see Plate XXX) and Goldsack went off in a canoe which we had been able to borrow to reconnoitre the river a little further up. The river was not very wide and there were a good many bends, and as he rounded one of these, a hippopotamus suddenly came up under the canoe and half-filled it with water. The boatmen made for the bank but the hippo chased them and again charged the canoe whilst one of the men hit it with a paddle. It was fortunately a large canoe or the occupants would have been thrown into the water and might not have got ashore. They waited awhile and then turned back, keeping close to the shore. But the hippo appeared again, and this time Goldsack was able to shoot it and it sank. Later the body floated and was pulled ashore by the combined efforts of all our porters. We hoped that we should be able to replenish our fat supply, but the animal proved to be an old one with many scars, which we put down to the teeth of other hippos, and without fat. We were disappointed but the porters were pleased and rapidly divided its meat, which they brought up to camp. That night Goldsack was turned out of his bed, and tent, by soldier ants which had been attracted by the meat. These ants, called locally " siafu," are the kind which travel in a long column and over-run everything in their path and bite fiercely.

The Akanyaru is one of the large tributaries and comes, like the Niavarongo, from the high country south-east of Lake

Kivu. When we saw it it had a small discharge and seemed to be completely overgrown by papyrus a short distance from its mouth. Looking up the valley all that could be seen was a plain of papyrus filling its floor. The Nyavarongo too was bordered by papyrus, but the water level was well below its banks so that the papyrus was dry. At the time of our visit the Akanyaru was discharging about one-third as much as the Niavarongo above the confluence. At the Ruvuvu confluence the Niavarongo discharge had more than doubled, and was about three times that of the Ruvuvu. Some of this was due to tributaries and some probably to a falling river draining water from the swamps. From our observations it seems as if the Niavarongo makes the most important contribution to the discharge of the Kagera, but this may depend on the season.

There are many miles of navigable waterways in the Kagera system, but unfortunately they are not continuous, but interrupted by rapids. The Germans had plans for bringing a railway from Tabora to Kahama and on to the Ruvuvu—Niavarongo confluence, with the idea that the produce of Ruanda could be brought by water to the terminus. The only part of this scheme which has since been undertaken is the railway from Tabora to Mwanza. Presumably the development of motor roads has been found less costly and more suitable than railways to the mountainous nature of the country.

When the territory was under German rule there was some discussion as to which of the Kagera tributaries was the source of the White Nile. It is not a very profitable question to discuss as there are many sources. If the principal source is defined as that of the stream with the largest discharge, then the Niavarongo probably has it. This was the opinion of the German administrator Doctor Kandt in *Caput Nili*.[1] If, however, it is to refer to the longest stream, then the Ruvuvu and the Luvironza, as we have already mentioned, have the honour. One of the streams whose claims have been put forward is the Mukungwa, and this certainly deserves to be mentioned on æsthetic grounds. At its head are the two beautiful lakes Muleru and Ruhonda in delightful mountain country at the foot of the volcano, Muhavura. Out of each lake the stream falls in cascades, and its clear water

[1] Berlin, 1905.

M 2

then flows down a narrow valley in a series of rapids and pools. If it only had trout it would be even more delightful, and I know of a no more suitable stream for their introduction in this part of the world.

The following thesis belongs to geology, and has been worked out by E. J. Wayland and his successors in the *Geological Survey of Uganda*, and pieces have been added to the picture by the archæologist L. S. Leakey and the biologist E. B. Worthington. I am neither geologist, archæologist nor biologist, so I can give only a general account of some conclusions from their books. There is evidence that the East African lakes have been, relative to their present condition, at both higher and lower levels. Some of the evidence supporting this is in the form of terraces above the present lakes, and which are the remains of old beaches. A beach was formed when the lake remained for some considerable time at about one level, and they usually contain the fossilized remains of animals, and sometimes the work of man in the form of stone implements. These changes of lake level may be due to earth movements, or to climatic changes causing a disturbance of the balance between the factors which determine lake level. When the level of a lake is steady, inflow by streams and rainfall on the lake is balanced by evaporation and outflow from the lake exit. Seepage should be added to the outflow but in general it is not important. It is obvious that if the outlet of the lake is raised or lowered, the balance will be upset and the outflow will be decreased or increased until balance is again reached with a higher or lower lake level. The change of level of the outlet may be caused by stream erosion, damming by volcanic eruption, or by a general tilt of the land surface. The balance can also be upset by climatic change when rainfall increases or decreases, and/or evaporation decreases or increases. Authorities agree that both earth movement and climatic changes have taken place on the Lake Plateau in recent geological times, and have been responsible for the changes in the level of the lakes which can be deduced from the geological evidence. It is generally thought that there have been in the past, periods of much greater rainfall than the present, and others when conditions were more arid, but agreement as to the details of these periods is not unanimous. The Nile Basin above the exit of the Bahr-el-Jebel from Lake Albert, has an area of 150,000 square miles or three-quarters of the area of Spain, and it is largely covered with vegetation. The number of geologists working over the area has been small, and it will be many years before it has been studied in such detail as to accumulate all the evidence bearing on the problem of its recent geological history, and then to fit it together to make a consistent whole.

One of the great events of African pre-history was the formation of the Rift Valley. The valley begins near to the Zambesi River and runs north up to the Red Sea, a branch separating north of Lake Nyassa and running up to the Sudan. All the great lakes of Central Africa—with the exception of Lake Victoria—as well as a number of small ones, lie in the Rift. Most valleys are drainage lines which have been gradually deepened by the streams which they carry, but the Rift Valley is of a different kind. As one stands on the plains south of Lake Albert or Lake Edward, one is on the flat floor of a valley twenty or thirty miles wide with steep escarpments on either side. It is true that there are rivers in the bottom, but they did not make the valley. Geological examination, where it has been possible, shows that the rocks underlying the floor of the valley are the same as those at the tops of the escarpments, the inference being that they once formed a continuous bed. This bed was cracked by parallel faults and either the piece in the middle sank, or the two sides, relative to the floor, were pushed up. Both opinions have been held. It is not supposed that it was a catastrophic cause which happened suddenly, but rather that the process has been spread over long periods of time, going by small steps, in fits and starts as it were.

Before the formation of the western rift the country sloped down from the eastern side of Lake Victoria westwards, and the drainage went to the Congo. This accounts for the fact already mentioned that the Kafu and Katonga Rivers have tributaries which converge on the main stream towards the west, indicating that at the time of the formation of their valleys, the general slope of the country was westwards. The formation of Lake Victoria followed this period of geological time, and was effected by the gradual sinking or warping of the area, so that portions of these west-flowing streams were caused to flow backwards to the lake. When the Rift was formed the west-flowing streams were captured by it and their waters went northward to the Nile. At a later date volcanic activity threw up the Mufumbiro chain of volcanoes right across the Rift Valley, leading to the formation of Lake Kivu and the diversion of some water from the Nile to Lake Tanganyika, and ultimately to the Congo.

Some of the old lake terraces have been examined and have yielded information bearing on the animal life, including man, of the age in which they were formed. Caves, as in other countries, have also supplied information about prehistoric man. From various sites in Kenya and Uganda it has been possible to arrange, in chronological order, a series of stone and other implements which enables us to get an idea as to whether two terraces on the sides of different lakes are of approximately the same date. Clearly, if several high-level terraces on different lakes appear to be of the same age, the assumption would be, that it was more likely that the high lake levels were due to climatic conditions rather than to earth movements.

Animal remains, particularly those of fishes, can give very useful information about past history. Some fish problems have already been mentioned, and the Worthingtons' book, from which I take the following, will provide interesting reading. The ordinary fish in the Nile extend from the sea to Lake Albert and the Murchison Falls, and the same fish, or fish with only very slight differences, occur in Lake Rudolf. Lake Rudolf is now completely separate from the Nile system, but the inference from the similarity of the fish, is that it was at one time connected with the Nile. There are well-marked beaches several hundred feet above the present level of the lake, showing that, at some distant date, it held much more water than it does now, and it is very probable that it once had an outflow north-westwards to the Nile. Some day a detailed survey of this inhospitable region may decide the question.

The fish of Lakes Edward and George and of Lakes Victoria and Kioga are, in the main, different from the Nile fish lower down, though a few species are similar. The evidence from a terrace on the Kazinga channel, however, shows that long ago when Lake Edward was higher than it is now, many of the Nile fish—such as the Nile perch and tiger fish, as well as the crocodile, which are now absent—existed in the lake, since their remains occur in this terrace. The explanation put forward to account for this is that in one of the arid periods the lake dried up and the original Nile fauna died. The existence of arid periods and the drying up of lakes is shown by large deposits of bones of aquatic animals in various parts of East Africa. When the lake again filled up a few species managed to get back from other waters, and from these, under the favourable conditions of a large lake, have evolved the present fish. The rapids on the Semliki were the obstacles which prevented the re-stocking of the lake from Lake Albert. A similar explanation will account for the fish of Lake Victoria. At some period the lake dried up, or at any rate was reduced to small swamps and muddy pools, in which such fish as Mud-fish and Lung-fish survived. These fish can burrow into mud and remain alive for long dry periods until the mud becomes wet and soft again. Perhaps some other hardy species managed to survive the arid period to re-stock the lake and evolve rapidly in the next rainy period. This must have happened after the formation of the Murchison Falls provided the block which prevented Lake Victoria from being re-stocked from the Nile lower down.

Chapter Eleven

CLIMATE, HEALTH AND VEGETATION

1. CLIMATE

THE subjects of this chapter have been touched upon in previous chapters describing the physical features of the Nile Basin. However, it seemed worthwhile, at the risk of some repetition, to go into them a little more fully and assemble the material within a single chapter. The climatic data for Egypt and the Sudan were put together by the Egyptian Meteorological Service under Mr. L. J. Sutton, which formed part of my department, though in recent years the Sudan has formed its own service. The Meteorological service of Egypt and the Sudan was started by Sir Henry Lyons about 1900. The data for the Lake Plateau comes from the East African Meteorological Service started by Mr. A. Walter in 1929. On my advice the Egyptian Government has made an annual contribution to the East African Service ever since its beginning, in view of the value of its work to the study of the hydrology of the Nile Basin.

As the Nile Basin extends from 31° north of the equator to 4° south and the country varies in elevation from sea level to 8,000 feet, with mountains rising considerably above this, it is obvious that it has a variety of climates. Without being too scientific in classifying these we make the following divisions.

1. The Mediterranean Coast.
2. The Delta and Upper Egypt to south of the Fayum (latitude 29° N.).
3. Upper Egypt and the Northern Sudan as far as Merowe, i.e. latitude 29° to latitude 18°.
4. The Central Sudan from Merowe to the latitude of Renk and Roseires, i.e. latitude 18° N. to 12° N.
5. The Southern Sudan, i.e. latitude 12° N. to latitude 4° N.
6. The Ethiopian Plateau.
7. The Lake Plateau, being Uganda and parts of Kenya, Tanganyika and the Belgian Congo.

It will be simplest to deal with these divisions in the order mentioned, and we will consider the temperature, humidity and rainfall, factors which have the most direct effect on human life. A study of the diagrams will best illustrate these factors and actual statistics will be found in the tables.

The characteristic of the Nile Valley from the sea to Khartoum is the smallness of the rainfall. Right on the Mediterranean coast from Alexandria to the most northern tip at Burullos about 8 inches of rain falls in the year. Inland the amount falls off rapidly until at Cairo it averages just over an inch. From there as far as Merowe it is less than an inch, and for the greater part of this distance the country is almost rainless. For example at Assiut the average rainfall is one-fifth of an inch and south of Assiut it often happens that years pass without rain, until one gets almost as far south as Merowe where the average rainfall increases to 1 inch. The rainfall of Egypt, as one would infer, is of Mediterranean origin, while at Merowe it is from the northern fringe of the tropical rain belt. The rain in Egypt falls mostly in the winter, while at Merowe and southwards to Khartoum it is mainly in July and August.

In the northern Delta rain creates very unpleasant conditions in the villages. The roads, with a few exceptions, are made of earth, excellent in dry weather, but after a little rain they become extremely greasy on the surface, making travelling difficult for animals, cars and their owners. As many roads lie along the banks of canals or drains it is by no means uncommon for cars to slide into the water.

The mean annual temperature increases from the Delta up to Merowe and then remains steady up to Khartoum; continuing southwards it falls slightly and remains steady over the Sudan plains. The rise of the country up to the Lake Plateau causes a considerable fall of the mean annual temperature, which here, and in Ethiopia, depends very much on altitude. From the Mediterranean coast as far south as latitude 12° N., January is the coolest month of the year; in Egypt and the Northern Sudan, June, July and August are the hottest months, except on the coast where July, August and September include the maximum temperatures. From Merowe southwards the effect of the rains is shown on the curve of mean monthly temperature

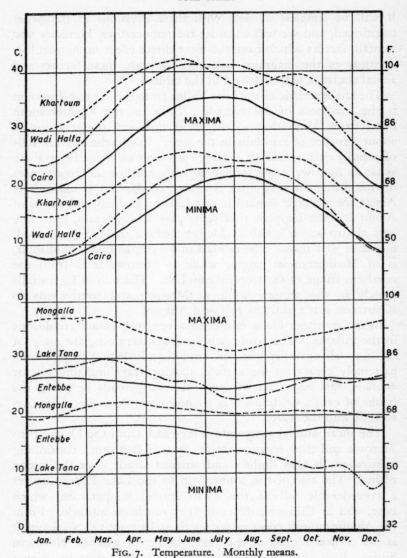

FIG. 7. Temperature. Monthly means.

but the effect is not appreciable until Khartoum is reached (see Fig. 7).

The climate of the Delta and Upper Egypt as far as Assiut,

170

is delightful from November to April. The days are usually clear and bright and the nights cool or even cold. In December, January and February, although it is usually warm in the sun, a fire will be appreciated at night, even as far south as Assiut, and in the desert, as many people know, it can be extremely cold. The weather though usually settled is liable to be disturbed in winter by the passage of depressions along the Mediterranean which bring strong winds and cold weather and sometimes rain. Their effect decreases as one goes inland, and in Upper Egypt the winter weather is generally agreeable. At this time of the year ordinary clothes as worn in England are suitable, but if one's time is spent mainly in the country or desert it is advisable to protect one's eyes by wearing sun-glasses. It occasionally happens that the ground temperature falls to freezing-point outside the towns, and in our garden in the country near Cairo it was usual to see hoar frost on the grass in the early morning a number of times during the winter. In the winter of 1939 hosepipes left out unemptied on the golf course at the Gezira Sporting Club were full of ice in the morning.

From March to the beginning of June Lower Egypt is affected by conditions known as "Khamsin" on the average about three times a month. These are due to the passage of depressions from the Sahara or along the coast from west to east, and during which the weather follows a definite course. The approach of a depression is indicated by an easterly wind and increasing temperatures, followed by dry southerly winds which can be extremely hot; in fact a temperature of 117° F. has been recorded in Lower Egypt. The high temperature may last for two or three days until the depression has passed, and then the temperature drops with extraordinary suddenness as the wind changes round from south to north-west, bringing cool moist air from the Mediterranean. During the Khamsin the atmosphere often becomes hazy owing to the presence of fine dust particles, and if the wind is strong sand storms may occur. A very striking example occurred in March, 1946. The air became hazy towards mid-day and began to carry a lot of dust so that the light gradually failed, becoming first orange and then red and finally it was almost dark. After about fifteen minutes it gradually became lighter and returned through red and orange to more normal conditions as the dust passed. It was a most impressive experience. Occasionally towards the end of Khamsin conditions, the phenomenon of a "blue" sun may be observed and may persist for several hours.

By the end of May or beginning of June summer conditions

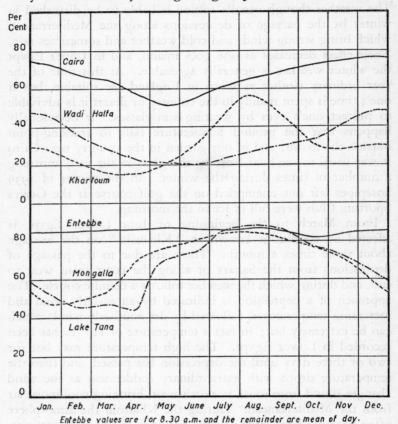

Entebbe values are for 8.30 a.m. and the remainder are mean of day.

FIG. 8. Relative humidity. Monthly means.

are established and continue until October. During this time the days are clear and the wind northerly, while very high temperatures rarely occur. In Upper Egypt and the Northern Sudan it is steadily hot from May to September, an important feature being the large diurnal range of temperature.

It is well-known that one's sensation of heat is greatly affected by humidity and that the temperature of the wet-bulb thermometer is usually a better index of comfort than the dry-bulb. The main characteristic, of the climate of a great part of the Nile Basin is its dryness (see Fig. 8). The relative humidity is greatest on the coast, except in winter when Cairo is damper than Alexandria and the humidity remains fairly steady up to Assiut, after which it decreases as one goes south as far as Khartoum. In summer the humidity decreases from the coast as far as Merowe, and then increases further south owing to the rains. The lowest humidities in the Nile Basin occur at Merowe where the average for the year is only 23 per cent. Sometimes in the Northern Sudan the moisture in the atmosphere decreases almost to zero, but at one time these low humidities were doubted. The matter was, however, settled beyond doubt by the experiments of the late Mr. B. H. Wade of the Physical Department of the Ministry of Public Works.

The prevailing wind over nearly all of Egypt and the Northern Sudan is northerly or north-westerly throughout the year. On the Mediterranean coast in winter the most frequent direction is west. Merowe during July and August is just on the northern limit of the tropical south and south-west winds. For the remainder of the year the northerly current extends right up the Nile Valley as far as Khartoum and southwards. The fact that the wind in Egypt is generally up the Nile is an advantage to the sailing boats which carry a great deal of the merchandise transported by the Nile. The north wind takes them upstream and they can drift down with the current. On the average the wind in Egypt is not very strong, but strong winds and sometimes gales occur in winter during the passage of depressions along the coast.

In the Central Sudan from Merowe to Roseires or Renk during the months of December, January and February the days are not unduly hot and the nights are cool. At the same time the humidity is low and it is a very pleasant time of the year. The rain in the south usually occurs from April to October (see Fig. 9), and the season is shorter as one goes north, until at Merowe rain is almost confined to July and August. The temperature is lowest in January and increases until May or June, when the

highest temperatures are recorded, after which it falls with the
increase of the rains and has a secondary minimum in August and

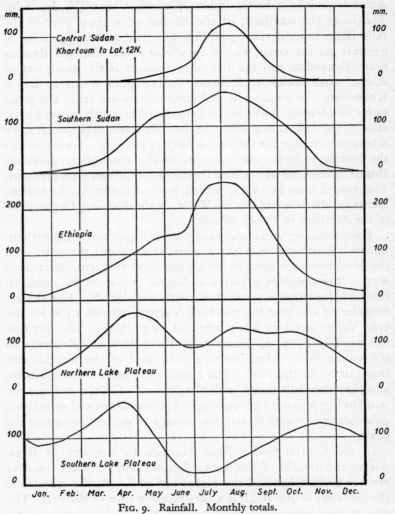

FIG. 9. Rainfall. Monthly totals.

a secondary maximum in September or October. September and
October are liable to be oppressive months.

During the rainy season the area is visited by "haboobs"

or storms carrying large quantities of sand and dust. June and July are the months in which such storms are most frequent, and they occur over a large area from Wad Medani and Dueim northwards to the borders of Egypt and right across the Sudan from Fasher to Tokar. Khartoum is frequently visited by "haboobs" and the average duration of the storm is about three hours, during which the strength of the wind may be considerable. An approaching "haboob" looks like a very dense cloud of sand or dust extending to a considerable height which may reach 2,000 feet or more (see Plate XXXI). Mr. G. W. Grabham, formerly Government Geologist, during his long residence in the Sudan has seen a good many of these storms, and a "haboob" appears to him as a collection of travelling circular storms, which present a buttressed appearance as they approach on a front which may reach twenty miles in length. Visibility in the midst of one of these storms is reduced to a very short distance. During the passage of the storm conditions are very oppressive, but there is always a fall of temperature afterwards and some rain may follow. Similar winds occur further south, but where there is vegetation and no dust on the ground the dust clouds are not present. In the Southern Sudan strong and sudden wind storms are liable to occur at the onset and the end of the rainy season, but they do not carry dust. When travelling on a river-steamer at these times it is advisable to be on the watch and prepared to tie the steamer up to the bank if necessary, as occasionally considerable damage has been done.

In the Southern Sudan rain may fall any time between February and November, the maximum being in August (see Fig. 9). The maximum temperature is in March and the minimum in July and August. Humidity is low from January to March, but is high at the peak of the rains. At this time of the year, however, the climate is pleasant and it does not rain all day long or every day. There are disadvantages, of course, if one has to travel otherwise than on the river, and the rainy season is a time of prolific vegetable growth and insects. A bright light attracts the latter in clouds, and if in camp a red shade over one's lamp helps to lessen the number which fall into one's food. In a permanent habitation the windows and doors must be covered with fine wire netting not only to keep out mosquitoes and flies, but also the many harmless but tiresome specimens. The wind is northerly from November to March and southerly for the rest of the year.

The climate of the Ethiopian Highlands was described in some detail in Chapter VI, and it is not necessary to say any more here.

On the Lake Plateau, as in Ethiopia, climate depends very much on altitude and on the shape of the surrounding country which influences the rainfall. The greater part of the Nile Basin is in Uganda, while those parts in Kenya and Tanganyika, as well as parts of Ruanda, are in the Basin of Lake Victoria. At any given station there is very little variation of the mean temperature throughout the year, and the diurnal range is not great. Similarly the mean relative humidity does not vary much throughout the year. This would be expected on the shores of Lake Victoria, but it is also the case inland. The average height of the country round Lake Victoria is about 4,000 feet, and the average maximum temperature is round about 80° F. The minimum temperature varies rather more with locality, and is about 60° F.,

Normal Temperatures in Degrees Fahrenheit and Percentage Relative Humidities.

Station	Mean Maximum Temperature				Mean Minimum Temperature				Mean Relative Humidity			
	Jan.	Apr.	July	Oct.	Jan.	Apr.	July	Oct.	Jan.	Apr.	July	Oct.
											Mean of day	
Alexandria .	65	74	85	83	51	59	73	68	69	69	77	69
Cairo .	68	84	97	87	46	56	71	64	74	58	61	72
Assiut .	68	89	99	87	43	58	72	65	69	41	42	62
Wadi Halfa.	75	97	106	98	46	62	74	68	45	22	22	32
Merowe .	85	103	108	105	54	69	79	74	30	14	23	23
Khartoum .	90	105	101	104	60	72	77	75	31	16	48	32
Roseires .	98	105	100	97	61	73	71	69	39	31	77	71
Lake Tana .	82	84	74	79	48	56	57	51	54	44	86	77
Malakal .	96	102	88	93	65	74	71	71	30	46	84	79
Wau .	97	99	89	93	64	73	69	69	40	57	78	76
Mongalla .	99	95	88	93	67	72	69	69	48	69	84	77
										8.30 a.m.		
Gulu .	90	85	80	84	62	64	62	62	64	85	89	79
Kampala .	83	79	77	81	64	64	62	63	78	88	89	83
Entebbe .	80	78	76	79	64	65	62	63	85	86	86	82
Eldoret .	79	78	71	77	47	51	49	49	56	67	82	62
Kabale .	75	73	74	74	49	52	47	51	94	96	90	93
Mwanza .	83	83	84	86	65	65	62	66	79	81	65	61

XXXI.   SAND STORM (OR HABOOB) OVER KHARTOUM
(*Photo by G. N. Morhig, Khartoum*)

XXXII.   RODA NILOMETER BEFORE THE RECENT REPAIRS.   ERECTED ABOUT 711 A.D.

so that the temperature may be described as equable. The relative humidity averages about 80 per cent. Altogether the

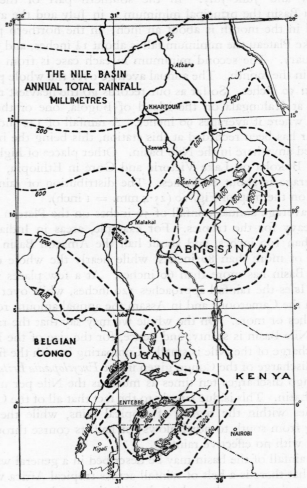

FIG. 10. The Nile Basin annual total rainfall.

climate is a very pleasant one, and the only complaint which might be made against it is the monotony of the temperature. The factor which varies most with the season of the year is the rainfall.

There are two dry and two wet seasons, but even in the dry seasons there is usually some rain, the minima occurring in January and June-July. In the southern part of the Lake Plateau Basin the principal minimum is in July and the average rainfall in the month is about an inch; in the northern part of the Lake Plateau the minimum fall is about 1½ inches, and occurs in January. The second minimum in each case is from 3 to 4 inches in the month. The annual average over the whole plateau is about 50 inches. So far as our records go the heaviest rainfall occurs at Kalungala on the island of Bugola, one of the Sese group, where it averages 90 inches. A rainfall of 140 inches in the year has been recorded at this station, this being the highest recorded anywhere in the Nile Basin. Other places of high rainfall are Bukoba on Lake Victoria and Goré in Ethiopia, where the average is about 80 inches. The distribution of rainfall is shown on the map of Fig. 10 (25·4 mm. = 1 inch).

The average annual rainfall of 50 inches on the Plateau is not very heavy for the tropics. For example, areas in India have more than 100 inches, and about half the Amazon Basin has a rainfall of more than 80 inches, while nearly the whole of the Congo Basin has more than 60 inches. At a few places in the British Isles the rainfall approaches 120 inches, while over small areas in the Cameroons and in Assam the annual amount reaches 400 inches or more. On the whole we may say that the rainfall of the Nile Basin is scanty, and hence, for the size of the Basin, the discharge of the Nile is small. Comparing it with the figures of the discharge of the Congo given in the *Encyclopædia Britannica*, the Congo discharges ten times as much as the Nile per unit of area of basin. This is due largely to the fact that all of the Congo Basin lies within the region of tropical rains, while the Nile running from south to north flows for half its course through a country with no effective rainfall.

The rainfall of the basin may be described in a general way by saying that there is a belt of rainfall across tropical Africa which moves northwards and southwards with the sun, but lags about two months behind it, and only moves half as far in latitude.

In the above description of the climates of the basin I have not gone into any detail. Those who wish for this can get it by a study of the diagrams and the climatic tables attached to this chapter.

There are often discussions amongst residents in Egypt as to whether the climate is changing, many people contending that the climate is hotter or damper than it was, say, thirty years

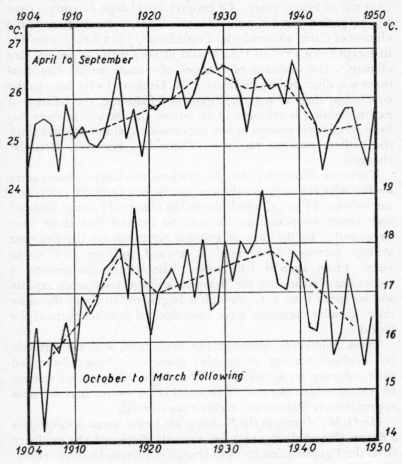

The dotted line shows five-year averages

FIG. 11. Mean temperatures at Helwan.

ago. The question of changes of climate is a difficult one on which to get evidence, since meteorological observations under properly controlled conditions do not cover a very long period.

N 2

Two kinds of change must be distinguished, one, a steady progressive change, and the other, an irregular change, such as, for example, a succession of warm summers which might extend over ten or fifteen years. Of progressive change extending over a long period there is no evidence. Thus, a description of the climate of Cairo written by an Englishman, John Antes, who was in Egypt from 1770 to 1782 would fit very well the present day climate. The question of changes of climate within historical times was discussed by Professor J. W. Gregory,[1] who came to the conclusion that, as regards Egypt and Palestine, the balance of expert opinion is strongly in favour of the view that there has been no climatic change of any importance in either country since the earliest existing records. There are, however, irregular changes.

These are shown by the observations at Helwan observatory made under the same conditions for the last forty-six years, and can be seen in Fig. 11, which shows the observed average summer and winter temperatures. It will be noticed that these vary irregularly. In the case of summer temperatures the five-year average increases from 25·2° C. around 1907 to 26·6° C. in 1927. From 1940 it falls away. The winter temperature is somewhat similar, but the five-year average rises more rapidly and by more than 2° C., though it begins to fall about the same time. Similar variations have been noticed in other parts of the world.

These differences, although not very great, and are certainly not evidence for any progressive change of climate, have had their influence on agriculture. They have led to earlier sowing of cotton, which because of this and other causes is now sown approximately fifteen days earlier than formerly.

Mr. G. W. Murray in the *Bulletin of the Société Royale de Géographie d'Egypte* (November, 1949) has recently discussed the evidence from the Egyptian deserts as to change of climate in recent times. The following is his summary of his paper:—

" After the last rainy interlude, which terminated about 4000 B.C., those inhabitants of the desert who did not invade the Nile Valley withdrew to higher ground in the south-west and south-east where they maintained themselves and their cattle till " C-group " times,

[1] *Geographical Journal*, 1914.

perhaps 2500–2000 B.C. Water near the surface at El-Shab and Tarfawi permitted people to live there in oases till about 3000 B.C., when the fall in the water table rendered these places uninhabitable. There was a doubtful recrudescence of rainfall in the Fayum in Old Kingdom times and, in the classic period, the Mediterranean rainfall moved a little farther south. This is the history of the Egyptian climate during the last 8,000 years."

2. HEALTH

The large range of climate in the Nile Basin leads to considerable variations in health conditions. It is doubtful, because of endemic diseases, whether any part of the Basin is as healthy for Europeans as the temperate regions of Europe, though the climate is often more pleasant. In Egypt and the Northern Sudan the winter climate is delightful but not really invigorating, while the summer climate is trying because of the high temperature. The climate of the Southern Sudan is almost always trying, except in the rainy season, when, although it is not particularly hot, there are other drawbacks. The climate of parts of the Lake Plateau is agreeable as to temperature, but this is only secured by its altitude, which in itself has ill effects on some people.

Some of the remarks about health in this section apply more to visitors or foreign residents than to the native population, since the latter usually acquire a certain amount of immunity to local diseases. Nevertheless some of the precautions suggested are of general application, and in order to keep in good health in most places in the Nile Basin it is necessary to take these precautions against disease. In the southern and central parts of the basin malaria is the most common disease. It is carried by the anopheline mosquito, which becomes infected by biting persons suffering from malaria or persons who have the parasite in their blood. When these infected insects bite another person they inject the parasite into his blood, and malaria will probably develop. New drugs developed during the war, of which paludrine is the latest, have replaced quinine in its treatment.

The mosquitoes breed in stagnant water, and it is advisable not to have any stagnant pools near one's house, and to sleep under a mosquito net. In many of the towns all over the basin, the draining of pools and oiling of stagnant water is carried out as a means of destroying mosquito larvæ. Up to the present malaria has not been common in Egypt, which at first seems remarkable, since conditions would appear to be favourable to its existence. The explanation may be that although the commonest Egyptian mosquito (Culex), which abounds nearly everywhere, can breed in any stagnant pool, the anopheles type, which carries malaria, is restricted in its breeding places. The particular anopheles which is the commonest carrier of malaria in Egypt, does not breed in open water, but requires the protection of vegetation, and hence only breeds in swamps, rice-fields and weedy drains or pools. Suitable breeding places for anopheles, therefore, are not as plentiful as for the ordinary Culex. In 1943 Upper Egypt was invaded by the *anopheles gambiæ*, a much more dangerous carrier of malaria than the *anopheles pharoensis* mentioned above, since it breeds in sunlit pools, even such tiny ones as might be formed by water in a donkey's hoof prints. This mosquito is known in tropical Africa, and occasional specimens have been found in Egypt, but apparently it never became established there, though it very nearly did. It appears to have come, carrying malaria from the south, and advanced as far north as just beyond Assiut, but got no further. The opinion seems to be that some climatic factor or physical condition further north was unfavourable to the insect. However, the incidence of malaria on a population unused to it, and lacking any means or knowledge of protective measures, caused many deaths before steps could be taken to cope with it. It will be remembered that the same mosquito had appeared a few years before in Brazil and had been the cause of a very serious epidemic of malaria, which had, however, finally been controlled. The experience of this Brazilian outbreak was available and the Government, with some foreign assistance, took large-scale measures, and finally the mosquito and the disease were stamped out.

Dysentery and typhoid fevers are common all over the Basin. The parasites which cause these diseases are usually taken in food or water, and flies are a means of carrying the infection. The precautions to be taken are good sanitation, good drinking water, doubtful water should be boiled, and cleanliness with regard to food. In Egypt, and some other parts of the Basin, bilharzia and ankylostoma, diseases due to microscopic worms, are common. They are either contracted by drinking infected water or by wading or bathing in it. During the South African war a number of the troops who went out from England contracted bilharzia, and the government was still paying disability pensions to them when the 1914–18 war came on. Mindful of South African experience the British Government sent out Dr. Leiper, an authority on parasitic worms, to devise measures for the protection of the troops in Egypt, where the disease is extremely common. Previous to this I had not heard much about bilharzia as it rarely occurred in Europeans, who are not usually exposed to the conditions favouring the entry of the worm to their systems. However, it did occur to me that wading in marshes and stagnant water when out snipe-shooting, might expose one to infection, so I consulted Leiper. He was of opinion that the chance of infection was not very great since, in the marshes and haunts of snipe, the water is usually slightly saline, and a very small percentage of salt is enough to kill the bilharzia organism. However, he did say, " If you do get it don't waste any money on doctors, as they can do nothing and you will just have to put up with it." Fortunately since that time a remedy has been discovered. In Egypt an attempt to eradicate bilharzia is now being made, the method being by putting very small doses of copper sulphate into the drains where the snail, which is the host of one of the stages of the bilharzia parasite, is found.

In the southern part of the Basin sleeping sickness occurs in some districts, and is carried by several kinds of tsetse fly which convey the infection by their bite. The cause of the disease is a microscopic organism called a trypanosome, which is in the blood of infected people and is taken up by the fly when it bites one so infected. After passing part of its life cycle in the fly it is passed on when the fly bites another person. A similar organism carried by another variety of tsetse fly, causes a fatal disease of cattle and horses called " nagana " or " nigma." A great deal of research has been devoted to these diseases and their carriers in the countries of the Nile Basin, and special research stations and organizations for dealing with them have been founded.

The tsetse is widespread on the Lake Plateau, and its activity as a spreader of animal trypanosomiasis seems to be more important than its direct action on people by way of sleeping sickness. Because of its effects on cattle it dominates large areas, for when the fly appears in an inhabited district and cattle fall sick, the natives drive them off to fly-free areas and the cultivation relapses to bush. The bush is the home and breeding ground of the tsetse, and this is what makes control so difficult, for it is not possible to clear all the bush and continue to keep the ground cleared. The tsetse sucks blood and largely lives on game, but if game animals were exterminated there are still many other animals and birds which are possible hosts for the trypanosome. Research is being devoted to the habits of the fly, and this involves, catching and counting many flies—marking some in such a way as to indicate when and where they were caught and then releasing them—experiments on clearing bush, destroying the fly by burning the grass when it is dry, spraying insecticides from aeroplanes, and the trial of synthetic drugs against the trypanosome, altogether a very wide field of work. The spread of the fly causes cattle to be concentrated in the fly-free areas and this leads to over-grazing and soil erosion.

Leprosy is common over the southern part of the Basin, but progress has been made in dealing with it, and new synthetic drugs have been produced which promise good results. In certain districts relapsing fever occurs. It is transmitted by the bite of a tick which lives in cracks in the ground and in native houses, and comes out at night. The precaution is to avoid sleeping in native houses or using old camping grounds.

Under-nourishment is a condition which is widespread in the more populous parts of the Basin, and is a predisposing tendency to disease. The rapid increase of population in the last thirty years is partly responsible for this, as the expansion of the cultivated land and food resources have not kept pace with the population increase. The immediate remedy lies in an increase of the cultivable area, where this is possible, and improved methods of agriculture, development of fisheries, and improvement of livestock. It is obvious, however, that these are only partial remedies, and which, together with attacks on disease, will probably lead at first to a more rapid increase of population. In past times disease, war, and slave-raiding, kept the African population more or less in equilibrium with the environment, but in this century slave-raiding and local wars have practically disappeared, while there has been a very considerable fight against disease all over the Nile Basin. Consequently many of the checks on population have been removed, and the only reasonable possibility for the future is some limitation of the number of births. Since with the great mass of the people of the Nile Basin the tradition is to have as many children as possible, ideas of birth control to limit the increase will take a very long time in becoming established. The spread of education, leading, as it generally does, to the desire for a higher standard of living, will gradually lead to a smaller birth-rate, but this will not affect appreciably the mass of the people for some time to come.

Some mention should be made of protection against the sun. When I first came to Egypt, a great respect for the power of the sun was prevalent, and nobody would have thought of doing a day's work in the open without a sun-helmet. During the First World War sun-helmets were issued to the troops. In Egypt, however, the fashion has gradually gone out and more risks are now taken; in fact in the second war sun-helmets were not used by troops in Egypt, and one very rarely sees one. In the Sudan they are worn, but in Kenya and Uganda stout felt hats with reasonable brims, sometimes of the double Terai pattern, are more common. It is said that some of the ill-effects of the sun come through its action on the eyes, and in one of my early journeys I suffered from glare in the desert. Since then I have been careful to protect myself with dark-coloured glasses and have had no further trouble. In hot weather one may sweat a good deal, and this diminishes the salt-content of the body. This diminution is said to be a condition which encourages heat-stroke, and it is therefore advisable to take plenty of salt to restore the balance.

3. VEGETATION

The main factor affecting vegetation in the Nile Basin, outside the areas where irrigation is practised, is rainfall. Hence the different zones of plant life run roughly east and west. In Egypt the vegetation near the river is almost entirely due to irrigation and cultivation and only a few wild plants occur. The principal crops of Egypt are cotton, wheat, barley, maize, berseem (a variety of clover), rice, beans, lentils, helba (or fenugreek) dates, melons, sugar cane and onions. Near the towns many kinds of vegetables and flowers are grown, including practically all those commonly grown in Europe. The following classification of the zones of vegetation is taken from Warming's *Oecology of Plants* (Clarendon Press), but it must be remembered that one zone shades into another. There is, in fact, no definite dividing line.

Large areas in, or near, the Nile Basin are desert and practically rainless. In these areas there is no vegetation except in a few favoured places, as, for example, the oases where the underground water reaches the surface, or along drainage lines where after rain the subsoil may remain moist for a long period. Along the drainage lines the vegetation consists of scattered plants comprising grasses, small herbs and stunted shrubs. In other desert areas there may be occasional rain at irregular intervals, or even a scanty annual rainfall, and where after rain small herbs germinate, bear fruit and die away in a few weeks. In these places at the right season it is an amazing sight to see the desert change from yellow or brown to green in such a short time.

As regions of scanty but regular rainfall are reached, the country becomes dotted with small thorny shrubs, mostly acacias, and this type of country is known as shrub steppe. It begins south of Merowe and, as one goes south and the rainfall increases, the shrubs grow more thickly together. After the rains the country becomes green with grasses and small herbs which quickly dry up after the rains have ceased.

Shrub steppe gradually passes into savannah country, which may be said to begin somewhere south of Khartoum. First there is thorny savannah containing small trees and, after the rains, grass and herbs. This is sometimes called orchard scrub, where the trees are not very close together. Where the trees are close together we get thorn bush and thorn forest. This type of country is called " nyika " in East Africa. In this zone of thorny trees, maize and millet are cultivated and the forest yields gum.

South of latitude 10° N. on the Sudan Plains the country is a mixture of patches of thin bush with many thorny trees and open grass plain or true savannah country, where the trees are scattered and not numerous, except along the banks of rivers or drainage lines. This country is covered with tall grass up to

6 feet, or more, high, and in the rains may be swampy. During the dry season, which lasts for about half the year, the grass dries and is set on fire by the inhabitants, and very shortly after the burning young green grass springs up. Fires play an important part in the life of African vegetation, for all over the Southern Sudan and parts of Ethiopia and the Lake Plateau the grass is burnt every year. This burning kills many species of trees and so limits the vegetation; the trees that remain are of stunted growth. Small ticks are common in the grass and their bites can cause considerable irritation.

On the Lake Plateau the drier parts at moderate altitudes are sometimes characterized by thorny bushes and euphorbias, and also by dom and borassus (or doleib) palms.

Ruanda and Urundi and the western part of Uganda consist largely of hilly country which is for the most part bare of trees, though covered with grass and herbs which support herds of cattle. Large areas of Uganda are covered with elephant grass up to 10 or 12 feet high, which is difficult to pass through except along tracks, elephant- or man-made. Most of the Lake Plateau is probably to be classed as savannah and has a general altitude of 4,000 to 6,000 feet. As rain is well distributed throughout the year the vegetation does not dry up to the same extent as it does on the Sudan Plains.

In the savannah zone the rivers are often fringed with reed swamp, more particularly the Bahr-el-Jebel and Bahr-el-Ghazal in what is known as the Sudd Region. In this swamp grow papyrus (*cyperus papyrus*); um soof (*vossia cuspidata*); boos or tall bamboo-like grass (*phragmites communis*); reed mace (*typha australis*) a plant like a bulrush; ambatch or turor (*herminiera elaphroxylon*) a small tree whose stem consists of a very light pithy substance and has prickly branches and a small yellow flower; water lettuce (*pistia stratiotes*) a small floating plant; a kind of convolvulus (*ipomoea aquatica*) which helps to bind swamp vegetation together and carries large blue or purple flowers associated with which are other climbers and twiners. The valleys of the Lake Plateau often contain swamps in which papyrus is the commonest plant, but in the higher country masses of reeds occur.

The true savannah country changes into savannah forest which

187

fringes the Blue Nile near Roseires and southwards, and covers the western slopes and parts of the Ethiopian Plateau, the southern Bahr-el-Ghazal and large parts of the Lake Plateau, including the slopes upward from the Sudan Plains. Savannah forest is composed of trees of medium height, casting little shadow and not usually growing thickly together. The ground between the trees is covered with grass and perennial herbs.

Tropical rain forest does not exist in great quantity in the Nile Basin, but is found in river valleys along the Nile-Congo Divide and in patches on the Lake Plateau. The middle heights of the Ruwenzori Range are thickly forested, as are certain parts of south-west Ethiopia. The conditions for the existence of rain forest are heat and copious rainfall, and it is characterized by a large number of species and several storeys of vegetation, so that practically all the space is utilized and a wonderful luxuriance of plant life results. The tallest trees have trunks bare of branches for 60 feet or more, and beneath these are smaller trees and again such smaller trees as low palms and the large herbs, the whole being often tied together by creepers so as to form an impenetrable mass. This rain forest produces a number of useful timber trees. On the high mountains of the Lake Plateau bamboo forest occurs at a height of 7,000 feet or more, as also does thick forest. Above the timber line at 9,000 or 10,000 feet alpine conditions marked by a special flora gradually succeed, and here are tree-heaths and giant relatives of some of our humble weeds and garden plants, such as lobelia and groundsel.

Chapter Twelve

THE EARLY HISTORY OF THE NILE BASIN

I. THE PEOPLE AND THEIR ORIGINS

SOMETHING has been said in the previous chapters of the people of the Nile Basin, but here a little more will be said of their probable origins and languages. The material for this chapter has been gathered from the works of Professor Evans-Pritchard of Oxford, Mr. G. W. Murray of the Survey of Egypt, and other authorities,[1] though they have no responsibility for any errors which I have committed.

The people of the Nile Basin are for the most part a mixture of the white or Caucasian and the black or Negro race, varying from pure Caucasian to pure Negro. In ancient Egypt the people were of Caucasian stock which became diluted to some extent by people of mixed descent from the south. The Negro is one of the original African races, and it is supposed that since very ancient times invaders of Caucasian race in successive waves from Asia have entered the Sudan and East Africa and have united with the peoples of the country. The result of this is that the pure Negro is to be found in West Africa but is rare in the Sudan. It is customary to talk of the Asiatic invaders as Hamites, but this is a rather vague term and very little is known of the original Hamites. The term is applied to brown people who are lean, slender and muscular, with thin, straight or aquiline noses, thin lips and frizzy hair. Some, but not all of these, speak related languages which are classified as being of the Hamitic group, or as showing Hamitic traces. The Hamitic peoples include Nubians, Bejas of south-eastern Egypt and the north-eastern Sudan (Fuzzy-wuzzies), Gallas, Somalis and the tall Hima aristocracy of western Uganda and Ruanda.

The people of ancient Egypt were a mixture of Semitic and Libyan (Hamitic) elements, and this race created the ancient

---

[1] E. E. Evans-Pritchard. *The Nuer ; Witchcraft, etc. among the Azande ;* both Oxford University Press; and article in Anglo-Egyptian " Sudan from Within." Faber and Faber. 1937. G. W. Murray. *Sons of Ishmael.* Routledge.

Egyptian civilization. Later they absorbed Negro and Hamitic elements from Nubia and the south, and Semitic and other Caucasian elements from Asia. The Arabs, a Semitic people, conquered Egypt in the 7th century A.D., and gradually pushed southward up the Nile Valley. Others entered the Sudan by way of the Red Sea, and all have become merged with the previous inhabitants. The people of the purest Arab descent are the Bedawin of Egypt, but the fellahin are probably not very different in appearance from their ancestors of three thousand years ago, the Arab invaders being relatively few.

In the Sudan people speaking Arabic and claiming Arab descent extend as far south as about latitude 12°, but the Arabs must have inter-married to a very large extent with the Negroid and Hamitic peoples who were already there and who greatly exceeded them in numbers. The Arab culture and language has spread all over the Northern Sudan, and Arabic is also spoken by a few people in towns or villages of any size in the Southern Sudan, but not to any extent beyond the Sudan frontier. With the Arabic language has spread Islam, but many of the indigenous population who have become Muslimin have kept their own language and customs, though in the Sudan they usually speak Arabic as well.

In the Southern Sudan the people are pagans and are of many tribes and languages, so that classification is difficult, especially as some of the languages are only just beginning to be studied, and have not yet been analysed. It is probable that something like one hundred languages are still current in the Sudan.

Dr. Evans-Pritchard has given a classification which depends partly on language similarity, and partly on the fact that people live in a particular area. There are three considerable groups based on similarity of language and culture: Nilotes, Nilo-Hamites, and the Azande; and three based on geographical distribution: the tribes of the ironstone country of the Bahr-el-Ghazal, the tribes of Kordofan, and the tribes of Darfung, the country along the Ethiopian Frontier from Roseires southward.

The Nilotes include three large tribes, the Shilluk, Dinka and Nuer, and are a tall, thin, long-legged people, with thin legs and arms, long heads and brown skins. They do not as a rule wear clothes and are contemptuous of foreigners and their habits, and are difficult people with whom to establish contact. They are cattle-owners and also cultivators, but cattle are their main interest, and life is largely built round them. With cattle the Nilote man buys a bride or pays compensation for the killing of a fellow being. Cattle are the main topic of conversation and contemplation, and about which songs are sung. Indeed, a man may be known by the name of his bull. They thus take the place of property and family possessions in other societies. The Nilotes have permanent villages, but the dry season forces them to move where there is grazing and live in camps with the cattle. They are people of the plains and swamps. Their mode of life has been very little affected by outside influences and they remain a primitive people whose outlook can, with difficulty, be understood by those of a higher culture.

The Shilluks are a single unit ruled by a King, who, in the past, was killed when he began to show signs of failing strength, and it was thought that his health was bound up with the welfare of the tribe. The Shilluks are thought to have come into their present territory from the south-east four or five hundred years ago. Dialects of Shilluk are spoken in the south and south-eastern Sudan.

The Dinka are divided into a number of independent tribes having the same culture. The most important person in a tribe is the hereditary rain-maker who, at one time, was buried alive when he reached old age. They are thought originally to have come from the neighbourhood of the Great Lakes.

The Nuer are an offshoot of the Dinka, and are also divided into independent tribes which are frequently at war with one another. The important persons are those with hereditary religious powers, and in recent times prophets have had a wide influence.

The Nilo-Hamites include the Bari and tribes which speak Bari as well as the Lotuko, Didinga and Turkana, and people who speak their languages. All these people are found in the hills which form the northern edge of the Lake Plateau.

The Bari are a people resembling the Dinka in appearance, inhabiting the country along the Bahr-el-Gebel south of Mongalla. They are the people with whom Sir Samuel Baker fought, and were once more numerous than they are now, and owned large herds of cattle which they have since lost. They are now becoming cultivators. Their language and culture do not resemble those of the Nilotes. The Bari-speaking people were probably subjugated by the Bari.

The Azande are a numerous tribe inhabiting the southern Bahr-el-Ghazal and the Belgian Congo over the Nile-Congo Divide. They originally came from the region of the Welle and Mbomu rivers, tributaries of the Congo, and invaded the Sudan at the beginning of the nineteenth century. They are people of medium height, copper-coloured, cheerful and sociable, and easily adaptable. Their country is largely thin savannah forest. They have no cattle and are cultivators of eleusine (millet), maize, bananas, ground nuts, manioc and other plants. They are good hunters and craftsmen and were formerly cannibals, and were nick-named nyum-nyum by their neighbours, which is supposed to represent the appreciative noise made in eating. They are ruled by a hereditary aristocratic class known as Avongara, into which no son of a commoner can enter. Their good organization enabled them to conquer most of the tribes of the Southern Bahr-el-Ghazal, and occupy large stretches of country.

The other groups, classified geographically, include scores of tribes and a diversity of languages, not all of which have been closely studied from the point of view of affinities.

The languages of Egypt and the Sudan are classified as Semitic, Hamitic and Sudanic. The principal Semitic language is of course Arabic, another being Tigre, spoken by the Beni Amer who live near the Red Sea on the Eritrean boundary, but this is outside the Nile Basin. Almost the whole of the Negroid peoples of the Southern Sudan speak Sudanic languages, or languages which have both Sudanic and Hamitic features, and are called Nilo-Hamitic. The only language supposed to be purely Hamitic is the language known as Beidawi, spoken by the Bishareen and Hadendoa of the eastern desert.

Further south on the Lake Plateau the largest group speaking related languages are the Negroid Bantu peoples, who are supposed to be an early mixture of indigenous Negroes and Hamitic invaders coming from the north-east. The earliest peoples, now remaining are the pygmies of the forests along the Semliki River, and similar small people in Ruanda and Western Uganda. Three types can be seen alongside each other in Ruanda; the Watusi, tall brown aristocracy with fine Hamitic features; the Wahutu, negroids of medium size who do the ordinary work; and Batwa, small people like the pygmies. The greater part of the people around Lake Victoria are Bantu, but in the north of Uganda there are Nilo-Hamites like those already mentioned living over the border in the Sudan. Many Bantu languages are spoken round the lakes, but the lingua franca is Swahili. This is a language of Bantu structure but with a vocabulary partly of Arabic origin, and which has arisen from the many Arabic-speaking people who have settled on the east coast in the last thousand years or more. Its name is derived from the Arabic word for Coast. Arabs and mixed Arab-Negroid people spread inland as traders, as they did up the Nile, carrying Arab culture and Islam, but as far as I could see have not left much trace on the mass of the people. Rarely did one meet any man who understood even a few words of Arabic, and a Mohammedan headman, in charge of my porters in Tanganyika, who had an Arabic name did not understand any Arabic, though he probably repeated some phrases in his prayers.

2. HISTORY

The earliest traces of man in the Basin are stone implements found in Egypt, in the Sudan, and on the Lake Plateau, some of these being made perhaps 100,000 years ago. These instruments gradually develop, and it has been possible, as in Europe, to arrange the different types in chronological order. The most recent in Egypt, which are found with early forms of pottery, date from about 8,000 to 4,500 B.C. The historical period begins about 3,400 B.C., and follows a period known as pre-dynastic, in which metal implements began to be used side by side with those of stone. When the early flint implement people lived the climate of North Africa was warm and humid, the country was covered with vegetation, and the mildness of the climate allowed men to live in shelters made of reeds and branches and did not force them to live in caves, as in northern countries; where traces of their occupation would have been preserved. Consequently the only remains of these early men are their durable stone implements. Some account of what is conjectured about the pre-history of the Nile Valley in Egypt was given in Chapter III.

Actual history in the Nile Basin begins in Egypt 5,000 or 6,000 years ago, and our knowledge is based on deductions from pottery, paintings, carvings and utensils found in tombs. Later we get the invention of writing and the records on the monuments which give accounts of contemporary events, and so we come down through Ancient Egyptian, Greek, Roman and Arab times until the present day. The history of Egypt is a large subject which can be read in many books, and little will be said about it here.

Little is known of the early history of the Nile Basin beyond Egypt, and that little comes from Egyptian monuments, which make occasional references to peoples further south, and from the excavation of sites in the Northern Sudan by Dr. Reisner and his successors. The Archæological Survey of Nubia made before the first heightening of the Aswan Dam, collected a great mass of information about the country and people living between Aswan and Wady Halfa.

The country south of Egypt to which Egyptian influence extended was known in ancient Egyptian times as the Southern Lands, and may have referred to the country as far south as a little upstream of Atbara. In the Bible it is called the land of Cush, and in later classical times, Ethiopia. It is an arid land poor in natural resources, but in ancient times occasionally rich, because it was the gateway through which passed the trade routes and goods from the south—ebony, gold, ostrich feathers, slaves and captive wild animals. In the third millenium B.C. many expeditions to the south are recorded, but it is doubtful if these went south of Sennar. A little later Egypt ruled the country as far as Dongola. It was then captured by the Ethiopians and sometime in the second millenium B.C. recaptured by Egypt. Scenes in the tombs show the receipt of the annual tribute from Ethiopia, with pictures of Africans, gold, and wild animals. The Scribes distinguished between the gold from the mines in the Eastern desert, which were worked by Ethiopian slaves, and the alluvial gold which probably came from the Blue Nile. For some time in the first millenium Ethiopian Kings ruled over Egypt, but later were forced to withdraw. However, they still ruled over a kingdom which stretched from Aswan to the swamps of the White Nile. The Ethiopian kingdom, though latterly of less extent, lasted until A.D. 350, when the King of Axum in Abyssinia came down the Atbara River and destroyed it. For a century now the Sudan has had a bad name in Egypt as a place of residence, perhaps because of the campaigns of Mohammed Ali Pasha and later expeditions, when many Egyptians died of malaria, dysentery or other tropical diseases. One wonders whether service in Nubia in ancient Egyptian times was looked upon as an honourable occupation, or one in which to banish people whose presence was not desired in Egypt.

It seems likely that the ancient Egyptians, although they traded down the Red Sea to the land of Punt (Somaliland) and up the Nile to Khartoum and beyond, knew nothing of the sources of the river. The first person to leave a written account of his travels in Egypt was Herodotus, who visited the country about 460 B.C., and travelled as far as Aswan. His account contains some information on the nature of the country, and his efforts to find out what was known about the Nile south of Egypt by questioning the priests. Herodotus was a good observer, and on the whole the account seems reliable, though some of it, particularly his theories, is a bit fanciful. A summary of that part which concerns the Nile will be given here.

He thinks that Egypt was once a gulf of the Mediterranean, and the black crumbly soil was brought down by the Nile. The Delta in his time was swampy and the Nile divided into three branches at its head, of which the middle one subdivided into three, and finally there were two more mouths belonging to artificial channels, so that there were seven mouths altogether. When the Nile overflows, as it did regularly in flood time, the country was like a sea and only the towns and villages were visible, like islands in the Egean. It was possible to sail from the seaside town of Canopus near Abukir to Memphis fifteen miles south of Cairo, and one passed close to the Pyramids in so doing. Something similar to this existed as far north as the head of the Delta when I first came to Egypt in 1906, for the basins had not then been converted to perennial irrigation, and though the sheet of water was not continuous, owing to the basin banks, the villagers still sailed from one village to another in the same

O 2

basin. Herodotus says the country swarmed with mosquitoes and the people slept on the roofs of tall buildings, and those in the marshes used fishing nets as a protection at night. The country was cut up by numerous canals in all directions with the object of supplying drinking water to towns away from the river, where previously they had only wells of brackish water. One would guess that perhaps this applied more to the Delta than to Upper Egypt. He says that after the Nile had flooded the land and the water had run off, the seed was sown and trodden in by pigs, who afterwards, when it had been harvested trod out the grain, but some authorities think the use of pigs was unlikely, as oxen are usually shown on the monuments.

With regard to the origin of the Nile, Herodotus made many inquiries and travelled to the boundary of Egypt at Aswan to see as much as he could for himself. Greek influence must have been strong in Egypt at the time or he could not have travelled as he did and have had access to so much information. One wonders how he travelled up the Nile, whether along the bank by donkey, as camels had not then been introduced to Egypt, or by boat, and also how he collected information. Did he speak the language or depend on interpreters, or did the priests who were his principal informants speak Greek? As to the sources of the Nile he only found one person, a scribe, who claimed any knowledge, but Herodotus did not think he was serious. This informant said that the Nile came from springs between two hills called Crophi and Mophi which are between Elephantine Island and Aswan. These springs, because of their depth and the force of the rising water, had defeated the efforts of the Egyptian King Psammetichus to sound them, even though he employed many fathoms of rope. From these springs half the water ran north to Egypt and half southwards to Ethiopia (the Northern Sudan). Had this been true some of the present political problems might have been simpler for Egypt, but the problem of finding enough storage capacity for present day needs would have been much greater, in face of the heavy evaporation in Southern Egypt.

What Herodotus gathered from his own inquiries was that south of Aswan the land rose, and it was necessary to tow a boat for four days, as the river wound about a good deal, after which there was an island, and then a lake, and above this, owing to rocks and cataracts, there was no navigation, so that it was necessary to travel along the bank for forty days. Then in twelve days by boat one arrived at the city of Meroe, an Ethiopian capital. Now Meroe was about sixty miles south of the mouth of the Atbara and about 1,000 miles by river from Aswan, so that fifty-six days for this journey or eighteen miles a day was possible, but it meant hard and steady travelling, as the greater part would have been on foot, where detours into the desert would have been necessary. On leaving Meroe a journey of about the same length of time brings one to the country of the people who deserted Psammetichus, King of Egypt, and joined the Ethiopians. Thus Herodotus says the length of the journey is about four months to this point, and the direction of the river is there from west to east. Above this point nothing is certainly known about its course since the country is uninhabited by reason of the excessive heat.

Calculating on a rate of eighteen miles a day the distance to the deserters' country from Aswan would be about 2,200 miles, but probably this estimate is too great as it would be difficult to keep up a steady eighteen miles a day. Following the White Nile the river flows from west to east above the Sobat mouth, and continues to do so up to the junction of the Bahr-el-Jebel and Bahr-el-Ghazal. This junction is about 1,700 miles from Aswan. Herodotus' information therefore corresponds in a general way with the course of the river as now known, though the details about the country immediately south of Aswan are not very correct. It is nevertheless possible that it may have been founded on tales picked up by some of the earlier Egyptian trading expeditions, or passed on by Ethiopians. The barrier to penetration south beyond the Bahr-el-Ghazal junction would not be excessive heat, but the swamp country with its blocks of vegetation, which turned back Nero's centurions 500 years later. Herodotus mentioned that crocodiles and hippopotami were abundant in Egypt, and that the crocodile was venerated in two towns, where a crocodile was tamed and adorned with earrings and bracelets. It was fed daily and occasionally with human victims. Tame crocodiles make one think of Lutembe, the tame crocodile in Lake Victoria near Entebbe, which a few years ago was regularly fed and came at call. In some places, however, Herodotus says the crocodile was caught and eaten. Crocodiles do not exist in Egypt in these days, though very occasionally one does get down the river, and some years ago several got through the sluices of the Aswan Dam and were killed in various places in Egypt. The hippopotamus also disappeared from Egypt a century or more ago.

Following Herodotus 130 years later Alexander the Great came to Egypt and with his visit began a period of several hundred years of Greek influence. Alexandria was built, and became one of the great commercial cities of the ancient world, which made it a very favourable place for the collection of geographical information about all the countries with which trade was carried on in Greek and Roman times. It was a great centre of Greek learning, having many scholars and a school of mathematics and its applications to geography and astronomy. From it traders pushed southwards up the Nile, and perhaps collected some information of what lay beyond the limits of their journeys, though the difficulties of getting tangible proof would be great, owing to the marshes and the great plains of the Southern Sudan, which are swampy in the rains and nearly waterless in the dry season. These must have been almost impassable obstacles to any travel between the Sudan and Central Africa with the means then available. One of the mathematicians and geographers of the famous Alexandrine school was Eratosthenes, sometimes called the father of scientific geography, who was in charge of the great library at Alexandria in the third century B.C. He was the author of a work on geography of which only fragments remain. His most important work was an attempt to measure the size of the earth by comparing the difference of latitude between Alexandria and Aswan with the distance between them on the ground. Owing to the difficulties in measuring the difference of latitude and the intervening distance, this last being probably an estimate based on the time taken to travel from one place to the other, the calculated size of the earth was about one-seventh too great. Some description of the Nile from Eratosthenes' geographical treatize has been preserved by Strabo, and I quote part of this from Dr. John Ball's *Egypt in the Classical Geographers*, from which some of the following is also taken:

" Two rivers empty themselves into it, which issue out of some lakes towards the east, and encircle Meroe, a considerable island. One of these rivers is the Astaboras (now called the Atbara) flowing along the eastern side of the island. The other (now called the Blue Nile) is the Astapus, though according to some its proper name is Astasobas, while the name of Astapus properly belongs to another river (now called the White Nile) which issues out of some lakes to the south and forms the direct stream of the Nile itself and is fed by the summer rains."

This is interesting as being the first recorded mention of the origin of the Blue and White Niles in lakes, though Eratosthenes was in error in thinking the Atbara also had its sources in a lake. It is true, however, that the head streams of the Atbara arise very near Lake Tana. Eratosthenes also mentions the great S-bend of the Nile between Atbara and Wady Halfa.

A long description of Egypt occurs in the geography of Strabo, written about the beginning of our era, and the largest descriptive work on geography of classical times. Egypt occupies about two-thirds of one of its seventeen books. In Strabo's day the Nile had seven main branches in the Delta, of which the eastern and western branches, the Pelusiac and Canopic, were the largest. Four of these branches apparently remained much the same as in the time of Herodotus, but it appears from the fact that Strabo mentions specifically lakes and marshes near the mouths of the river, that the marshes were less widespread than in the time of Herodotus. He says that the cause of the annual rise of the Nile was the summer rainfall on the mountains of Abyssinia, and this was known from the elephant-hunting expeditions sent by the Ptolemies.

By the time of the Roman occupation of Egypt, trade down the Red Sea to India and the east coast of Africa was well established. Hamitic people from southern Arabia had for centuries been making their way into East Africa and diffusing amongst the indigenous people. There must have been trade between the coast and the interior, and it was probably due to this trade that rumours of snow-capped mountains and great lakes in the interior were current in the first century A.D. In view of the obstacles to travel in the Sudan it does not seem likely that the rumoured connection between the lakes and the Nile could have been definitely established, and it is more probable that it was an intelligent guess. The tale of a Greek who said that he travelled inland from the coast of East Africa for twenty-five days journey and reached the neighbourhood of the two great lakes and the snow mountains, from which the Nile has its origin, does not seem very probable. In such short time he might have reached some of the lakes in the Eastern Rift Valley and seen the snows on Mts. Kilimanjaro and Kenya, but hardly Lake Victoria, and certainly not Ruwenzori or Lake Albert.

One of the most brilliant of the many learned men who worked in Alexandria was Claudius Ptolemaeus, who lived in the first half of the second century A.D., and wrote treatises on astronomy and geography, which remained in use for well over 1,000 years. The astronomical book, usually known by its Arabic name of Almagest, remained the basis of astronomy until Copernicus, Kepler and Newton, while the geography was only superseded by the discoveries of the navigators of the fifteenth and sixteenth centuries. The geography contained descriptions and maps of countries and, amongst these, material relating to the Nile. Not very long before Ptolemy a map of the known world had been produced by an eminent geographer, Marinus of Tyre, whose works have disappeared and are only known from Ptolemy who made use of them.

Ptolemy thought that the White Nile came from high snow-covered mountains in Central Africa called the Mountains of the Moon, and that it was supplied by the melting of the snows thereon. The stream produced flowed northwards and passed into two lakes. From these two lakes there flowed two streams which joined together to form the main stream (White Nile), and flowing north received a tributary, the Astapus (Blue Nile), coming from the south-east from a lake called Coele (Lake Tana). Further north the river received the Astaboras (Atbara) coming also from the south-east, while the land between the Astaboras and Astapus was called Meroe (called by previous writers an island). Continuing north the details he gives show that he knew of the big bend of the Nile north of Atbara. The general correspondence of these features with what actually exists is good, and Ptolemy's map and account of the Nile is a considerable advance on those of any of his predecessors, though it still could have been only an intelligent collation of all the information then current as travellers' tales. He was naturally a good deal in error as to the latitudes and longitudes of the main features of the Southern Nile and of the shape of some of them, but, considering the nature of the evidence likely to be at his disposal, it was a good first approximation, and remained the basis for many centuries.

The east coast of Africa from the Sudan to Mozambique continued to be colonized by Arabs until modern times, with more and more penetrations into the interior. The Arabs no doubt continued to believe that the sources of the White Nile were in the lakes and mountains of Central Africa, and when they conquered North Africa and entered Spain, the idea would be passed on to mediæval Europe. No manuscript of Ptolemy's geography earlier than the end of the twelfth century exists, and amongst those which are still extant is an Arabic translation made in the fifteenth century. Definite knowledge as to the sources of the White Nile was obtained only in the nineteenth century.

We now turn to the Blue Nile and Ethiopia (Abyssinia, not the Ethiopia of the Ancients which was in the Northern Sudan). During the time of the Ptolemies the Greeks established trading posts on the Red Sea and inland as far as Axum, which became the capital of Abyssinia and was, judging by its remains, a city of some importance. Not much information about the country has, however, come down from those times, and it was not until the Portuguese expeditions of the fifteenth and sixteenth centuries that we had any written account. A little previous to these, however, several itineraries and maps were published. They are based on travellers' tales and many of the names can be identified, though some of the features are quite imaginary. Two maps of the middle of the fifteenth century, before the Portuguese reached Abyssinia, have been discussed by Mr. O. G. S. Crawford in *The Geographical Journal*, September, 1949. They are the Egyptus Novelo of about 1454 and the map of Fra Mauro of about 1459. It is clear from these and from the identity of names established by Mr. Crawford, that there was a good deal of information available in the Mediterranean countries about Abyssinia before the great period of exploration which began in the fifteenth century, one source of which might have been the connection between the Coptic and Abyssinian churches.

Mr. Crawford thinks that the identification of the Mountains of the Moon, the traditional sources of the Nile, with the Ruwenzori range is an error, and claims that they should be identified with the range to the east of Lake Tana, of which the highest peak is Mt. Abuna Josef (13,740 feet). He bases his argument on a statement by Fra Mauro that the Nile rises near a high mountain called Chamir, and which he thinks became identified with *qamar* the Arabic for moon. This is a question on which I offer no opinion.

The successful wars of Portugal against the Moors in the fifteenth century, led to a spirit of adventure and discovery which was encouraged by the enlightened Infante Dom Enrique, known to us as Prince Henry the Navigator. As a result, Portugal was a centre of studies in navigation, and Portuguese expeditions made their way gradually down the west coast of Africa until, in 1488 the Cape of Good Hope was rounded by Bartholomew Diaz. Portuguese stations were gradually established on the east coast of Africa at the same time as Columbus was making his American discoveries. Portuguese fleets entered the Red Sea and a Portuguese mission reached the court of "Prester John" in 1520. With this mission was a priest Francisco Alvarez, who remained in Abyssinia for some years and wrote an account of it. These adventurous journeys were made with very crude means of navigation based largely on the compass and dead reckoning, and the way was made easier for others to follow by the construction of charts and the fixing of the positions of important places by latitudes observed with a quadrant of wood (see *Second Voyage of Christopher Columbus*, S. E. Morison). A point to be noted is that south of the equator the pole star is not visible as a guide, and new constellations and stars have to be learned. One of the objects of these expeditions was to capture the rich trade with India and East Africa, which up to that time had been in the hands of Egypt, Turkey, and Arabs from Arabia and the Persian Gulf. The spices and other goods from India and the East African coast travelled up the Red Sea to Suez and across to Alexandria, which was one of the great trading centres of the world, and by establishing posts, as they did at the southern end of the Red Sea, the Portuguese were in a position to close the principal trade routes from India to Europe, and enjoy the trade themselves.

The era was disturbed with the conflicts of the Portuguese with Egyptians, Turks and Arabs in the Red Sea, and at the same time Abyssinia was invaded from the south by Somalis under Ahmed Gran, who, between 1528 and 1540, overran most of the country. The Abyssinians appealed to the Portuguese for assistance, and a fleet was sent under Stephen da Gama, a son of the famous navigator Vasco da Gama, who was the first to reach India by sea. With Stephen was another son, Christopher, who was in command of a ship, and later a member of the party that went to the help of the Abyssinians who were in great difficulties. This party started from Massawa and fought several battles with Ahmed Gran, who was reinforced by some Turks with artillery. Ultimately the Portuguese were defeated by superior numbers and Christopher, who had been severely wounded, was captured, tortured and executed. A tradition soon arose that where he was executed a spring appeared which had miraculous healing powers. During the next few months the Abyssinians and Portuguese, who were reduced to little more than a hundred, gathered their forces and, in 1543, attacked Ahmed Gran somewhere near Lake Tana. The Portuguese were determined to discover and kill the Somali leader and, it is recorded, that finally one of them shot him in the head, and he fell from his horse. Most of his supporters then ran away except the small Turkish force, who, however, were soon surrounded and destroyed. The country was then completely cleared of invaders, and Portuguese influence seems to have been exerted partly by missionaries, one of whom, Father Pedro Paez, recorded that he was shown the spring at Sakala, called the source of the Blue Nile, and was the first European to see it. Kammerer in his *La Mer Rouge, Abyssinie et l'Arabie*, published by the Royal Geographical Society of Egypt, has collected a great mass of information about the Portuguese voyages, on which I have drawn. He describes Paez as a well-educated and able man who was respected by the Abyssinians. It was by chance that, in his travels with the Negus in 1618, he came to the two tiny springs which are the source of the Blue Nile, and he says, " I cannot express my delight in seeing that which Cyrus, Cambyses, Alexander and Julius Caesar had so strongly and so unavailingly desired to know." The little rivulet flowing from these springs, is joined by others and rapidly becomes a considerable stream, and Paez says that it enters a great lake through which it flows rapidly without mixing with its waters! (This is of course impossible.) Below the lake is a great waterfall where the water falls with such violence that one would think it would disappear in spray. Below this again the Blue Nile is so shut in by rocks that one can hardly see it, and the passage is so narrow at the top that a really agile man can jump across. The emperor and his army crossed this gorge over planks, where afterwards a bridge was built by masons brought from India, and this bridge remains to the present day.

Following Paez, two other Jesuits, Emmanuel d'Almeida and Jeronimo Lobo, wrote accounts of Abyssinia, where both remained until the expulsion of the Jesuits in 1633. D'Almeida's account was edited to its detriment by Tellez, and Lobo's was translated into English by Sir Peter Wyche in 1669. One remark may be taken from Lobo to the effect that Abyssinia is the country where there are more priests, more churches, and more monasteries than anywhere else in the world. The journeys made by d'Almeida and Lobo were full of dangers and hardships, and included battles by sea and captivity on land.

I need only mention Poncet, a French surgeon who travelled to Abyssinia via Sennar and the Rahad, and was there from 1698–1700, before coming to Bruce, of whom I have written in Chapter VI. Prior to Bruce, Abyssinia was, from time to time, visited by European priests, some of whom have left accounts of the country. Bruce saw the source of the Blue Nile in 1770 and, in eight volumes, gave a full description of his journey. He describes how after many difficulties he arrived at the long sought-for source of the Nile, and he and his companion drank a health to King George III in the pure water of the spring. From there he returned to Gondar, having travelled all round Lake Tana. During his journeys he had crossed the Blue Nile by the bridge below the falls of Tis Esat, which he saw and admired. The homeward journey from Gondar was made by way of the Sudan, through Ras-el-Fil near Gallabat, and parallel to the River Rahad as far as Sennar. From there he followed the Blue Nile to its junction with the White Nile and continued along the main Nile, probably to Abu Hamed, whence he took the route to Aswan. On his arrival in England he found that the French Geographer

D'Anville had anticipated him by producing a map on which was shown the source of the Blue Nile, its location having been obtained from the accounts of Paez and Lobo. Bruce apparently did not know of the visits of these travellers about 150 years earlier, though he refers to the visit of Lobo to the falls of Tis Esat. His own account of his travels was received with some scepticism in London, and this possibly led him to delay the publication of his great work, *Travels to Discover the Source of the Nile in the Years* 1768–73 until the year 1790.

Chapter Thirteen

EXPLORATION IN MODERN TIMES

MODERN exploration of the Nile Basin may be said to begin with the conquest of the Sudan by Mohammed Ali Pasha and his sons in 1821 and the following years. The Arabian expeditions of Mohammed Ali had impoverished Egypt, military manpower was lacking, and the Albanian troops were ill-disciplined and caused troubles in Cairo. In Egypt at this time the Sudan was looked upon as a country where such fabulous riches as gold, copper, ivory and other valuable products might be found, and an expedition to the Sudan seemed to be a remedy for all Mohammed Ali's difficulties. A mixed force was organized under Ismail, the third son of Mohammed Ali, and included a collection of doctors, naturalists and mineralogists, who were to get from the country anything in the way of treasure which the ignorance of the inhabitants had left undiscovered. Ismail defeated the Shaigia tribe at Korti, then marched south on Sennar, the capital of the Fung Kingdom, and in May, 1821, camped on the site of Omdurman, whose name was said to be that of the sole inhabitant, an old woman. The site of Khartoum, on the point of land between the White and Blue Niles, was selected for a permanent military camp by Mohammed Ali himself when he visited the south in 1823, and later it was chosen as headquarters and capital of the Sudan by the Governor, Khurshid Pasha. The word means an elephant's trunk in Arabic, and is also the name given to a garden hose. Because of disputes amongst the Fung rulers in Sennar the Egyptians were welcomed as liberators, and, without fighting, the king became a vassal. The search for gold was, however, fruitless, but many people were seized, the men for soldiers and the women and children for slaves. Ismail went south up the Blue Nile accompanied by Caillaud, a French mineralogist, to look for the Eldorado supposed to be in the Fazoghli district on the Blue Nile. The expedition was laborious, though it was undertaken in December and January, the best time of the year. There were continual fights with the inhabitants, and the fabulous quantities of gold turned out to be only small grains in the beds of the torrents, insufficient in quantity to be worth working on a large scale. The rumours of gold further south were also exaggerated, and Ismail could not get even an ounce a month. Out of the 1,500 men who left Sennar, Ismail brought back only a few hundred, and practically none of his horses and camels. In those days nothing was known of the causes of malaria, dysentery, and the diseases which attack transport animals, so the ordinary precautions of the present-day could not be applied. Ibrahim, the son of Mohammed Ali who had gone to the White Nile, had been forced by illness to return, and Ismail applied to his father for permission to come home. Mohammed Ali, after first refusing permission, granted it when he knew of his son's state of health, and Ismail set off northwards with a small escort. At Shendi he stopped to inspect the garrison and to demand from the local chief a sum of money and a quantity of slaves. The chief temporised and made a feast for Ismail and his officers. Whilst they were eating the chief's followers surrounded the house and set fire to it, burning all the guests to death.

While Ismail was up the Blue Nile, his brother-in-law, Mohammed the Deftardar had conquered Kordofan. He was a well-educated man of an old Turkish family, a good soldier, but absolutely ruthless, and his massacres of the ill-armed and primitive inhabitants were remembered in Kordofan and Sennar eighty years afterwards. After the conquest he also set out to find gold and slaves. There was little gold, but long columns of slaves were marched to Egypt and many people were massacred to revenge the death of Ismail.

Ibrahim Pasha wished to extend his journeys, and was no doubt drawn on by the maps then current on which figured imaginary sources of the Nile. On this doubtful information he built up vast projects of exploration and conquest, but his illness and the death of Ismail left the country to the Deftardar. In 1822 the empire of Egypt extended as far as the plains and marshes of the Southern Sudan, owing to an army in part built up of negroid Sudanese on whom Mohammed Ali could rely, and who were not so subject to disease as people foreign to the country. Sixteen years later Mohammed Ali made his last visit to the Sudan, and, although over seventy years of age, he visited Fazoghli where he remained for some time. During this visit he put into practice an idea which he had had in his mind for a long time, to send an expedition to explore the White Nile as far as was possible, and to solve the problem as to its origin, a problem which had interested the civilized world for hundreds of years. Several sailing dahabias were brought up from Cairo over the cataracts, a large quantity of stores collected, and the expedition of some officers and several hundred troops was put in charge of Selim Bimbashi. With them was Monsieur Thibaut, a Frenchman who had been in the Sudan for some time and had made several journeys to the Shilluk country, and it is from his report that the following account is taken.

Before the expedition sailed from Khartoum, Mohammed Ali Pasha called the officers together to give them final instructions as to the conduct of the journey. It was not to be a voyage of conquest, and the troops were only for defence in case of attack. Good relations were to be cultivated with the inhabitants, and their friendship was to be obtained by presents and kindness. The expedition took some time to fit out, and finally sailed in November, 1839.

Thibaut remarks on many familiar features of the White Nile, the islands, the forests of sunt and other trees, the difficult shoals at Abu Zeid—where my own ship was once aground for two days—and the villages of the Dinkas and Shilluks. After passing the Sobat mouth and seeing the hills some distance inland from the mouth of the Zeraf, which, however, is not mentioned, the expedition was hindered by masses of floating vegetation, but ultimately reached Lake No, at the junction of the Bahr-el-Ghazal and Bahr-el-Jebel, after a month of travel. Here they had some difficulty in finding the channel, and apparently spent two days in the Bahr-el-Ghazal, disliking its marshy nature and the taste of the water. Ultimately they retraced their steps and found the Bahr-el-Jebel, up which they travelled and presently saw people of the Nuer tribe on the bank, with whom they conversed, a Sudanese soldier acting as interpreter. The people appeared to be friendly and brought as presents a goat and some tobacco, but the interpreter said that he had heard some one say that these were poisoned. This resulted in soldiers firing on the crowd and some of the tribesmen were killed; the rest disappeared in the tall vegetation. There were more affrays later, and the impression one gets is that the interpreters, either through stupidity or malice, were responsible for some of them. In most places the natives were disposed to be friendly, and brought gifts of cattle and even helped to tow the ships. Sometimes they took the visitors for gods and prayed them not to kill them with thunder.

The navigation of sailing dahabias in the winding stream of the Bahr-el-Jebel, shut in by tall vegetation and travelling against the current, was difficult and towing was often necessary. Ultimately the expedition reached a bifurcation in the Aliab country, where one branch was narrow and deep and had a strong current, while the other was wide with little current. The former was an impossible passage for the ships, and the expedition therefore tried the wide channel. After towing for some distance, the method became impracticable, and men went overboard to push the ships over the shallows. Ultimately a council was held, and it was decided that it was not possible with the means at their disposal to get any further, so they began their return journey on January 26th, 1840, having reached latitude 6° 30′ N., some distance short of Bor.

A second expedition was sent in 1840–41 under Selim Bimbashi, who was accompanied by Thibaut, d'Arnaud, Sabatier and Werne, several of whom produced accounts of the journey. D'Arnaud, who was in charge of the scientific side of the journey, produced a map, a tracing of which is in the Institut d'Egypte in Cairo, and which now shows signs that it is more than a hundred years old. Some account is given of the expeditions in letters from d'Arnaud, which can be found in the bulletins of the Geographical Society of Paris in 1842 and 1843. A full account was also written by Werne.[1] This expedition and a third which followed in 1841–42, succeeded in getting as far as latitude 4° 42′ N. just beyond Rejaf, where the river is shallow and the rapids begin. The river was low and d'Arnaud wished to wait for it to rise, but a general council decided against his proposal. They had reached the point where the hills begin and the country

---

[1] Werne F. *Expedition to Discover the Sources of the White Nile* (Translation C. W. O'Reilly, London, 1849).

is park-like and very pleasant. D'Arnaud thought from native report that, once the first rapids were passed, the river could be navigated for fifty or a hundred miles, to a point where different branches unite. These are shown dotted on his map, but in fact do not exist. He makes no mention of the Kit river, a torrent which comes from the east just below the terminus of the expeditions, perhaps because it was only carrying a trickle of water. The expeditions disproved the tradition that the White Nile came from the west, but got no hint of the great lakes to the south. This was not surprising, as the African, until recent times, never travelled beyond the limit of his tribal country, and knew nothing of what was beyond. On the third expedition many of the members suffered from scurvy, and a considerable number died. This third expedition was the last effort of Mohammed Ali Pasha to discover the sources of the Nile. D'Arnaud returned to Cairo, and on the journey was shipwrecked in the 4th Cataract, and nearly lost both his diaries and his life.

In the following years the Southern Sudan was opened up by merchants from Khartoum, ostensibly for the trade in ivory, gum and other products, but added to this was the trade in slaves, " black ivory." These merchants recruited private armies, mainly of Nubians from the country round Dongola, known as Dongolawis, and established trading stations in Darfur, the Bahr-el-Ghazal and southern fringe of the Sudan. Austrian missionaries founded missions on the Bahr-el-Jebel at Kenisa and Gondokoro. These were, however, given up after a few years owing to the unhealthy nature of the country and the high mortality—fifteen out of seventeen Europeans died. It was from these missionaries in 1850 that reports came of the existence of large lakes to the south.

The Bahr-el-Ghazal was explored by Petherick in the eighteen-fifties, and he was probably the first European to do so. He was a mining engineer employed by Mohammed Ali Pasha to search for coal in Egypt and the Sudan, and afterwards became a merchant and British Consular Agent in Central Africa. He will be mentioned later in connection with Speke and Grant. Between 1853 and 1858 he made an annual expedition up the Bahr-el-Ghazal, the first of which, with a single sailing boat of the common Sudan type known as a "nugger," only got as far as Meshra-el-Rek. A "nugger" is a boat rather like an elongated saucer, built of thick planks, carrying a mast and sail, and usually covered over near the stern with a roof of thatch as a protection against the sun and rain. On this journey he had difficulties in finding a passage into the Bahr-el-Ghazal through the thick reeds. On later journeys his party left the boats at Meshra and penetrated inland going due south, and ultimately reached a point in what is now the Belgian Congo, about $3\frac{1}{2}°$ N. of the Equator. Here he first encountered the Azande who proposed to eat him, but were thoroughly scared by the discharge of a gun which they had never seen before. Petherick had no serious troubles with the people inland, and was the first European to penetrate into the Bahr-el-Ghazal Basin. His route was roughly parallel to the Jur and its main tributary the Sueh. His object was trade in ivory, and he established trading posts in the Bahr-el-Ghazal and on the Sobat. At the same time as Petherick's earliest expeditions, de Malzac penetrated the country to the west of the Bahr-el-Jebel somewhere about the latitude of Ghaba Shambe, and contemplated writing a book, but unfortunately died before he was able to do so. Petherick returned to England in 1859, and was engaged by the Royal Geographical Society to meet and assist Speke and Grant on the northern part of their journey, and to supply them with the necessary boats and stores at Gondokoro.

It has been previously said that for very many years Arab traders on the East African coast had been making journeys into the interior. In the eighteen-forties the missionaries Kraft, Rebmann and Erhardt, were travelling in East Africa for the Church Missionary Society, and during their travels saw the snow-topped mountains Kilimanjaro and Kenya. They also heard much talk by traders about their journeys and the places they had seen. This talk, although vague and confused, agreed on the existence of a great inland sea, which might be continuous, or might consist of several bodies of water. Putting things together, the missionaries thought that Kilimanjaro and Kenya and other mountains, although isolated, might form a line leading up to the legendary Mountains of the Moon, and that from the north of these flowed the springs of the Nile.

Their reports led to renewed interest in the sources of the Nile. There were, at this time, in the garrison at Aden, two British officers, Richard Burton and J. H. Speke, both of an adventurous disposition and full of enthusiasm to penetrate the mysterious hinterland of East Africa. After an abortive expedition into the interior of Somaliland, another, partly on funds from the Royal Geographical Society, was organized, and started along a regular trade route of the Arabs which led to Lake Tanganyika. When Burton and Speke arrived near what is now Tabora, the Arabs resolved for them the great inland sea into three separate lakes. They continued westwards and saw the great Lake Tanganyika, part of which they explored and found that no river flowed out of the northern end. On their return Burton, who had frequently been ill on the journey, again fell ill near Tabora. Speke was able to get Burton to agree that he should go north to find the " sea of Unyamwezi," and having got together some porters, he set off. After some days he came to Smith Sound, the long indentation south of Mwanza (see p. 157), and following this up he saw, on August 3rd, 1858, a great lake looking like a sea, with many islands on its coast. Speke thought this large sheet of water might be the source of the Nile and inquired its name, to which the natives replied " Nyanza," which in its various forms is a Bantu word meaning a large body of water. Speke therefore called the lake Victoria Nyanza in honour of Queen Victoria. He then returned to join Burton and the two travelled back to the coast, from which Speke sailed to England, while Burton remained to finish the affairs of the expedition.

When Speke announced the news of the discovery of Lake Victoria and the possibility that it might be the source of the Nile, the Royal Geographical Society immediately planned a new expedition so that Speke might develop his discovery. Funds were collected by public subscription, and assistance was given by the governments of India and South Africa. It was also arranged, as already mentioned, that Petherick would help the expedition when it reached the neighbourhood of the Bahr-el-Jebel.

The party, which started in 1860 from Zanzibar, consisted of J. H. Speke in command, and J. A. Grant as second, with a mixed company of Indians, Arabs and Africans as guards, servants, interpreters and porters. A full account of the journey is given by Speke in *Journal of the Discovery of the Sources of the Nile*, from which the following short summary is taken.

From Bagamoyo they took the route to Kazé (Tabora) and then, instead of following Speke's previous route to Mwanza on Lake Victoria and then exploring its south coast, they took the trade route N.N.W. to Karagwé, the country of King Rumanika. Up to this point they had continually to pay tribute to every petty chief and put up with all manner of extortions. Rumanika was an enlightened person of Wahuma race, ruling in an orderly fashion and forbidding exactions by local chiefs. The Wahuma, of whom the Watusi of Ruanda are a branch, are Hamitic people only slightly mixed with negroes. From Rumanika's village, the expedition saw, more than a hundred miles away, the cones of the Mufumbiro Mountains in Ruanda, which they thought must be the traditional Mountains of the Moon. After some stay with Rumanika, Speke moved on northwards to Uganda, but Grant had to be left behind because of some disease of his leg. Rumanika appears to have humbugged Speke by telling him that the regulations of Uganda were very severe, and that no sick person could enter, nor could his donkeys even be admitted unless they wore trousers!

The streams of the district all ran into the Kitangule or Kagera, whose head waters were in the Mountains of the Moon, which Speke thought, from his own observations and the reports of travellers, was the most important tributary of Lake Victoria. This being so one would have thought he might have turned aside to see something of its course and origin. On all the long journey so far the party had not seen the Nyanza, and first saw it from a hilltop when they were three-quarters of the way along its western side, but from then, until they reached the palace of M'tesa, King of Uganda, it was often in view. Speke was much impressed by the fertility of the country and the tidiness of the houses and gardens. After staying for some time with the capricious and cruel M'tesa, Grant arrived, and permission was given for their departure to Unyoro to the north, and for a visit to the outlet of the lake. Speke saw the outlet at the Ripon Falls, as already related, but owing to the stupidity of his local escort, he was not allowed to go on the lake in a canoe. From there they made their way northward to the village of Kamrasi, King of Unyoro, at the mouth of the Kafu, and again had to submit to the rapacity of a petty king. Here they heard of the large lake to the west into which flowed the stream which they thought to be the Nile. After delays they took canoes down the Nile and reached the head of the Karuma Rapids,[1] and from there left the river without following it up to Lake Albert, because of difficulty over porters and local feuds. The route was N.N.W., and after some days they came to an advance post of the merchant de Bono, whose agent or wakeel, Mohammed, had instructions to assist them and bring them to Gondokoro. They struck the river at the Nimule Bend and arrived at Gondokoro in February, 1863. Here they met Samuel Baker and his wife, and Petherick appeared from the west a few days later.

Speke considered that Petherick had not fulfilled his obligations to the Royal Geographical Society, and seems to have behaved harshly towards him. It is difficult, however, after nearly ninety years have elapsed, to come to a just conclusion on the question. Speke arrived later than he had expected, and Petherick also met with difficulties and delays outside his control. In any case savage Central Africa was not a place where a time-table could be arranged as for a journey from London to Cairo. The unfortunate Petherick suffered considerable losses on the expedition, incurred the dislike of slave traders because of his arrest of one of them, and was finally out of employment because the British Government suppressed his post. It was unfortunate that the search for the sources of the Nile should be marred by disagreement between Speke and Burton, and then between Speke and Petherick. Speke was killed in 1864 in an accident, while out shooting, caused by an oversight which would hardly have been expected in such an experienced person.

At Gondokoro Speke told Baker of the lake called Luta Nzigé lying to the west of the Victoria Nile, and Baker's discovery of this, which he called the Albert Nyanza, has already been described in Chapter X. These discoveries of Speke and Baker are now commonly held to have settled the questions of the origin and course of the Nile, but at the time the unexplored gaps and the very elementary state of the science of hydrology made many people think there was still an element of doubt. At

---

[1] Where the river turns west.

a meeting of the Khedivial Geographical Society in 1875, Schweinfurth, perhaps the most scientific of the African travellers of those days, in discussing a map which he had prepared of the Nile sources, said, " It is probable that Lake Albert belongs to the régime of the Nile, but one cannot be certain," and he then mentioned the possibility of an outlet to the Congo. The course of the Nile was not followed completely from Gondokoro to Lake Albert, and then to Lake Victoria, until Gordon was Governor of the Equatorial Province of the Sudan, when his officers followed the river and mapped parts of it. Meantime other explorers travelled in the Bahr-el-Ghazal, of whom we may mention Miss Tinné, during whose expedition up the river, her mother, her aunt and Dr. Steudner died from blackwater fever. This lady, young, charming and very accomplished, and full of the wish to discover things, came to a tragic end. A few years after her river expedition she organised a caravan to cross the Sahara to Lake Chad, and from there to reach the Nile Basin from the west. On this journey, while still only thirty-three years of age, she was brutally murdered by people of the Tawareg tribe.

Schweinfurth, who spent the years 1869 to 1871 in the Bahr-el-Ghazal Basin, was a traveller of a different calibre to his predecessors, inasmuch as he was a trained botanist and scientific observer. He did not travel with a large party, but made an arrangement with Ghattas, a Coptic merchant of Khartoum, who had trading posts on the tributaries of the Bahr-el-Ghazal. The contract stipulated that Ghattas would provide Schweinfurth with food, porters, transport and guards, and would arrange for him to join any excursions made by his people. The Governor in Khartoum made the principal merchants trading in the Bahr-el-Ghazal responsible for his safety. Under these conditions Schweinfurth was able to live at the zaribas (posts) of various merchants, and to travel from the Nam or Rohl river in the east to the Biri in the west, and as far south as the Welle river, a tributary of the Congo. He entered the country by boat to Meshra-el-Rek, and then south to the principal station of Ghattas near the present village of Tonj. His map, which must have been compiled, in part, from his own travels, but more from information supplied by the traders, shows the principal tributaries of the Bahr-el-Ghazal, and the whole region dotted with the zaribas of merchants. His book *The Heart of Africa*, in two large volumes, gives a full description of all he saw, illustrated by wood cuts from his own excellent drawings. He gives much description of the various tribes and their habits, the animals and the vegetation. In the extreme south in the neighbourhood of the Welle River he saw specimens of the Pygmies from further south. Up to this time these small people were to some extent legendary, and mention of them had come down from classical Greek authors, though specimens had been reported by various travellers. Schweinfurth gave a description of them, thus clearing up some of the myths, and brought away a Pygmy boy who had been given to him. This boy accompanied him to Khartoum, but unfortunately died on the way to Cairo. There is a good deal of information about the slave trade in his book, where he says it was definitely separate from the trade in ivory. By the arrangements made for him with the merchant Ghattas and others, Schweinfurth was able to travel about and get information untroubled by the restrictions, exactions of petty chiefs, and other troubles with the natives which embarrassed the expeditions of Speke and Baker.

The next steps in exploring the untraced parts of the White Nile occurred when General C. G. Gordon became Governor of the Equatorial Province in 1874, in succession to Sir Samuel Baker. Gordon was accompanied from Cairo by Colonel Chaillé-Long, a member of the American Military Mission to the Egyptian Army, who has written an account of his experiences in Central Africa and other places in *My Life in Four Continents*. Chaillé-Long's first work was a journey from Gondokoro to visit M'tesa, the King of Uganda with whom Speke had stayed. His instructions were to conclude a treaty with M'tesa whereby the Nile Basin became a Protectorate of Egypt. Having arrived with half-a-dozen attendants, Chaillé-Long put on his Egyptian Army uniform of blue tunic and red trousers, mounted his horse and rode to the palace. The horse was an unknown animal in Uganda and made a great impression, but caused some consternation when Long dismounted, as the crowd had thought him a Centaur and not a man. The presents he had brought also made a good impression on M'tesa, particularly the battery and the induction coil with its brass terminals. Long had carefully drilled his servant that when he himself held the terminals the battery was to be switched off, and switched on only when the king or his courtiers held them. The shock from the current was a considerable surprise and shook the king and his courtiers heavily. Long's prestige was immediately established, since the current apparently made no impression upon him whatsoever. The treaty was signed and arrangements were made for the return journey. Before starting away, however, Long was able to sail on the lake in one of a fleet of canoes, and to see a little of the shores to the east of Murchison Gulf. On the return he embarked at Kakindu, where Speke had left the river. Going north with the stream, after several days he discovered a large lake previously unknown, which the Khedive subsequently named " Lake Ibrahim." It has, however, since reverted to its local name of " Kioga." On arriving at the mouth of the Kafu the party was attacked by several hundred men in canoes of the fleet belonging to Kaba Rega, King of Unyoro and son of Kamrasi. Long was unfortunately wounded in the face when his servant shot an attacker at close quarters. The fight continued until nightfall, when the enemy retired having suffered heavy losses from the firearms of the party, who a few days later reached Foweira, the most advanced Egyptian post. This journey settled the identity of the stream leaving Lake Victoria with that entering Lake Albert.

The following year E. Linant de Bellefonds, son of the engineer mentioned in Chapter III, travelled up to the court of M'tesa as Egyptian Ambassador, and there received H. M. Stanley on his circumnavigation of Lake Victoria. A description of his journey from Gondokoro to the lake is published in the first bulletin of the Khedivial Geographical Society. Unfortunately he and all his party were killed by tribesmen on his return journey.

In 1876 Gordon, who was an engineer officer, made surveys of the course of the Bahr-el-Jebel from Dufilé to Lake Albert, and of the Victoria Nile from Lake Albert to Foweira. The Bahr-el-Jebel from Gondokoro to Nimule had been surveyed by officers under Gordon. The question had been debated as to whether Lake Albert emptied its waters to the Congo or the Nile. This was settled in 1876 by Gessi, one of Gordon's officers, who went up from Dufile with two boats and circumnavigated the lake. It had no outlet except to the Nile, though he could not explore a forest to the south which would seem to have been composed of ambatch growing in shallow water. He missed the mouth of the Semliki flowing into the south end of the lake, which was left for Colonel Mason, an American officer with Gordon, to discover in 1877. Mason steamed round the lake in the *Nyanza*, a steamer originally bought by Sir Samuel Baker, which was probably carried up in pieces and put together near Nimule, as it seems very unlikely that it could have been got over the Fola Rapids. Mason found a river flowing into the south end of the lake, which he entered and ascended for an hour, but which was so shallow that the steamer scraped the bottom. It is interesting to read that looking up the valley he saw a big mountain. This can only have been Ruwenzori, which I have seen myself, both from the plain near the Semliki mouth and from the middle of Lake Albert. The snow peaks were probably in cloud, as they were when I saw the mountain. Mason produced a very creditable map of the lake and determined the longitudes of Gordon's stations on the Bahr-el-Jebel between the lake and Gondokoro. Before he discovered the Semliki there seems to have been some idea that Lake Albert was just a backwater of the Nile.

At the end of 1874 H. M. Stanley arrived at Zanzibar, with the object of completing the discoveries of Speke, Burton and Livingstone. With him were three Englishmen and a boat in sections, the *Lady Alice*. Some of the sections, however, were too large to be carried along narrow bush paths which were in many places the tracks they would have to follow. Fortunately a skilled ship's carpenter was found who was able to divide the sections into manageable size. Stanley took one of the regular routes to Lake Victoria and reached a spot on the Speke Gulf at the south-east corner of the lake. Here the boat was put together, and they started up the east side of the lake, passing many islands and indentations before they got to the country of M'tesa. They were received with great ceremony, and while there visited the Ripon Falls, and gathered as much geographical information as possible. Stanley also met Linant de Bellefonds, whom he found a very charming companion. After staying for some time,

Stanley left in order to circumnavigate the lake, promising to return later. He was accompanied by some of the fleet of canoes belonging to M'tesa. These were large canoes built of planks, and capable of holding many men; they were necessarily large since the lake can, when the wind rises, be as rough as the sea. On the journey down the west coast the mouth of the Katonga River was seen; this is really a swamp, but does occasionally have floods. One of these once held me up as it had washed away the bridge and some of the embankment across the swamps. Further on, the mouth of the Kagera was explored, and Stanley managed to get up it for about three miles, but the current was too strong for further progress. He says the Kagera issues into the lake in a powerful deep stream, whose iron dark colour can be recognized several miles out in the lake. The mouth of the Kagera evidently changes from time to time, as when I measured its discharge in 1924 there were three entrances, each closed by a bar over which the water was shallow and nothing of bigger draft than a rowing boat could have got in.

After circumnavigating the lake, not without trouble from some of the people on its shores, Stanley returned to M'tesa, with whose help he hoped to travel westwards to Lake Albert. M'tesa sent an army with him, and the expedition travelled up the Katonga swamps to where it joins the Mpanga River coming from Ruwenzori, and then to the escarpment overlooking Lake George. Stanley was anxious to be able to stay on the lake side, and a request for permission was sent to the local chiefs. The presence of the large force had, however, disturbed them and permission was refused. A reconnaissance party could find no easy way by which the boat and other loads could be got to the lake, and by this time the nerves of the Waganda were a bit unsettled at the prospect of a war, so there was nothing to do but to return. Stanley then said farewell to M'tesa and marched south to Karagwé, the kingdom of Rumanika. He spent a month exploring some of the Kagera, and afterwards had a long conversation on the geography of the country, its rivers and lakes. When he left Rumanika he went south and presently reached Lake Tanganyika, and from there made his way down the Congo to the sea. He had made a memorable journey right across Africa, explored the headwaters of one of the great rivers of the world, and followed nearly the whole course of another, and completed this by producing one of the most readable of all accounts of travel.

By 1877 the course of the White Nile had been traced completely from Lake Victoria to Khartoum, and it was known that Lake Victoria had a large tributary, the Kagera, which remained to be explored, as did also the Semliki, the only important tributary of Lake Albert. Lake Edward had still to be discovered, and this was done by Stanley's expedition when taking Emin to the coast in 1888, as already recounted in Chapter IX. Of Emin I have already spoken and may again mention the scientific work which he did as a naturalist. Another scientific traveller of about this time was Junker, who visited the Atbara, Sobat and Bahr-el-Ghazal, but most of his work was done in the basin of the Congo.

Following the work done by Gordon and his staff, the rise of the Mahdi led to the closing of the Sudan to all outside influences. Penetration to the headwaters of the Nile still continued from the east coast, and a good deal of this was done by missionaries, and later by the Imperial British East Africa Company. Germans occupied the coast south of the British sphere of influence and entered what is now Tanganyika and Ruanda-Urundi. All these influences led to the gradual exploration of the Lake Plateau, and we may say that by 1900 the great period of purely geographical exploration of the Nile Basin was over, and no startling discoveries remained to be made. The tributaries of the Nile in Ethiopia were still very little known, including the Blue Nile itself, and much exploration was done in the twentieth century, some of which has been mentioned in previous chapters.

In the Sudan immediately after the reconquest the work of creating law and order and organising a settled government began. An essential part of this was the detailed exploration carried out by district officers, and which was described in route reports and sometimes accompanied by sketch maps. At the same time a Survey Department was formed and the systematic mapping of the Sudan began. By 1905 sufficient was known for the compilation of *The Anglo-Egyptian Sudan*,[1] an official report in two volumes, geographical, descriptive and historical. Similar

[1] H.M. Stationery Office, London.

exploratory work was taking place under the British and German Governments in East Africa.

However, although the course of the Nile was known and mapped in a general way, practically nothing was known of its hydrology. Occasional travellers had given estimates of the amount of water flowing in the main stream and in some of its tributaries, but usually these estimates are quite unreliable. The study of the Nile from the point of view of its water supply has been carried out almost entirely in the twentieth century, and an account of this aspect will be given in the next chapter. In bringing to an end this chapter on exploration one may pay a tribute to the fortitude and endurance of those people who gradually made the Nile Basin known to the outside world, and to the many of them who perished and left their remains to be absorbed into its soil.

Chapter Fourteen

HISTORY OF HYDROLOGICAL STUDIES
IN THE NILE BASIN

IT is not proposed to discuss hydrological matters in detail, but since the present regulation of the river, and the projects proposed for the future, depend on scientific studies, no description of the Nile would be complete without some account of how they have developed. It may be said that at the present time there is no great river in the world upon which such an accurate and extensive system of measurement is carried out. At the present time (1950) the levels and discharges of its principal tributaries are measured regularly throughout the year by the Egyptian Irrigation Service and the Uganda Hydrological Survey from the sea to the Kagera River beyond Lake Victoria. Each day the river level is observed at a hundred points in its basin, and several times a month the quantity of water flowing is measured at a hundred gauging stations. The level is measured on a scale, usually of marble, set in a concrete pillar which is built into the river bank (see Fig. 12). The quantity of water flowing is measured by dividing the river into a number of sections by imaginary vertical lines, and the velocity of the water is then measured by means of a current meter (see Fig. 14, p. 229) at one or more points on the middle vertical of each section (see Fig. 13). Also the depth and width of each section are measured. From the velocity observations the mean velocity over the section is calculated, and from the depth and width, its area is found. Then the area multiplied by the mean velocity gives the quantity of water passing through the section per second. Adding up the quantities passing each section we get the total quantity flowing, or the discharge of the river. On the Nile we measure all quantities in metres, and so the discharge is given in cubic metres per second. A cubic metre of water weighs approximately a ton.

During the low half of the year, all the water naturally flowing in the Nile, together with what has been stored from the flood-

FIG. 12. Gauge on the Upper Nile.

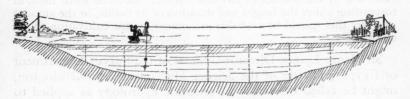

FIG. 13. Measurement of discharge.

time, is used for irrigation. Throughout this time, therefore, it is important to know exactly how much water is flowing, in order that it may be divided in proper proportions between Egypt and the Sudan, and between the various irrigation districts. In the nineteenth century it was only important to measure the water at the low time of the year, but as the irrigated area increased and projects were made for increasing it to the maximum possible, the amounts passing throughout the year also became of importance. Previous to the twentieth century the velocity of the water was measured by timing floats over a measured distance, but at about 1900, current-meters were introduced by Captain (afterwards Sir Henry) Lyons, and the era of scientific measurement began. Previous to this it was known that the rise of the Blue Nile and Atbara were responsible for the flood in Egypt, while the White Nile was a more steady stream, but the amounts contributed by these tributaries were unknown. Chélu, in his book *Le Nil le Soudan, l'Egypte*, published in 1891, says, that in flood, the discharges of the Blue Nile, the White Nile and Atbara are approximately equal; whereas the actual proportions are now known to be roughly 70 per cent., 10 per cent. and 20 per cent. respectively. There is nothing surprising in this ignorance of hydrology, as from about 1882–98 the Upper Nile was closed by the Mahdi's rebellion, and previous to this, irrigation engineers were fully occupied in putting the small funds at their disposal to the immediate practical uses of improving conditions of irrigation in Egypt. Speaking of the time of the Mahdist régime, Sir William Garstin (Adviser to the Ministry of Public Works), said:

" During this period, those in Egypt, charged with the control and distribution of the waters of the river, were seriously handicapped in their efforts, by the thick veil that had settled down upon the Upper Nile, and by the absence of any information that could assist them in forecasting either the height and duration of its floods, or the amount of water that should be available in summer for the cultivation of the cotton crop."

Sir Henry Lyons, Director-General of the Survey Department of Egypt, and later of the Science Museum, South Kensington, might be called the father of scientific hydrology as applied to the Nile Basin, and he was the initiator of a number of other scientific studies, of which we may mention the foundation of a meteorological service for Egypt and the Sudan, and the enlargement and transfer of the Khedivial Observatory to Helwan. In 1902, officers of the Survey measured the discharge of the White and Blue Niles, and for the first time established their relative importance.

By the end of 1902 the Aswan Dam and the Barrages at Assiut and Zifta were completed. The Aswan Dam as it then was, added about one thousand million cubic metres of water to the summer supply of Egypt, and the Assiut Barrage enabled a large area of land in Upper Egypt to be irrigated perennially. By this time it was realized that supplies of water in addition to that to be stored in the Aswan Dam would ultimately be required by Egypt, and also that the increasing population in the Sudan would necessitate the extension of irrigation in that country. Both for this reason and also to assist the routine of irrigation work in Egypt, it became necessary to study the Upper Nile, and with this object, gauges were gradually erected at important points on the principal streams. In December, 1902, two Irrigation Department expeditions started, the one under Mr. C. E. Dupuis to visit Lake Tana, the source of the Blue Nile, and the other under Sir William Garstin to visit the Lakes Victoria, Albert and Edward. An account of these will be found in Sir William Garstin's *Report on the Basin of the Upper Nile*.[1]

The journeys of Sir William Garstin and the discharges measured by Mr. J. I. Craig, who accompanied him, enabled a proper appreciation of the régime of the White Nile to be formed. For the first time the great losses of water in the Sudd region were discovered, and it was possible for Sir William to suggest in outline a scheme of projects to be studied so that the low-stage discharge of the Nile could be increased. This scheme showed a considerable grasp of the régime of the Nile, and forms the skeleton of most subsequent proposals.

In 1905 the Sudan branch of the Egyptian Irrigation Service was formed with the immediate object of surveying, levelling, and measuring the volume of the different rivers throughout the year; erecting gauges; and generally collecting data for the different projects for the improvement of the water supply of Egypt, and

[1] Cairo Government Press 1904, and *Blue Book Egypt*, No. 2, 1904.

the development of perennial irrigation in the Sudan. In the same year, a thorough investigation of the Nile valley from Aswan to Khartoum was begun in order that new reservoir sites might be found. In connection with this, all likely sites were mapped by the Survey of Egypt, and a line of levels was run from Halfa to Khartoum. At the same time a new method of river measurement by means of a large masonry tank, was introduced by Mr. (now Sir Murdoch) MacDonald, Resident Engineer at the Aswan Dam, and later Adviser to the Ministry of Public Works. This has already been described in Chapter III. Sir Henry Lyons in 1906 published *The Physiography of the River Nile and its Basin*,[1] which gave a general description of the Basin, its geology, hydrology and climate, as far as they were then known, and for which the works of almost every traveller in the Nile Basin had been examined. I arrived in Egypt in 1906, so that developments since that date are within my personal knowledge.

From 1906 to 1913 the members of the staff of the Sudan branch of the Egyptian Irrigation Service under Mr. P. M. Tottenham were collecting material for the drawing up of projects for the improvement of the summer water supply of Egypt, and for the irrigation of a portion of the Sudan Gezira, as the land in the angle between the Blue and White Niles is called. Records of their work will be found in the Annual Reports of the Ministry of Public Works. Early in 1914 it was decided to build a dam at Gebel Aulia on the White Nile, 45 kilometres above the junction of the White and Blue Niles, to form a storage reservoir for Egypt, and another at Makwar on the Blue Nile, about 360 kilometres above the junction, for the irrigation of the Gezira.

During this period a great deal of scientific work was done by members of the Survey, whose activities were very diverse. In fact it was said that the work of the survey concerned the heavens above, the earth beneath, and the waters under the earth. One of these activities was the study of the river, to which Mr. J. I. Craig contributed a good deal, besides starting sound methods of analysing and tabulating hydrological information, which are the foundation of those in use to-day. One piece of work of great value was the levelling of high precision, which was carried from the sea to the Great Lakes. By this it is possible

[1] Cairo Government Press.

to know within a few inches the height of the river above sea-level at any point on its course. This is important information, both for the design of projects and for the study of hydrology, and it is surprising that such accuracy can be obtained over a line several thousand miles long.

The scientific activities of the Survey of a physical nature were combined and transferred to the Ministry of Public Works in 1915 as the Physical Department, under my direction, with a greatly increased scope and responsibility. They included Hydrology, Meteorology, the Helwan Observatory, the Weights and Measures Service and the Scientific Instrument Workshops. After the 1914–18 war, we were able to add some very able people to the staff, and in particular Dr. P. Phillips and Mr. R. P. Black in the Hydrological Service, and Mr. L. J. Sutton in the Meteorological Service. As time went on we were able to add to these, Egyptians, who had been trained in England and had taken good degrees in mathematics or physics. We started immediately to collect all the hydrological information in the possession of various branches of the Ministry, and to prepare it for publication. *Nile Control*, by Sir Murdoch MacDonald, which contained a description of the projects for dams on the White and Blue Niles, with estimates of the water requirements of Egypt and the Sudan, and, following Garstin, suggested further projects for reservoirs in Lake Tana and Albert and the conservation of the water lost in the Sudd Region, was published in 1920. This contained some of the data which had been put together and made as homogeneous as possible. It was clear that the observations of the water flowing at various points of the Nile system needed to be considerably extended, partly as a scientific study, but mainly because of their vital practical importance for the regulation of the river, and for the design of projects to use more of its water supply. It was also clear that if the data was to be of use it must be analysed systematically, and the results published regularly. This led to the publications of *The Nile Basin*, begun by myself and the late Dr. Phillips, and continued by myself, Black and Yusef Simaika Bey. This contains all the measurements of the discharge of the river and its tributaries, its levels, and the rainfall in its basin, in all, eight volumes and eleven supplements, four of which describe the

Basin and discuss its hydrology in detail, the remainder being devoted to statistics. One more volume is needed to complete the description and discussion of hydrology, and perhaps a supplementary volume to go over the whole field and bring it up to date, as the first volume was published in 1931. The question of keeping the publication of hydrological data up to date is one for my Egyptian successors, and is of the greatest importance for the future of the country.

By 1912 the Irrigation Service had established discharge sites at some of the most important points on the river, but little was known about the hydrology of the Blue Nile or the White Nile beyond the Sudan boundary, or about some of the tributaries. From 1919 onwards various reconnaissances were made. Lake Tana, which had previously been visited by Mr. Dupuis and later by Mr. A. Burton-Buckley, was studied by a mission which was started by Grabham and Black and continued by Herbert and Bambridge, whose work extended over the period 1920–24. As in the case of the earlier expeditions, work was at first restricted by the suspicions of the Ethiopians, but these gradually disappeared as it was realized that the curious habits of the intruders did no harm, and even produced money for the district, while medicines and treatment could be got from the doctors. Mr. G. W. Grabham, from 1907 to 1939 Sudan Government Geologist, wandered over most of the Sudan in the course of his work, and collected a great deal of information about the country in addition to that on geological matters. In 1923 Mr. P. M. Tottenham, then Under-Secretary of State for Public Works, went up to the Great Lakes, accompanied by Mr. Grabham, Mr. E. M. Tabor and Hussein Sirry Bey. Sirry was a son of Sir Ismail Sirry Pasha, who held the portfolio of Public Works for a longer time than any other Minister within my recollection. Hussein was afterwards Minister of Public Works and later Prime Minister, and acquired a great knowledge of irrigation matters and of public affairs.

From 1920 onwards I was able myself to make many journeys to the Upper Nile, and carried out reconnaissances of the Kagera, the Lake Edward and Semliki system and the tributaries of the Bahr-el-Ghazal, as well as travelling over all the principal tributaries of the Nile in the Sudan. In arranging these journeys, and in the matter of transport, I have to thank my colleagues of the Egyptian Irrigation Service, who have always been very ready to help, and with whom I have had much pleasant companionship.

Between the Wars there was a great deal of investigation of the hydrology of the Sudd Region, and surveys of the swamps, and of the country to the east of them, were carried out from the air and on the ground, in order to draw up a project for the preven-

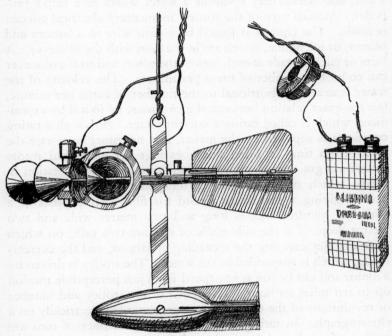

FIG. 14. Current Meter.

tion of the large losses of water which occur. This will be discussed later in the chapter on projects.

However, to return to the scientific side of things, a matter of great importance is the accuracy of the measurement of the discharges of the river and its tributaries. The relevance of this will be seen later on. By the direct measurement of water by means of the large tank at Aswan, which has already been described, Egypt had a fundamental and absolute method which existed nowhere else, and as far as I know, has not been repeated on any other large river. The method provides a standard with which the ordinary method of measurement, by means of current-meters, can be compared. Before mentioning the results of this comparison it is necessary to give a little detail on the working of a current-meter (see Fig. 14).

The instrument has a rotor which is turned by the flowing water, and which may resemble a water wheel or a ship's propeller. At each turn of the rotor a momentary electrical contact is made. The contact is joined by a twin wire to a battery and buzzer, or telephone, which are in the boat with the observer. A buzz or click is made at each turn of the rotor, and so the observer can count the number of turns per minute. The velocity of the water is nearly proportional to the number of turns per minute, but the exact relation between the two must be found by experiment, which is called rating a current-meter. Although a rating certificate is supplied by the maker, it is necessary to re-rate the meter from time to time, since bearings get worn and rotors sometimes get dented. There is an automatic rating station in Egypt which makes the rating independent of the observer, besides giving a permanent record for filing. It consists of a tank one hundred metres long and two metres wide and two metres deep. On the side walls of this are two rails, on which runs a trolley carrying the recording apparatus, and the current-meter, which is suspended in the water. The trolley is driven by a motor and can be run at any speed from just perceptible motion up to ten miles an hour. The speed of the trolley and number of revolutions of the current-meter are recorded electrically on a chronograph. In rating a current-meter, a number of runs are made backwards and forwards at different speeds, and the traces made on the chronograph paper will contain all the data necessary for making the rating-table of the current-meter.

In the process of rating, it is the current-meter which moves through the water, but when in actual use the water moves past the meter. The two phenomena would be the same if the water immediately surrounding the meter were all the time moving steadily in the direction of the stream. In any stream, however, this is not exactly the case. In slow-moving streams where the channel is fairly uniform, any motion, other than the steady forward flow, is hard to detect, although it exists. In more rapid streams, however, eddying motion occurs as well as the steady streaming, and is easily detected. The motion is then said to be turbulent. This is the case in the Nile in flood-time.

In the case of turbulent motion the combination of the down-stream motion and the irregular motion produces a somewhat greater velocity than the downstream component alone, although the actual velocity is continually varying slightly in direction. The cup type of current-meter, like the ordinary cup-anemometer, registers the actual velocity and not the velocity downstream only. Thus it tends to exaggerate the velocity of the stream. The amount of this effect was unknown previous to 1920. It is also difficult to separate from other sources of error, most of which also exaggerate the quantity of water passing in the river, and have an increased effect as the velocity of the stream increases. The effect of turbulence was investigated by the late Mr. B. H. Wade in the very turbulent water below the Aswan Dam, and in other places.[1] His conclusion was that it was utterly improbable that the correction to the measurements of the flood discharge below Aswan due to turbulence, would reach 2 per cent.

Another source of exaggeration of the discharge of a deep and rapid stream occurs in sounding. The pressure of the water tends to carry the sounding weight downstream as it is lowered, and also to bend the sounding wire into a curve. This makes the length of wire in the water longer than the true depth, and so increases the discharge calculated from the measurements. This effect was investigated by the late Dr. P. Phillips, and corrections to soundings were found by an ingenious piece of work.[2] His conclusion was, that on a good discharge site on the Main Nile at the top of the flood, the correction for exaggerated soundings might be as much as 1 per cent.

The comparison of the measurements of the discharge of the Nile at Aswan by current-meters, and by the sluices (see p. 65), has settled the question of the reliability of current-meters on such streams as the Nile and its tributaries. Several hundred comparisons showed that the methods gave identical results up

[1] " Report on Investigations into the Improvement of River Discharge Measurement," Part I. Physical Department, Paper No. 4. Cairo Government Press, 1921.
[2] " An Experiment to Determine Corrections to Sounding in River-gauging." Physical Department, Paper 18. Cairo Government Press, 1925.

to 170 million cubic metres per day, at which the average velocity is about 70 centimetres a second. From 170 mlpd. to 340 mlpd. (mean velocity 1 metre per second), the current-meter measurements on the average were 1 per cent. higher than the sluices, while at higher discharges the difference was about 2 per cent. These comparisons cover all conditions on the Main Nile and its tributaries, up to the peak of an ordinary flood. There are, however, indications that at the peak of a high flood, current-meters may exceed the sluices by somewhat more than 2 per cent., but there are not enough observations to establish this definitely. The conclusion is that at all discharge sites on the Nile and its tributaries, current-meters of the cup-type are very reliable measurers of the quantity of water flowing, and only very exceptionally would results be slightly exaggerated.

For about eight months the sluice discharge measurements are based directly on the big tank, as was explained on p. 66.

When the river is in flood and the reservoir is empty the method based on the big tank, which is applicable when the reservoir contains water, can no longer be applied. It was necessary, therefore, to invent some other method which would enable the flood discharge to be related to the absolute standard of the big tank. This was rather a complicated business, but I was able to devise a method, and the necessary apparatus was made partly in the Physical Department workshop and partly in the workshop at the Aswan Dam. The apparatus was tried out, and a long series of experiments was carried out under Watt by the staff at the Dam. The method and apparatus and the result of the experiments are described in a paper by Hurst and Watt in the *Proceedings of the Institution of Civil Engineers in* 1924. Thus the discharge of the Nile in flood was known to a high degree of accuracy, and I do not think this can be said of any other large river in the world. The current-meter could then be compared with sluice measurements up to the top of the flood, with the results already given.

There are now 300 current-meters in use in the Nile Basin, and every one has a dossier containing its life history. The result of a very great amount of experience is that the Price pattern current-meter, in competent hands, is a very reliable instrument, and that under good conditions it is possible to measure a discharge with, on the average, an accidental error of 1 per cent. This is a high degree of accuracy, but it has been constantly attained in the past in acceptance tests for the efficiency of pumps, for which a special technique was developed by the Physical Department. An improved current-meter of the vertical axis type has been developed by Mr. Black, making use of the Savonius S-rotor. This has the advantages over the Price pattern that the rotor is more robust, simpler to make, and gives more rotations for the same speed of the water. Hence it is more accurate at low velocities. It is also less sensitive to rocking of the discharge boat, which has an appreciable effect on the Price pattern meter. It is being manufactured by Messrs. Watts and Hilger.

A current-meter with its bright plated rotor spinning in the water must look an attractive object to the large fish in the Upper Nile, but it has only once happened that one was lost while working, and that met its end on the Sobat in the jaws of a crocodile.

Another interesting application of the tank experiments was in connection with models, which are now largely used to predict the behaviour of hydraulic structures while they are still only on the drawing-board. In 1918 Watt made the first scale model of a portion of the Aswan Dam with its different types of sluice, and set it up in a tank to imitate the reservoir, with a measuring box below it to imitate the tank. He found that, when the depth of water in the model reservoir was also to scale, the discharge of the model was proportional to the discharge of the full-scale sluice over a wide range of reservoir levels. The proportion turned out to be very nearly what would be expected from theoretical considerations. In the case of a model of 1/25 scale its discharge would be very nearly $1/(25 \times 25 \times \sqrt{25})$ or 1/3,125 of that of the original. The first model was made of wood to a scale of $1\frac{1}{2}$ centimetres to the metre, and we made others of larger scales very carefully in metal. They all showed the theoretical proportionality of discharge. This was the first time that the discharge of a small model had been compared with the discharge of a large sluice which had been directly measured in a tank; three-quarters of a ton in the tank of the model, compared with 20,000 tons in the large tank. No direct comparison on this scale has ever been done elsewhere. The practical outcome of this experiment was to make two models of the sluices of the Sennar Dam on the Blue Nile, which was then being built. The discharge of the full-scale sluice was inferred from the model experiments, and on these rests the division of the Blue Nile water between Egypt and the Sudan. Since the original experiments of Watt and myself established the validity of models as measurers of discharge, their use has become an established practice in Egypt. There are, however, some limitations, and they cannot be used blindly with the idea that they will give an answer to any hydraulic problem.

A great many experiments have been made at the Delta Barrage with models of regulators, weirs, outlets and other works by the late Mr. A. D. Butcher and his successors, with the object of improving design[1]. Recently a large and well-equipped hydraulic laboratory has been built to replace and extend the previous installation. This forms part of the Inspectorate General of Nile Control, a branch of the Irrigation Service which has been formed to carry on the study of the Nile and the scientific side of irrigation in place of the Physical Department, which has been split up and its parts redistributed.

Other important work which was done by the Physical Department between the wars was the study of the material carried in suspension by the Nile. When the river rises owing to the rains in Ethiopia, a great deal of mud and sand is washed into it, and the finer parts are brought down to Egypt. Later, when the river falls, it gradually ceases to carry mud and becomes clear. The sediment is both a blessing and a trouble. It is the cause of the existence of the cultivated land of Egypt, on which each year it deposits a thin layer of new soil. Some of this new soil, however, gets deposited in the canals, which have periodically to be cleared at a considerable cost. As an offset to the cost, however, the soil so obtained is used on the land. The presence of silt in quantity also prevents the water from being stored in reservoirs, for some of the silt would be deposited and the reservoir would gradually fill up and disappear. This has

---

[1] For example see Vaughan-Lee, *Jl. of Inst. of Civil Engineers*, London, June 1941, where experiments on models of the Gebel Aulia Dam by Dr. Hassan Zaki Bey are described.

happened all over the world where the waters of streams carrying loads of sand and mud have been stored. The practice, therefore, at Aswan is to start filling only when there is little silt in the water. It does, however, happen, when there is a high flood which looks like endangering the river banks in Egypt, that the reservoir is partially filled with flood water in order to reduce the height of its crest in Egypt. This would be likely to cause the deposition of some silt. It has also become important, since the two heightenings of the dam and the consequent increase in the volume of the reservoir, to find out how early it is safe to begin to fill. This has led to a systematic study of the quality and quantity of the suspended material by the collection of hundreds of samples of the silt-containing water at different depths and different points across the river. These samples are then analysed to get the proportion of sediment to water by weighing the sample, evaporating the water, and then weighing the sediment. From the analysis of the complete set of samples it is possible to calculate how much sediment is being carried by the river. By doing this regularly for several seasons it can be decided when it will be safe to begin to fill the reservoir. All these results have been put together by my colleague Yusef Simaika Bey in a paper called *The Suspended Matter in the Nile.*[1] Another connected investigation has been the careful survey of the reservoir from time to time to find whether sediment has been deposited, but so far there has been no significant amount.

The manner in which silt is suspended and carried by the water is a very interesting one. If the water moved steadily in parallel lines in what is known as streamline motion, there would be no suspended matter, but this form of motion can only be made to occur under special conditions in a laboratory. In a natural channel, although the general motion is parallel to the bed, on this are superposed random motions like those of the bees in a swarm. It is these random motions which pick up and keep the finer particles suspended. I investigated this in the laboratory by stirring a mixture of mud and water in a vessel like a churn in such a way as to make the motion as nearly haphazard as possible. The very interesting result was that the amount of suspended mud was greatest at the bottom and

[1] Physical Department, Paper No. 40. Cairo Government Press.

decreased with the height above the bottom, in exactly the same way as the pressure in the atmosphere falls as one ascends.

In 1925 the Sudan formed an Irrigation Service and took on the management of its own irrigation affairs, which had previously been of small extent, and had been looked after by the Egyptian service. In 1929 the Nile Waters Agreement was concluded between Egypt and the Sudan, and in 1932 an agreement was made to cover the operation of the Jebel Aulia reservoir. These two agreements, with their Working Arrangements covering technical details, have worked without a hitch. The need for further water supplies for both Egypt and the Sudan makes it necessary in the near future to extend them to cover the further works which are now projected.

Just recently the Uganda Government has formed a Hydrological Service to investigate water supplies arising in Uganda, and this Service has taken over the measurements of the principal tributaries of the Nile on the Lake Plateau, previously made under the Inspector of the Southern Nile Division of the Egyptian Irrigation Service.

I have written the previous paragraphs to indicate the important part played by scientific measurement and experiment in the study of the régime of the river, and I shall later show how these studies are applied to the practical business of regulating the river for irrigation, and for devising projects to produce more water at the time when it is needed. The Egyptian Government has spent a large sum of money on the study of the Nile, and it has returned its cost a hundred fold, and perhaps even a thousand fold, to the country. Now much greater facilities are available for experimental work than when the work I have described was done. It is to be hoped that the enthusiasm and interest of the pioneers will descend to their successors and enable them to produce results worthy of the days, 2,000 years ago, when Egypt was the home of the most famous mathematicians and natural philosophers of the time.

Chapter Fifteen

HYDROLOGY

1. THE NILE IN GENERAL

THE following description of the water supply of the Nile, the parts played by the tributaries, the swamps and the Great Lakes, cannot be given without some unfamiliar and apparently abstruse ideas. The abstruseness is however, more apparent than real, and the subjects discussed are of general interest. The fundamental principle on which nearly all investigations concerning water are based, is that water is neither created nor destroyed; if it disappears in one place it reappears in another. The rest is largely ordinary arithmetic, and due warning will be given if there is anything really difficult to be discussed.

The dependence of Egypt on the Nile has led to intensive studies of the quantities of water carried by the main stream and its tributaries throughout the year. These studies may be said to have begun at a very early date, as the ancient Egyptians recorded river levels on nilometers, some of which still remain. The nilometer on Roda Island, Cairo, dates back to 860 A.D. and records on its predecessors for 220 years earlier have come down to us, though unfortunately with many gaps. There is no other series of observations of a meteorological phenomenon comparable in age with these Nile records, except those derived from the measurement of the rings of the big California trees, which take us back even further. However, previous to the present century, there was very little detailed knowledge about the Nile water supply and its origin, and the greatest developments have taken place since the war of 1914–18. The levels and discharges of the principal tributaries and of the main stream are now measured at many points from Tanganyika to the sea, with the exception of the Blue Nile beyond the Sudan boundary.

A river gauge consists primarily of a scale, usually of marble, on which the level of the water is observed. The standard type of Nile gauge consists of a series of steps or pillars built into the river bank to each of which a section of the scale is fixed (see

237

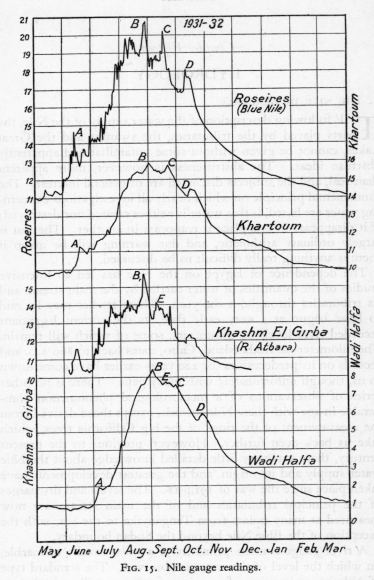

FIG. 15. Nile gauge readings.

Fig. 12, p. 223). There are 140 of these gauges scattered over the basin outside Egypt, and many more on the Nile in

Egypt, to say nothing of the numbers on the canals in Egypt. Most of them are observed daily, and the readings of the more important are telegraphed to Cairo. For convenience these gauge readings are plotted day by day to form diagrams such as those shown in Figs. 15, 22 and 23.

River levels are important for certain purposes, but a more important quantity is the discharge of the river. Discharges are usually reckoned in cubic metres per second,[1] or millions of cubic metres per day. All irrigation programmes and practice are based on quantities of water, hence the measurement of discharge is a fundamental proceeding, and has already been described on pp. 65 and 222. The discharge of the river varies from place to place and from day to day, but it is not necessary to measure it every day at an observation station, since there is usually some relation between level and discharge. Thus, if the level is observed every day and the discharge at intervals of a few days, or in some cases of even a month, a sufficiently close approximation can be found to the discharges on the intervening days when no measurements were made.

In describing the water supply, we shall begin with the Main Nile at Wady Halfa, as it was before the filling of the heightened Aswan Reservoir and the Gebel Aulia Reservoir had modified its régime, i.e. previous to 1934, and deal later with the modifications of flow introduced for the advantage of irrigation. The Sennar Reservoir on the Blue Nile was first filled in 1925, but its effect is small. Fig. 15 shows the levels of the river in the year 1931–32, which was a fairly average year. Halfa may be taken as representing what would take place in Egypt if there were no dams, barrages or irrigation, to interfere with the natural flow of the river. The river began to rise in June, and in the next two months rose about 7 metres (23 feet), reaching a maximum at the beginning of September, and then fell away more slowly than it rose, to reach a minimum the following May. Three streams, the Blue Nile, White Nile and Atbara, are responsible for the Main Nile at Halfa, and the levels of these are also shown on the diagram. Levels are not exact indicators of quantities of water, particularly at the junction of two streams. For example, the effect of the

---

[1] 1 milliard (mlrd) = 1,000,000,000. 10 millions a day (mlpd.) = 116 per second = 3·65 mlrds. per annum. 1 cubic metre = 35·3 cubic feet.

White Nile is hidden by the more powerful stream of the Blue Nile.

Roseires on the Blue Nile is not far from the Ethiopian mountains, and the river there, by rapid fluctuations, shows the effect of the rain falling on them, occasionally rising and falling two metres in ten days, or even rising four metres in a week. In the 620 kilometres from Roseires to Khartoum these rapid fluctuations are considerably damped, but their main features persist. Notice the peaks marked A, B, C, and D, on the Roseires and Khartoum curves. When we get to Halfa the Atbara also affects the levels. On the whole it rises similarly to the Blue Nile and often, though not always, a peak on the Blue Nile is accompanied by one on the Atbara. Naturally, since both streams draw their supplies from Ethiopia a widespread rain will affect the two. Khashm-el-Girba gauge on the Atbara, however, is nearer to Halfa than is the Roseires gauge, so a peak on the Atbara arrives at Halfa two or three days before one which started at the same time on the Blue Nile. The Atbara carries much less water than the Blue Nile, but the effect of a peak may be considerable because, owing to the shorter journey, there is less damping. The peak B, at Khashm-el-Girba, happens at the same time as B on the Blue Nile, but it gets to Halfa two or three days before the Blue Nile peak, and is responsible for the actual maximum B, at Halfa. Peak E, on the Atbara, does not coincide with anything of importance on the Blue Nile, and corresponds to E, at Halfa. C, at Khartoum, which occurs when the Atbara has fallen, is responsible for C, at Halfa.

This slight analysis illustrates an important calculation, namely the forecasting of the height of the flood in Egypt from what happens on the Blue Nile and Atbara. In a high flood, what happens on the tributaries is followed day by day in Cairo with the closest attention, as on the forecast which is made, depends the measures to be taken to reduce the danger from a high flood.

Another critical time occurs when the flood is first beginning to rise, and the Aswan Reservoir is nearly empty. In a year when the flood is late, as in the year 1943, the most careful attention is needed in June and July so as to make full use of the reservoir water, and at the same time not have the reservoir empty before the natural river supply is enough for the crops.

Failure to make full use of the water increases the difficulty of irrigation and some crops suffer, while a mistake in the other direction may lead to serious loss of crops through lack of water. Consequently a daily forecast is made based on the quantities of water passing Roseires on the Blue Nile, Malakal on the White Nile, Khartoum, and Khashm-el-Girba on the Atbara, and the

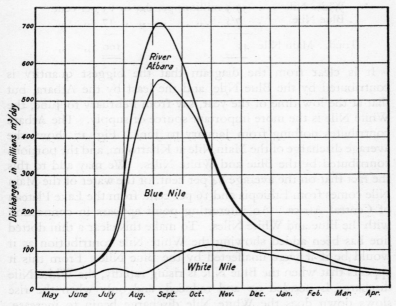

FIG. 16. Discharge of the Nile at Aswan.

water released day by day from Aswan is governed by these forecasts.

We now leave levels and deal with quantities of water. Fig. 16 shows the average discharge of the Main River at Aswan unaffected by reservoirs, whose effects have been removed. The upper line shows the discharge of the main river at any time, and the other lines the component discharges. Let us take the maximum discharge occurring on about September 8th. It is made up as follows:—

White Nile	.	70 millions per day or 10 per cent.					
Blue Nile	.	485 ,,	,,	,, ,, ,, 68	,,	,,
Atbara .	.	157 ,,	,,	,, ,, ,, 22	,,	,,
Total. Main Nile	712			100	,,	,,

The minimum discharge is about 45 millions per day on about May 10th, and is made up as follows:—

White Nile	.	37·5 millions per day or 83 per cent.					
Blue Nile	.	7·5 ,,	,,	,, ,, ,, 17	,,	,,
Total. Main Nile	45			100	,,	,,

It is clear from the diagram that the biggest quantity is contributed by the Blue Nile, and the least by the Atbara, but that at the low time of the year, say from February to June, the White Nile is the more important source of supply. The Atbara contributes nothing from January to June. Fig. 17 shows the average discharge of the Main Nile at Khartoum, and the portions contributed by the Blue and White Niles. We may add to this the fact that on the average 84 per cent. of the water of the Main Nile comes from Ethiopia and 16 per cent. from the Lake Plateau of Central Africa. An interesting point appears in connection with the Blue and White Niles. To make this clear a thin dotted line has been added showing the White Nile contribution as it would be if it were unaffected by the Blue Nile. From this it appears that when the Blue Nile is rising rapidly, the White Nile discharge is ponded up and reduced, and only when the rise slows down does the White Nile discharge begin to increase. When the Blue Nile falls the White Nile discharge is increased by water which has been ponded. The effect of the Blue Nile is therefore to make a natural reservoir of the White Nile, and this effect is now produced artificially on a greater scale by the Gebel Aulia Dam situated some little distance up the White Nile. The White Nile when low is only a few hundred metres wide, but as it lies in a flat shallow valley the effect of the reservoir when full is to increase its width to three or four kilometres.

In reading the following the maps inside the covers should be consulted. The Atbara draws its supply from the northern part of the Ethiopian Plateau, but little is known of the hydrology of its tributaries. The rainfall which causes its flood comes from the same source as that falling in the Blue Nile Basin, and this is probably the South Atlantic, of which more later. In flood its

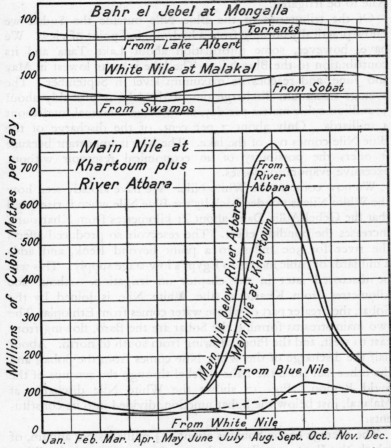

FIG. 17. Discharges of the Nile and its main tributaries. Average 1912–36.

level fluctuates like that of the Blue Nile, and after the flood it soon ceases to flow.

The Blue Nile receives two tributaries in the Sudan, the Rahad and Dinder, both coming from Ethiopia. They are strong streams in flood, but like the Atbara, are later reduced to pools. When at their maximum they produce together about 10 per cent. of the Blue Nile discharge. Above these tributaries is the Sennar Dam, which enables a large area to the west of the Blue Nile to be irrigated.

Of the tributaries of the Blue Nile outside the Sudan we know practically nothing from a hydrological point of view. We have, however, some information about Lake Tana and its contribution to the Blue Nile. The lake is at its lowest in May and June, and reaches its maximum level in September. The average maximum discharge out of the lake is probably about 35 million cubic metres per day, and the mean annual total about 4 milliards. Only about 7 per cent. of the discharge of the Blue Nile comes out of the lake. The lake is important because it offers the possibility of an economical reservoir without excessive evaporation losses.

We now come to the White Nile. We have already seen how the White Nile is ponded back by the Blue Nile when it rises, and that the Gebel Aulia Dam, about 45 kilometres from Khartoum, increases the ponding effect. The reservoir so produced affects the river for 300 miles, to a point beyond Renk, and adds 2 milliards of cubic metres to Egypt's low-stage supply. This will be discussed later in the chapter on irrigation. About 800 kilometres from Khartoum the White Nile is joined by the Sobat, the greater part of whose water comes from Ethiopia. The two main streams forming the Sobat are the Baro, flowing from east to west, and the Pibor, flowing from south to north. About half the discharge of the White Nile comes from the Sobat, and the other half from the Bahr-el-Jebel through the swamps of the Sudd Region. Fig. 17 shows the White Nile discharge at Malakal, just below the Sobat junction, divided into its constituents.

The average of the Sobat is about $13\frac{1}{2}$ milliards per annum, of which the Baro contributes about 72 per cent. and the Pibor 17 per cent., and the remainder enters by small channels. About 90 per cent. of Sobat water comes from Ethiopia. It might be expected that the Sobat and Blue Nile drawing their waters from Ethiopia would have similar characteristics. To some extent this is true, but the flood on the Sobat is modified by the fact that all its tributaries are liable to overflow their banks and inundate large areas of plain. In fact in a year of heavy rain practically the whole country, from the Ethiopian foothills to the Bahr-el-Jebel and the slopes of the Lake Plateau, is under water. The effect of this is to smooth out all the peaks which occur on the headstreams, and delay the arrival of the maximum at the mouth by two or three months. The Sobat, like the Blue Nile and Atbara in flood-time, brings down mud from Ethiopia, though only a relatively small amount gets into the White Nile.

The average discharge of the White Nile is about 28 milliards per annum, of which the Sobat produces 13·5, and the rest, except for a negligible amount contributed by the Bahr-el-Ghazal, comes from the Bahr-el-Jebel or its branch, the Bahr-el-Zeraf. This remainder is called swamps discharge in Fig. 17. It will be noticed that the Bahr-el-Jebel discharge varies very little throughout the year. This is due to the regulating effect of the large swamps of the Sudd region on the Bahr-el-Jebel. When a rise occurs upstream of the swamps, most of it flows out of the river into the marshes, and only a very small part of the increase is felt at the tail of the swamps. When the river falls there is a tendency for the marshes to drain back to the river, but large areas are below the river level and cannot drain back. The water which enters these is lost by evaporation and by transpiration from the luxuriant vegetation, and in fact there is very little return of water to the river, with the result that the Bahr-el-Jebel loses nearly half its water in the swamps. Fig. 17 shows the average discharges entering (Bahr-el-Jebel at Mongalla), and leaving the Bahr-el-Jebel swamps. (Swamps at Malakal.)

If one travels down the Bahr-el-Jebel one of the features one notices is the number of side channels. Water is continually leaving and returning to the main channel, and sometimes nearly half the water is carried by alternative channels. One of these systems, which lies to the east of the main channel, is the Atem-Awai, which carries a considerable discharge. This fact led to the proposal of the late Mr. A. D. Butcher to make the head of the Sudd Diversion Channel at Jonglei where the Atem runs along the edge of the dry ground. There is little at Jonglei but a few Dinkas and their huts, but owing to this project, which will be described later, and the investigations made by the Sudan

Government through the organization known as the Jonglei Team, the name is now well-known. To get to Jonglei and back to the Bahr-el-Jebel lower down requires some intricate navigation, as the channels change from time to time, old ones becoming blocked by vegetation, and new ones opening up. I have twice been into Jonglei lagoon, and each time the route was different. Below the tails of the Awai are the Cuts leading from the Jebel to the Bahr-el-Zeraf. The Zeraf gradually separates from the Jebel, but the two rejoin above the junction of the Sobat with the White Nile. One-third of the total discharge is carried by the Zeraf and two-thirds by the Jebel.

In the case of the Bahr-el-Ghazal, which drains a large area having a fair rainfall, the tributary streams in their upper courses carry considerable volumes of water in flood (July to October), although they are practically dry from January to April. Of this quantity which drains into the tributaries, estimated to be rather more than the discharge of the Sobat, only a trickle reaches the mouth of the Bahr-el-Ghazal. Some day, no doubt, works will be undertaken to conserve some of this water, which renders large areas uninhabitable for half the year, and whose only economic benefit is to provide grazing for cattle on the edges of the permanent swamps. The two main tributaries of the Bahr-el-Ghazal are the Jur and the Lol, and both of these are big streams in flood above where they spill and create swamps.

Returning to the Bahr-el-Jebel, we have said that half of its water is lost in the swamps. It derives its water mainly from the Equatorial Lakes, but there is in addition a contribution, averaging about 17 per cent. of the total, from torrential tributaries joining between Lake Albert and Mongalla in the Sudan Plain (see Fig. 17). These torrents rise very rapidly, and large quantities of water come down in a few hours, but when the rain ceases the flood subsides nearly as rapidly as it rose. In the rainy season, however, the traveller may have to camp for a day or two before he can cross some of these streams. On the road from Juba to Nimule they are now all bridged. During the dry season their contribution is negligible. The effect of these torrents is shown on Rejaf and Mongalla gauge readings in Fig. 23, p. 273.

2. THE GREAT LAKES

The Jebel immediately below Lake Albert does not fluctuate rapidly since it is entirely controlled by the lake, which, owing to its size, can change its level only slowly. Thus it takes several years of rainfall in excess of the average to build up a high level in the lake, and this level, once established, will take two or three years to fall away. The project to use Lake Albert as a reservoir will be described later.

Lake Albert receives supplies from two principal sources, the Victoria Nile and the Semliki, and from other small streams. The Semliki comes down from Lake Edward and receives on the way the drainage from the western side of Mt. Ruwenzori, and some small streams from the Belgian Congo. Its contribution to Lake Albert is about $3\frac{1}{2}$ milliards in the year, of which 2 milliards comes from Lake Edward. The Victoria Nile has an average discharge of 20 milliards, and is by far the most important contributor. The amount brought in by the small tributaries can be estimated from the rainfall, the size of the streams, and the nature and area of the country. This is usually called "run-off," and estimates of run-off based entirely on rainfall and the nature of the country, are often the only data available in some European countries for the design of hydro-electric schemes.

To understand the economy of the lake we shall attempt to make a balance sheet of gains and losses. Measuring water is not quite like counting money, since we cannot know any of the quantities to the last cubic metre, and some we cannot measure directly at all. We are therefore driven to the resort of the amateur accountant, and must credit amounts which are unknown, to general expenses. In our case the uncertainties are put into the item, evaporation. The annual balance sheet is as follows:—

Annual inflow :

From the Semliki	3·6	milliards
Estimated amount from other tributaries	1·7	,,
From the Victoria Nile . . .	19·7	,,
From rain on the lake	4·6	,,
Total	29·6	,,

Annual outflow:
       By the Bahr-el-Jebel   .   .   .   22 milliards
Difference
       which is put down to evaporation .   7·6   ,,

This difference represents an average depth of evaporation of 1·4 metres a year, or about 3·9 millimetres a day.[1] The figures given above cover the period of ten years since regular measurements of the Semliki and Victoria Nile discharges began. It will be noticed that the largest quantities in the balance sheet are the inflow from the Victoria Nile and the outflow from the Bahr-el-Jebel.

Lakes George and Edward are practically one lake, though Lake George is at a slightly higher level than Lake Edward. The area of Lake Edward is 2,200 square kilometres, and that of Lake George 300. Hydrological information is still scanty, but be it remarked, it is more abundant than that available for several lakes in Scotland on which power schemes are being constructed. There is, however, enough information to enable us to get out a balance sheet, as in the case of Lake Albert. The following are the details:—

Annual inflow:
       From tributaries   .   .   .   2·2 milliards
       From rainfall on the lake   .   3·4   ,,

           Total   .   .   .   .   5·6   ,,
Annual outflow:
       By the Semliki   .   .   .   2·0   ,,

Difference:
       To be put down to evaporation   .   3·6   ,,

This difference amounts to 1·44 metres in the year, or 3·9 millimetres a day. The inflow from the tributaries is based partly on a few measurements, partly on the examination of the streams and the country made by myself, and partly on inferences from the amount of rain falling in the basin.

In 1938, when the late Dr. Phillips and I were writing volume V of *The Nile Basin*, we had less information about Lake Edward. However, by a careful analysis of rainfall, estimation of the

---

[1] Area of Lake Albert is 5,300 square kilometres.

amount brought in by tributaries, evaporation from such observations as existed on the Lake Plateau, and four measurements of the discharge of the Semliki River at different places and times, we were able to make an estimate of the normal rises and falls of the surface of Lake Edward. At that time there was no gauge on the lake, and no record at all of its variations of level. Phillips and Black and I were very doubtful about publishing the investigation, and its results as it seemed somewhat academic and speculative. There was also one feature which did not occur on Lakes Victoria or Albert and which made us pause. This was that there appeared to be two very definite maxima and minima in the year. However, it was finally decided that we should include the investigation and its results. Now, with ten years of observations of the level of the lake, our estimate made in 1938, and our forecast of a double period in its annual variation, is amply confirmed. The range of lake level in ten years has been a little more than a metre, i.e. about 4 feet. Lake Edward, like Lake Albert, is a potential reservoir in which over-year storage could be carried out.

Returning to Lake Albert and following the Victoria Nile to Lake Kioga, we find that in this stretch it receives some drainage from swamps, but there is no tributary of importance. Lake Kioga is joined by many swamp-filled valleys where the water-surface has usually a considerable slope. There are well-defined limits to the lake set by higher land, so that it is not like the Sudd Region of the Bahr-el-Jebel, where water can spread over very wide and indefinite areas. It receives drainage from a large area of country, but owing to the swampy nature of the valleys, the run-off is usually small, except perhaps in the case of the tributaries which arise on Elgon and the mountains to the north-east. It sometimes happens that, when there is a very heavy rainfall, Lake Kioga and its tributaries add a large volume of water to the Victoria Nile, and this is a factor which has to be considered in drawing up projects for storage in the Great Lakes.

In drawing up a balance sheet for Lake Kioga difficulties occur which were not present to the same extent in the case of Lake Albert. The basin has a large area, much of which is undulating country and from which the percentage of rainfall (or run-off) which finds its way into the lake will not be large. We may assume that the run-off is the same as that of the Aswa River to the north, whose discharge has been measured for a number of years, and whose run-off is about 3 per cent. This may seem surprisingly small, but most Nile Basin run-offs are much smaller than those of temperate climates. This is accounted for by thick vegetation, strong evaporation and the existence of swamps. Assembling all the information for a balance sheet for Lake Kioga we have:—

Annual inflow:

From Victoria Nile	.	.	.	20·6 milliards
By tributaries	.	.	.	3·5 ,,
By rain on lake and swamp	.	.	8·0 ,,

Total . . . . . 32·1 ,,

Annual outflow:

By Victoria Nile . . . . 19·7 milliards

Difference to be put down to evapo-   12·4 ,,
ration from open water and
transpiration by plants.

We may assume that the evaporation from the open water of Lake Kioga is similar to that which has been found for Lakes Albert, Edward and Victoria, whose mean is 3·9 millimetres depth per day. As the swamp has an area of about 4,500 square kilometres and the open water about 1,800, this leaves 2·2 metres depth, or 6 millimetres per day for loss by evaporation and transpiration from the swamp. Thus losses from swamp are at the rate of about 1½ times the loss from open water. Evaporation and transpiration will be discussed more fully later.

We now consider Lake Victoria, where work has begun on a dam at the Owen Falls, about one and three-quarter miles below the Ripon Falls, which will transform it into a reservoir, and at the same time produce power for use in industry in Uganda. The area of the lake is 27,000 square miles, the Equator crosses it, and it stretches over 180 miles in latitude. In this long distance the incidence of rainfall varies. Most of the rainfall stations are on the shores of the lake, though a few are on islands. The centre of the lake, however, has very few islands and these are not commonly visited, so that observations over a large proportion of the lake are almost impossible. The lack of observations from the central portion of the lake makes the drawing of lines of equal rainfall (isohyets) a little uncertain. This affects the estimate of the total rainfall on the lake, but the uncertainty is not very great. The newly founded Uganda Hydrological Service is doing its best to extend information, but there are difficulties in maintaining observations on remote islands which can be visited only very occasionally, and where it is extremely hard to find a local observer. Even self-recording instruments require some attention, and an unattended rain-gauge may quickly become a receptacle for rubbish.

The lake has an average rise and fall during the year of about a foot, and the maximum range during the forty-five years over which the records extend, is 1·74 metres, or about 5 feet 9 inches. Its main tributary is the Kagera, whose discharge has now been measured regularly for ten years. All the other tributaries are much smaller than the Kagera, but those on the north-eastern part of the lake have a fair discharge in the rainy season. On the basis of the Kagera, and the others which have been measured, we can make an estimate of the percentage of the rainfall which enters the lake.

The balance sheet is:—

Annual inflow:

From tributaries	.	.	.	.	16 milliards
From rainfall on lake	.	.	.	.	98 ,,
		Total	.	.	114 ,,

Annual outflow:

By Victoria Nile	.	.	.	21 ,,
Difference to be put down to evaporation.				93 ,,

This difference amounts to 1·4 metres in the year, or 3·8 milli-metres a day. The balance sheet shows that the main source of supply is the rainfall on the lake itself and the main outgoing is by evaporation, and that evaporation and rainfall are roughly equal and about five times as big as inflow or outflow by the rivers.

The approximate equality of rainfall and evaporation in the cases of Lakes Victoria, Albert and Edward, is a very important result. It means that these lakes have a great advantage as reservoirs, inasmuch as rainfall and evaporation compensate each other. When, therefore, the water surface is raised and its area increased, the unavoidable increase of loss by evaporation is compensated by an equal increase in the gain from the rainfall which falls on the surface. In the case of a reservoir in a rainless country, like the Aswan Reservoir, the uncompensated evaporation loss due to increase of surface is important.

These balance sheets are very slightly different from those got out for the Nile Basin fourteen years ago, owing to the fact that we now have much more precise information about the discharges of the rivers, thanks to the efforts of the Sudan Branch of the Egyptian Irrigation Service. We should have been in a still better position if my proposals for the study of the hydrology of the Great Lakes made in 1927 had been accepted at the time. The value of a record of any natural phenomenon increases with its length, and this applies particularly to river and lake statistics. Had systematic measurement on the Lake Plateau begun in 1930 instead of 1940, we should have a very much more extensive and valuable body of knowledge.

3. EVAPORATION AND TRANSPIRATION

In the preceding section we have deduced evaporation as a residual in the balance sheets of the lakes, with very concordant results. Evaporation is also measured by evaporimeters of various types, but these do not give correct values for the evaporation from a large sheet of water like a river or a lake. The apparatus in use at meteorological stations in Egypt and the Sudan is a Piche evaporimeter, which consists of a graduated tube filled with water and closed at its open end by a piece of blotting paper held in place by a metal disc. The metal disc has the same diameter as the outside diameter of the tube, and the blotting paper projects a millimetre or two beyond this all the way round. The tube is inverted and hung up and evaporation takes place from the projecting ring of blotting paper. It is measured by the fall of the water surface in the tube. In the dry conditions of Egypt and the Sudan, a Piche evaporimeter in a screen at some distance from a sheet of open water will evaporate about twice as much as the open water surface. It is the latter which concerns the hydrologist, and many attempts have been made to measure it, but not with complete success in all cases. The best results have been obtained with an iron tank in the shape of a cube of 1 metre side. The tank is floated on a river or lake by means of a wooden raft, so that the rim of the tank is a few inches above the level of the outside water surface. The tank is filled to outside water level, and the loss every day is measured by a gauge which indicates the level of the water in the tank. It has been found from experiments in Egypt and the Sudan that the evaporation indicated by the floating tank is a little more than half that shown by a Piche evaporimeter in a meteorological screen some distance away from the water. There are difficulties, however, with the floating tank on windy days in preventing waves splashing into it, and for this reason it has never been successful on the Great Lakes, where waves of considerable size occur. The deduction of the evaporation from a sheet of open water from readings of a Piche evaporimeter, is not very certain, since a lot depends on the exposure of the instrument. The best procedure for a particular district in Egypt or the Sudan is to take the mean evaporation from several stations in the district and halve it. The Great Lakes, however, produce a local climate, so that a Piche evaporimeter in a town on the shores of Lake Victoria will not indicate twice the evaporation from the lake itself, but something appreciably less. This is because the damp atmosphere over the lake extends some distance inland. Evaporation is affected by the dampness of the atmosphere, and by the wind and temperature. In the case of a small body of water or an evaporimeter, a wind continually removes the damp air produced by evaporation and replaces it with drier air, thus increasing the evaporation.

The observations of evaporation deduced for open water in Egypt and the Sudan, and the evaporation from the balance sheets already given for the Great Lakes, produce a fairly consistent picture, which is indicated in the table, on p. 254. The evaporation in the Southern Sudan seems a little low compared with the neighbouring areas.

It is interesting to see how the evaporation increases from the Delta up to Khartoum, and then decreases as one goes

Average Evaporation. Millimetres a day

	Piche	Open water
Mediterranean coast	6·1	3·0
Delta	4·6	2·3
Cairo and neighbourhood	5·5	2·8
Fayum	7·9	4·0
Oases	13·0	6·5
Upper Egypt	9·0	4·5
Northern Sudan (Halfa to Atbara) . .	15·1	7·6
Khartoum and neighbourhood . . .	15·5	7·8
Central Sudan (Dueim to Roseires) . .	12·6	6·3
Southern Sudan (Malakal and south outside the swamps)	6·8	3·4
Lake Albert		3·9
Lake Edward		3·9
Lake Victoria		3·8

further south. In Egypt the evaporation is a maximum in June and a minimum in December and January. In the Northern Sudan it is the same, but May has practically the same evaporation as June. In Khartoum neighbourhood the maximum is in April and May, owing to the reduction later caused by the monsoon rains, of which this area is on the fringe. In the Southern Sudan the minimum evaporation is in the months of July and August, at the height of the rains. Evaporation in Egypt and the Sudan, on the whole, follows the temperature.

The heavy evaporation and general dryness of the climate in Egypt, and most of the Sudan, have various implications. A common device for keeping drinks cool is a large, porous pot, known as a zeer. The zeer is partly filled with water, which percolates through the pores and evaporates on the outer surface, thus cooling the water inside. When travelling, a canvas bag, known as a zamzamia (from the well Zamzam at Mecca), which is filled with water and placed in the wind in the shade, serves to provide a cool drink. When water evaporates the dissolved salts are left behind, and this fact has bearings on agriculture and health. In the case of a soil which is perennially irrigated, unless there is a good downward drainage so that the salts can be carried away by watering and not allowed to accumulate in the soil, the soil will contain more and more salt until it ceases to be able to support crops. It is a common experience on impermeable land to see a white incrustation of salt. In the case of the human body, exertion in hot weather produces perspiration, which evaporates leaving salts on the skin. The more one drinks the more one perspires, and the more salts are lost from the body, It is necessary, therefore, to take extra salt to make up the loss, as loss of salts is one of the causes of heat stroke. This is conveniently done by taking Salt Tabloids.

4. THE ORIGIN OF THE NILE FLOOD

There must have been speculations from early times about the origin of the Nile flood, and Herodotus has given us his version. He thought that, in winter the sun is driven south by storms into the upper parts of Libya where the streams rise which feed the Nile. The proximity of the sun causes strong evaporation and the streams shrink. When, in summer, the sun returns northwards the Nile again augments and is at its highest. His account is not clear as to where the water comes from, as he first derides the idea that it is due to melting snow, and later says the Nile derives none of its bulk from rains. The discovery, in the sixteenth century, that the flood was due to rain on the Ethiopian Highlands was a satisfactory answer so far as it went, but in the nineteenth century the study of meteorology developed, and the physics of the atmosphere and its circulation began to be studied. By the end of the century it was realized that the causes of phenomena like the Indian Monsoon and the Nile flood, must be sought in the general circulation of the atmosphere. The features of this circulation were to be discovered from a study of the variation of barometric pressure and the winds. In Egypt various attempts were made to relate the Nile flood with conditions in north-east Africa. Mahmoud Pasha el Falaki in 1882 suggested that the Nile flood might be predicted by a study of temperatures and pressures observed at Cairo. Later Ventre Pasha thought that the force and direction of the winds at Aden and Zanzibar might be a base for forecasts. Sir Henry Lyons in his *Physiography of the Nile* (1906), discussed some of the earlier suggestions and made an examination, from which he concluded that the two principal factors to be considered are, firstly, the strength of the south-east trade winds as they progress from the south to the north of the Equator along the eastern coast of Africa, and secondly, the excess or deficit of atmospheric pressure in the area represented by Aden, Cairo, Beirut and the region lying to the west of this; the sub-equatorial rainfall in early summer must also be considered: all of which pointed to the Indian ocean as the source of the Ethiopian rains.

In 1910 Mr. J. I. Craig wrote a paper in *The Journal of the Royal Meteorological Society*,[1] in which he gave reasons for thinking that the origin of the Ethiopian rainfall is a current from the South Atlantic which crosses Africa and precipitates most of its moisture on the Ethiopian Highlands, and is similar to the Indian south-west monsoon. The information about wind-directions over Central Africa was then scanty, but Craig's thesis was also supported by a relation between barometric pressure at St. Helena in the South Atlantic, and the volume of the flood. When pressure was high the flood tended to be above the average, but the relation has not always been maintained.

The reasons which point to the Atlantic origin of the rain are as follows. The possible sources of water are the Mediterranean, Red Sea, Indian Ocean and South Atlantic. The Mediterranean is ruled out since its rainfall is confined to a narrow coastal belt between which and Ethiopia is 1,400 miles of desert. In the case of the Red Sea, there is a small rainfall along the western coast which, however, is not nearly enough to produce a perennial stream. The streams which flow down the eastern slopes of the Ethiopian Plateau disappear in the desert long before they reach the sea.

On the whole the winds of the flood season blow across Africa from the Gulf of Guinea towards Ethiopia. The rainfall is heaviest on the west coast and over the Congo Basin, falls off over the Sudan Plains, and is again fairly heavy over the Ethiopian Plateau. South and east of the Plateau, rainfall is scanty and large areas are desert or semi-desert. Again, the rainfall on the high mountain masses of Central Africa, such as Ruwenzori and Elgon, is heavier on the western slopes.

More recently, Dr. C. E. P. Brooks and S. T. A. Mirrlees of the British Meteorological Office have studied the atmospheric

[1] " England—Abyssinia—the South Atlantic, a Meteorological Triangle."

circulation over Central Africa, with much more data at their disposal (*Geophysical Memoirs*, *No.* 55, 1932). Their general conclusion is that the heavy rainfall over Ethiopia in July (a flood month) appears to be due partly to the south-west monsoon rising over the high ground, and partly to a concentration of air. Looking at their map of air movements, most of the air which reaches the portion of Ethiopia from which the main part of the flood is derived, comes from the south-west. There is, however, a current from the Indian Ocean which impinges on the south-west current and helps to produce the concentration mentioned, though it affects country mainly to the south and east of the Nile Basin. During the recent war, research on the meteorology of Central Africa was carried out by Major Solot of the American Army. His map of the July circulation resembles that of Brooks and Mirrlees, and my conclusion after reading his paper, was that the main rain-bearing current to Ethiopia in flood-time is from the South Atlantic. There is a current from the Indian Ocean which would affect the eastern Lake Plateau and southern Ethiopia, and perturbations of this might occasionally cause Indian Ocean rain to fall in the Nile Basin. From the circulation maps for April in both papers, it appears that the early rains in Ethiopia are of Indian Ocean origin. All evidence so far produced therefore goes to confirm Mr. Craig's theory, but a more extended analysis of the data which has now been collected, particularly from the upper air, would be valuable in filling up some of the unavoidable gaps of the past.

Another line of research was started by Sir Gilbert Walker, and both Craig and myself made use of it. This was to look for connections between the Nile flood and other phenomena by the statistical method of correlation, which gives a definite measure of the closeness of any connection which may be found. The method of correlation was invented by Professor Karl Pearson, and was first introduced into Egypt by Craig (see p. 267). Unfortunately in the case of meteorological phenomena, a relationship after persisting for a number of years, may sometimes completely disappear, and in some cases has even been reversed. It is not safe, therefore, to rely on relationships, even though they are numerically sound, unless a good physical explanation for them can also be provided. The best statistical relation found up to the recent war was given in the form of an equation by Mr. E. W. Bliss in a paper on " Nile Flood and World Weather " in the *Memoirs of the Royal Meteorological Society*, Vol. I, No. 5. In this paper correlations were found between the Nile flood, the temperature at Dutch Harbour, Alaska, the temperature at Samoa in the Pacific, and the pressure at Port Darwin, Australia. The temperatures and pressures all related to times preceding the flood, and in each case a high value tended to be followed by a low flood. It is interesting that all these places are on the opposite side of the world to the Nile. Bliss's formula was published about 1927, and I have tried recently to bring his correlations up to date with what data could be obtained. The result was that in each case the closeness of the relation had become less (see later, p. 269).

5. RODA GAUGE AND THE SEARCH FOR PERIODICITIES IN NILE PHENOMENA

The Gauge and its long series of records have already been mentioned. It was built about 711 A.D. and consists of a marble pillar built up in sections, and standing in the middle of a large square well whose walls carry Arabic inscriptions of a religious nature (see Plate XXXII). The well has passages which connect it with the river, and a staircase enables the observer to go down to water level to read the scale, which is cut on the central pillar. The scale is in pics and qirats, a pic being a cubit of about 54 centimetres, and a qirat a twenty-fourth of a pic. A gauge, with a metric scale, on the river wall near the original gauge has replaced it in recent times. The old gauge and its well were completely restored recently under Kamel Ghaleb Pasha, Under-Secretary of State for Public Works, to the designs of Dr. S. Leliavsky Bey. The restoration renewed in their former style the buildings round the well which had disappeared, and surrounded the whole structure by a reinforced concrete vessel to protect it. Water cannot now enter, and the building will remain as the oldest Arab monument in Egypt. The gauge is now roofed over with a pyramidal roof as it was in former times, and Shakespeare's lines

> " They take the flow o' the Nile by certain
> scales i' the pyramid "

are said to refer to this pyramid, and not to the royal tombs

(Pyramids).[1] Kamel Ghaleb Pasha has always taken great interest in the gauge and its history, and has just published a book giving the results of his researches, which will enable the old readings to be more correctly reduced to a metric scale, having due regard to the recorded changes which have occurred to the pillar.[2]

The original records are said to have been in Coptic, and when Sir Henry Lyons first came to Cairo, about 1894, and made some investigations, he was told that Ali Pasha Mubarak, a former Minister of Public Works, had borrowed the originals to enable him to write a book, *El Khitat el Taufikia el Guedida li Misr el Kahira*, which is a sort of calendar of events, and gives many of the maximum and minimum readings of the gauge. The Pasha had died some years before, and Sir Henry made some inquiries of his heirs to see whether the records could be found, but without success. At a later date I attempted some searches, through one of my Egyptian colleagues, in the Government archives and in various libraries, and also inquired of Dr. Margoliouth, Professor of Oriental Languages at Oxford, but without any success. I doubt the recent existence of any originals, as I think that Prince Omar Toussoun, who made a considerable study of old information concerning the Nile, would have known about them, and would have probably been in a better position than anybody else to trace them. That there should have been any very old records in the archives of the Public Works Ministry is to me incredible, and I think the story was only rumour, like some which are continually arising, or was, perhaps, just an invention to explain to Sir Henry Lyons why there were no records.

Prince Omar Toussoun's studies are contained in *Mémoire sur l'Histoire du Nil*, published by the Institut d'Egypte, 1925. In this he has collected a great mass of information from ancient and modern writers about the history of the Nile, and has much to say of the many ancient Nilometers scattered up and down the river, and particularly about that at Roda, and its records. The following is taken from his memoir.

From the time of the Arab invasion, the authorities seem to

[1] In support of this Kamel Ghaleb Pasha gave me the following references. Prince Radziwill (1583) describes the Nilometer as " Pyramide mensuræ Nili." The 16th century atlas by Braun and Hogenberg called " Civitates Orbis Terrarum " shows the Nilometer on the map of Cairo as a pyramid with the inscription " Columna hic posita est ut ex ea Nili incrementum hoscatur."
[2] Memoires de l'institut d'Egypte 1951, " Le Mikyas ou Nilometre de l'Ile de Rodah."

have taken care to preserve the records of the level of the Nile. However, two curious facts appear. There is no reference to these levels in ancient writers before the fourteenth century A.D., that is 800 years after their beginning, and their beginning is twenty years before the Arab invasion of Egypt. These writers give no indication of the sources from which they compiled their lists, and we can only surmise that they were taken from documents which are now unknown. From 622 to 1470 A.D. three authors, Ibn Abik, Aboul Mahasin and Shihab el Din el Higazi, have produced lists, and these seem to have been drawn from more than one source. The Prince gives a list of flood and low-stage levels compiled from these authors, and for the succeeding period from a number of later writers. The list is much more complete for the first eight centuries than it is after, and until we come to the thirteenth, i.e. the nineteenth century A.D.

This long series of records of the Nile has always been attractive to students, and much work has been done and many papers published on the subject. The most complete series, but with gaps, extends from 622 A.D. to 1522 A.D.,[1] and gives maximum and minimum levels. Although they contain many sources of error, and naturally have not the precision of modern scientific observations, nevertheless they are probably as reliable as many of the statistics collected to-day about such less well-defined phenomena as health or social conditions. In spite of uncertainties due to repairs and renewals of the gauge, change of the river channel, and vagaries of gauge-observers, a good deal of useful information can be extracted from the records. One use to which they have been put is to estimate the chances of high or low floods; another is the search for periodicities. With this latter aim they have been analysed by several people who have found many periods varying from two to 240 years. None of the periods, however, is pronounced enough to be discoverable except by refined and painstaking analysis. A glance at the records when plotted on a fairly large scale shows that there is no period which is directly evident to the eye. It is not a case of Joseph's seven fat and seven lean years, but something more irregular. The principal feature is the occurrence of fairly long terms of years when, on the whole, floods have been high, and others when they

---

[1] Those previous to about 711 A.D. are from some other Nilometer near Roda.

have been low. Nevertheless a low flood may occur in a high series, and high floods in a low series. In recent times, for which records are well-established, 1869–98 was a period in which floods were high, while 1899–1942 was a period of low floods. When Aswan gauge reaches 93·30 a flood is considered dangerous, but watchers are called out, and the organization for flood protection put in force before this level is reached. At the

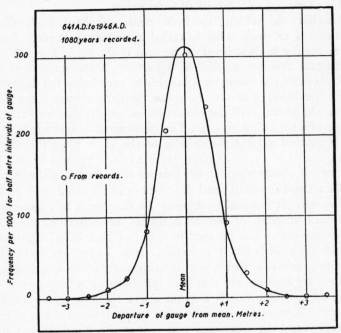

FIG. 18. Roda gauge. Frequency curve: maximum readings.

present time floods which pass 93·0 at Aswan would be considered high.

In the period 1869–98, out of thirty floods twenty-two passed 93·00, while sixteen of these passed 93·30. In the following period of forty-four years ten floods passed 93·00, and only two passed 93·30. In the first period the highest and lowest floods occurred in successive years, with a difference of 2¾ metres (9 feet) between their peaks.

The periodicities which have been found all have small amplitudes of the order 10 cm. The most pronounced has an amplitude of 17 cm. The difference between a high flood and a low flood, if they were regulated by this periodicity alone, would be $\frac{1}{3}$ of a metre, or about 1 foot. This may be contrasted with the difference of 9 feet between successive floods already mentioned.

It is clear from the above discussion that any periodic variation in Nile floods is negligible compared with the irregular changes, and is of no use as a means of forecasting.

Another use which has been made of these Roda Gauge readings is to draw what is called a frequency curve. Such a curve for the highest level of the year is shown in Fig. 18. The horizontal axis has a scale of departure of the maximum level at Roda from the mean, the plus side of zero being for departures when the flood is above the mean, and the negative for floods below the mean. All the observations are divided into sets, the range of a set being 50 cm. The number of observations in the set is plotted against the middle of the set. Thus the sets are — 25 cm. to + 25, + 25 to + 75, — 25 to — 75, and so on. The number of observations in the first set is plotted at 0, the number in the second at 50 cm., and the number in the third at — 50 cm., and so on. It is usual to express the frequency as numbers per thousand instead of actual numbers of observations. This frequency curve can be used to find out how often a particular height of flood is likely to occur. It is a very interesting type of curve, and one which occurs quite commonly as a frequency curve. Its features are that it is symmetrical, which means that there are as many floods a metre above the average as there are a metre below, and so on; the most frequent flood is one near the average; and the frequency gets less as the flood departs more and more from the average. This means that very high or very low floods are rare, which of course is a matter of common knowledge. This symmetrical form of curve, usually known as the normal, or Gaussian frequency curve, occurs if one measures the height or girth of a large number of men and plots a frequency curve from the results, and in many other natural phenomena. It is a curve which also arises in the case of chance events, where it is an equal chance whether the event happens or fails to happen. The curve was found as a result of mathematical analysis by Demoivre, and later by Gauss, who developed it, and whose name is generally attached to it. There is sometimes a belief on the part of practical people that this form of curve, which is the basis of what is known as the method of least squares, is a mathematical law to which nature must conform. The truth is that it is a formula which describes fairly accurately the frequency distribution of many natural events, though it does not describe the frequency of all natural events. As an example the frequency curve of peoples' ages, sometimes called a mortality curve, is a different type altogether.

6. SUNSPOTS AND THE NILE

There is a widespread, and as I shall show, unfounded, belief in the connection between the water of the Nile and sunspots. The theory began with a paper by Dr. C. E. P. Brooks, published in 1923 on " Variations in the Levels of the Central African Lakes," [1] in which he pointed out a connection between the levels of Lakes Victoria and Albert and the frequency of sunspots. In 1928 Sir Richard Gregory supported Brooks' conclusion,[2] and gave a diagram of sunspot numbers and Lake Victoria levels, which is reproduced in Sir James Jeans' book *Through Space and Time*.[3]

More recently the American journal *Sky and Telescope* had an article on sunspots [4] in which it is stated, " Thus while a tropical river such as the Nile shows a maximum height near sunspot maxima, the reverse has been found for rivers in temperate regions such as the Parana River in the Argentine area." This example is given with a warning against hasty generalizations about solar-terrestrial relationships. In none of these is any fresh evidence added to that given by Dr. Brooks. In *The Nile Basin*, Vol. V [5] Phillips and I pointed out that there were reasons for thinking that the apparent connection was only a coincidence. Sir Gilbert Walker [6] also raised some objections to the evidence

[1] Brooks, C. E. P. Meteorological Office, London. *Geophysical Memoirs*, No. 20, 1923.
[2] Gregory, Sir R. " Weather Recurrences and Weather Cycles." *Quart. Jour. Roy. Met. Soc.* April, 1930.
[3] Jeans, Sir J. Cambridge University Press, 1934. Reprinted 1944.
[4] Bowerman, W. G. *Sunspots in Review. Sky and Telescope*, Sept. 1944, published at Harvard College Observatory.
[5] Hurst and Phillips, *The Nile Basin*, Vol. V. Government Press, Cairo, 1938.
[6] Walker, Sir G. " Variations of Level in Lakes: Their Relations With Each Other and With Sunspot Numbers." *Quart. Jour. Roy. Met. Soc.* July, 1936.

of control of the lake by sunspots. In view of the interest shown in the matter it seems advisable to give here the reasons for thinking that the connection is accidental.

Fig. 19 shows the annual mean lake levels and sunspot numbers for the period 1896–1950. A sunspot number corresponds

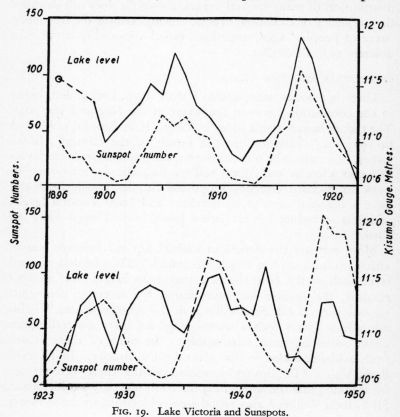

FIG. 19. Lake Victoria and Sunspots.

approximately to the area covered by spots, and a sunspot number of 100 corresponds roughly to a spot area of 1/100 of the visible disc of the sun. The upper half of the figure covers the period 1896 to 1922, which was that available when Brooks wrote his paper. From this it will be seen that the lake level and sunspot numbers move up and down together, and the maxima and minima of both occur at the same times at intervals of about eleven years. Taking the second half of the diagram, maxima and minima on the lake occur twice as often as sunspot maxima and minima, thus high lake levels occurred both with high and low sunspot numbers. Hence in the second set of years there was clearly no relation between lake levels and sunspot numbers, and the supposed connection of the first period does not exist in the second. The inference is that the supposed connection is accidental.

I shall now examine the question in more detail and, to do this, return to the balance sheet idea based on the fundamental hydrological conception, that water cannot either disappear altogether or appear from nowhere. The sources of supply of a lake are its tributaries and the rainfall on its surface. The tributaries are supplied by the rainfall on the basin, so that the whole source of supply is rain. The sources of loss are evaporation and the discharge out of the lake. There is a further possibility that some of the water may soak away through the bottom of the lake, but this can be ignored. When there is a heavy rainfall the lake rises, and when there is no rain the tributaries decline, and evaporation and outflow make the lake fall. If the lake is small, like those in the Highlands of Scotland, a day or two of rain makes it rise, and as soon as the rain ceases it falls again. In the case of a great lake like Victoria, rapid rises and falls do not take place. The lake will rise slowly as the result of the rainy season and fall again in the dry season, but several seasons of rain above the average are required before it builds up to a maximum. The level of the lake is determined not only by what has happened in the preceding rains, but also by what has happened in several preceding seasons. The effect on the lake in a particular year, however, will be due to rainfall on the lake, plus inflow from tributaries, minus evaporation from the surface and outflow through the exit during the year. This effect will be added to the condition of the lake at the beginning of the year. If the gains are greater than the losses the lake will rise, and the extent of the rise will be the difference, gains minus losses, spread over the lake surface. All this is simple arithmetic and quite obvious. The sunspots, therefore, can only act on the lake by affecting rainfall or evaporation. There are no other factors. Therefore, to find whether sunspots have any effect we must consider, not the comparison with lake levels, but the comparison with rises and falls of the lake, and this is quite a different matter. To make

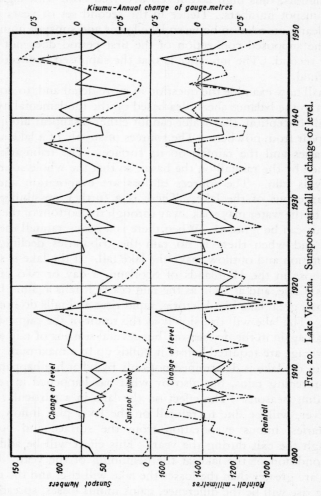

FIG. 20. Lake Victoria. Sunspots, rainfall and change of level.

this comparison we tabulate the average sunspot number for a year with the change of lake level during the year, counting rises as positive and falls as negative. This comparison is shown in

266

the upper half of Fig. 20, where the dotted line represents sunspot numbers and the full line, not the lake level, but the amount by which it rises or falls in the year. Rises and falls are measured from the zero line. For example, in 1917 the lake rose 55 cm., and in 1918 fell 68 cm. When we examine Fig. 20 we see that there is no relationship whatever between sunspot numbers and rise or fall of the lake. There is no relation either between the sunspot number and the rainfall of the year, even in the first term 1890–1922. There is, however, a close relationship, as our hydrological explanation predicts, between rainfall and change of lake level, and this is also shown in the lower part of Fig. 20. In the first few years of this century the rainfall stations were too few to give a fair representation of the rainfall.

The closeness of a relation is measured statistically by the coefficient of correlation. This is a formidable name, but it is easy to understand and to calculate by ordinary arithmetic. When there is a perfect relation between corresponding values of two variable quantities the coefficient of correlation is 1·0. This would be the case if a Centigrade and a Fahrenheit thermometer were placed in a jug of hot water and simultaneous observations of both were made at intervals as the liquid cooled. When there is no relation between corresponding values of two variable quantities the coefficient approximates to 0. This would be the case if there were two bags of coins, let us say those taken at two different railway ticket offices, and a coin was drawn from each bag, the dates of these being written down, then a second pair of coins, and so on up to say, thirty or forty. There would be no significant relation between the two sets of dates, and the coefficient would approximate to zero. If one had a bag containing 50 coins and took out one coin leaving 49; two leaving 48, and so on, there would be a perfect correspondence between the two sets of numbers 1, 2, 3, etc.; 49, 48, 47, etc.; but this time one set would increase while the other decreased, and the coefficient would be — 1·0.

Between no relation and a perfect relation there are all degrees with coefficients ranging from 0 to + 1, or 0 to — 1. As an example, fathers and sons tend to have similar heights, and a coefficient of 0·5 has been found from the measurement of 1,078 cases. If the heights of twin brothers of the type known as identical twins were considered, the coefficient would be much closer to 1·0.

The significance to be attached to a correlation coefficient increases with the size of the coefficient, and also with the number of observations on which it depends. Thus, with 25 pairs of observations of two phenomena a coefficient less than 0·35 would not be worth considering as evidence of a connection between the two phenomena. Similarly, with 50 pairs of observations coefficients less than 0·25 would have no significance. This explanation will enable the following table to be appreciated. In this table are given the coefficients of correlation which have been calculated from the annual mean values of lake levels and the phenomena which may influence them. These coefficients are the statisticians' method of summarising the evidence contained in Figs. 19 and 20.

Lake Victoria Levels and Sunspot Numbers

Phenomena—annual means	Coefficients of correlation		
	1896–1922	1923–1950	1896–1950
Lake levels and sunspots . . .	0·83	0·23	0·38
Change of lake level during the year and sunspots	0·12		0·10
Rainfall and sunspots . . .	0·10	− 0·06	− 0·05
Rainfall and change of lake level (1902–49)	0·53	0·87	0·69

The table shows that the coefficient of correlation between sunspots and lake levels, was large in the first period and insignificant in the second. There was never any significant correlation between sunspots and change of lake level, or sunspots and rainfall. The correlation between rainfall and change of lake level was fairly large in both periods.

The only factors affecting lake level which we have not considered are the discharge out of the lake and the evaporation. There is a definite relation between discharge and lake level, since the discharge increases with increase of lake level. Unfortunately we have not continuous records of evaporation near Lake Victoria, but if we had, it is clear that the connection should be with change of lake level and not with the actual levels. The nearest we can get to the desired comparison is to use the data for sunspots and evaporation at Mongalla, the nearest station for which a long series of observations of evaporation exists. The correlation from a period of years is practically zero. Apropos of correlation, it may be remarked that correlations are occasionally found when the connections are due to chance, and that these disappear as more records are accumulated. The case of Lake Victoria levels and sunspots appears to come in this category.

In one of the references quoted above, Brooks' statement about the Equatorial Lakes has been transferred to the Nile as a whole. I have, therefore, correlated, with sunspots, the annual discharge of the Nile at Aswan since 1870, and this gives a coefficient of 0·02. That is to say that there is no connection whatever between the discharge of the main stream of the Nile and sunspots.

In view of all this, the inevitable conclusions must be that there is no evidence of a connection between the levels of Lakes Victoria and Albert [1] and sunspots, nor of the quantity of water flowing in the Nile and sunspots. Neither have I come across any phenomenon connected with the Nile in which a relationship with sunspots has been established.

7. FORECASTING THE RIVER

Forecasts of the flood depending on the general circulation of the atmosphere, and the relations found by Bliss have already been mentioned (see p. 258).

Recent computations show that Bliss's coefficients of correlation between the volume of the flood and temperatures in Alaska and Samoa, and the pressure at Port Darwin, have decreased from an average of $-0·55$ to $-0·40$. The greatest decrease was for Dutch Harbour, but this may be partly due to change of the place of observation.

The original formula of Bliss accounted for about half of the variation of the flood, and this is now reduced; the rest is due to causes outside those included in the formula. This is, within our present experience, about as much as this type of research

[1] The largest source of supply of Lake Albert is from Lake Victoria, so its levels follow those of Lake Victoria. See p. 247.

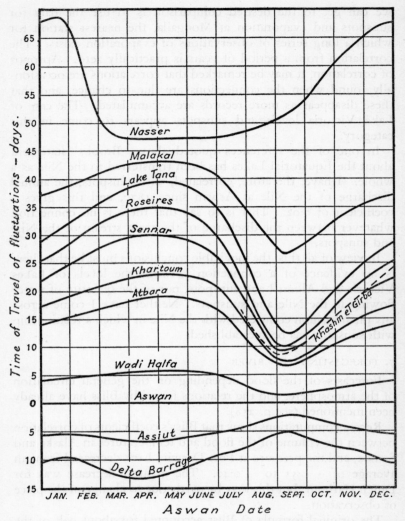

FIG. 21. Normal time of travel of fluctuations along the Nile between various stations and Aswan.

can do. If the flood could be traced to two or three definite causes which could be measured, a fairly exact formula could be deduced. In actuality we have not, however, so far found these definite causes, but only indications or symptoms of them, and which leave a lot still to be discovered. Until we have a clear-cut physical explanation we cannot hope to make a long-range forecast exact enough to be of practical use. It is still possible that the intensive study of the upper air over Africa, may lead us to an understanding of the mechanism which produces the flood, and so enable forecasts of value to be made some time in advance. Egypt should, therefore, continue to support the efforts of the East African Meteorological Service, and encourage any attempts to extend meteorological observations in Ethiopia.

Periodicity has also been mentioned as a possible means of forecasting the flood, but the analysis devoted to the long series of records of Roda Gauge shows that periodic effects are small and completely masked by irregular fluctuations, so that they are useless for the purpose.

Two types of forecast have been successful and are in regular use. The first may be called the railway time-table method, in which, when a well-defined rise or fall of the river is recorded at some station, the approximate time of its arrival at places lower down can be predicted. This was referred to in Chapter XV in the case of the Blue Nile, Atbara and Main Nile. It is on these rivers that the phenomenon is best defined, and has been well-studied. Fig. 15 shows that well-marked flushes or peaks can be traced all the way from Roseires to Wadi Halfa, and major features can be followed even to Cairo (see p. 238). The flushes change slightly as they travel, and from reference to the diagram of river levels we may say that minor fluctuations are gradually smoothed out. In fact the tendency is for a rise or fall of level to be reduced or flattened as it travels. On these rivers there is very little spilling or loss of water, and these are the reasons why the features are traceable for such long distances.

Fig. 21 gives the times of travel between various stations throughout the year, and shows that on the Blue Nile, Main Nile and Atbara as the river rises the time of travel shortens. For example, it is shortest in August and September when the river is in flood, and longest in April and May when it is low. The time from Roseires (Blue Nile) to Aswan, a distance of 1,540 miles, varies from ten days to thirty-five days, and the average speed from 154 to 44 miles a day. Forecasts are made by what are called " Lags and Losses." The lags are obtained from the time-table diagram, and, what are called losses from the analysis of past occurrences. They include the effect of flattening and spreading out of the flush as it travels.

A very interesting case of travel of disturbances, and the only

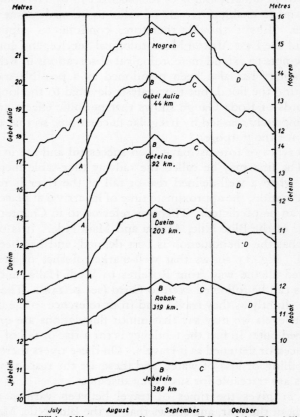

FIG. 22. White Nile gauge readings 1931. Effect of the Blue Nile.

one of its sort which has been recognized on the Nile, is the travel up the White Nile of disturbances caused by the Blue Nile. It occurs when the Blue Nile comes down in flood, and the sudden flushes already mentioned, travel down the Blue Nile to Khartoum, and on down the Main Nile. Sometimes the effect also travels up the White Nile, and in about 220 cases has been traced to Dueim or Rabak, the latter a distance of 200 miles from the junction (see Fig. 22). In a number of cases the same disturbance has been followed from Sennar down the Blue Nile to Mogren, and then up the White Nile to Rabak. Curiously so, the velocity down the Blue Nile in these cases was the same as that up the White Nile, and averaged about seventy-five miles a

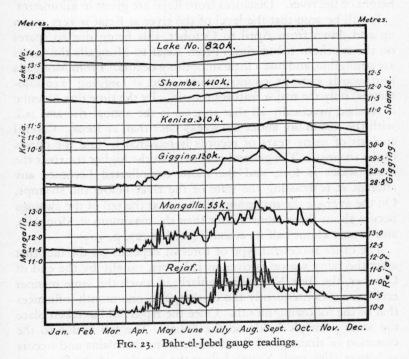

FIG. 23. Bahr-el-Jebel gauge readings.

day. The velocity increases with the height of the river in both cases.

When a river loses water by spilling over its banks the rate of travel of a rise is slowed down, and the greater the losses the more it is slowed, so that usually the rate decreases as the river rises instead of increasing. In addition, the height of the rise decreases more rapidly as it travels. These effects occur on the Bahr-el-Jebel in the swamps of the Sudd region, and on the Baro in flood, in both cases due to these rivers losing water by overflowing their banks. Fig. 23 shows the gauge readings on the Bahr-el-Jebel in 1931, an average year. They begin at Rejaf, where the river leaves the hilly country and enters the Sudan Plain. The horizontal lines are drawn at intervals of half a metre on the gauges, but the vertical distance between one curve and the next is chosen for convenience, and has nothing to do with the actual height of the river. Distances from Rejaf are given in kilometres.

It will be seen that the level of the river at Rejaf is very much up and down from April to October, this being due to spates on the southern tributaries. From Rejaf to Mongalla the losses are negligible, and just a little smoothing occurs. From Mongalla northwards swampy country begins, and at Gigging (130 kilometres) only the major features remain. By the time that Shambe is reached practically all that appears is the annual rise and fall, with the maximum about six weeks later than at Rejaf. Careful analysis of many years of records is required to find the effects of the swamps. The general result is that the higher the river the more water is lost, and the more complicated becomes any attempt at forecasting the state of the river below the swamps. On the average the maximum discharge at the tail of the swamps occurs about three months later than the maximum at Mongalla, and is only about half its amount (see Fig. 27, p. 305).

The other successful type of forecast depends on the fact that after the rainy season is over in Ethiopia, usually by the end of October, the Blue Nile falls regularly in much the same manner each year. Consequently the discharge in one month influences that of the following month. Once the rapid fall has taken place the same principle holds on the Sobat. The fall is due to the cessation of drainage of flood water from the plains and occurs at Nasser (also spelt Nasir), below the junction of the Baro and Pibor, about three weeks before it takes place at the Sobat mouth. By tabulating the discharge of one month against those of the following months for the Blue and White Niles, correlations can be found, so that in November a forecast can be made for the following months up to May, or even June. This forecast improves as time goes on, and a better one can be made in December than in November, and so on. It is extremely useful because it gives a good indication of the supply likely to be available for the summer crops, and whether the prospects are favourable for a large area under rice. The correlation forecast for June is not very good, as by this month the river is beginning to rise, and its discharge depends on the Ethiopian rains, which, in the present state of our knowledge, cannot be foreseen. As July depends almost entirely on the rising river and not on the preceding flood, nothing can be forecast until the Blue Nile and Atbara are rising. It is necessary, therefore, to keep a reserve in Aswan Reservoir for July in case the river should be late in rising, and this is not released until it is justified by the state of the upper tributaries.

Nile forecasting is not always extremely exact, nor can it be reduced entirely to formulæ. Experience and judgment, therefore, will always play a considerable part. There is no doubt, however, about its importance, for filling and emptying reservoirs, for drawing up the programme for summer irrigation, and particularly when the flood looks as if it might be a dangerous one.

8. THE SILT IN THE NILE

Most streams when in flood carry along solid matter which has been washed by the rains off the catchment area, or eroded by the stream itself from its bed. In mountainous country where the slope is steep, the stream bed may consist of boulders which are rolled along in time of spate. The headstreams of the Nile in Ethiopia and some on the Lake Plateau are of this nature. With more gentle slopes the velocity is not enough to move boulders and these are replaced by pebbles, which in turn give place to gravel as the slope decreases. These coarse materials are found in the Nile tributaries in the mountains. In the Blue Nile there are boulders in the upper reaches, and lower down pebble banks extend to north of Roseires, while on the Atbara pebbles are found for some distance north of the Setit junction. They are rounded by being rolled along the river bed and rubbed against their fellows, and this grinding produces sand, still finer particles known as silt, and, finest of all, clay. The coarser sand rolls and bounces, and some is carried in suspension near the bed; the finer silt and clay is carried in suspension at all depths.

The average motion of the water is parallel to the bed, but in addition to this there are eddies and irregular motions in all

T 2

directions, and generally known as turbulence. It is these haphazard motions which keep the particles continually moving up
and down, so that there is a cloud of them in the water decreasing
in density from the bottom upwards. The theory of this mode

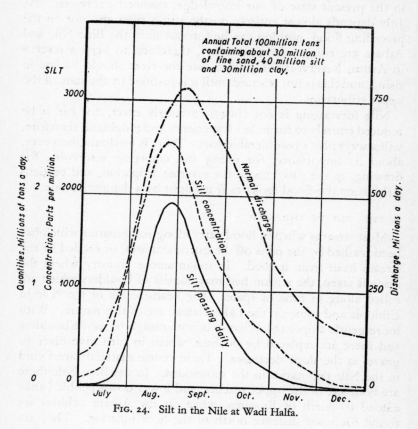

FIG. 24. Silt in the Nile at Wadi Halfa.

of suspension and the experiments by which it was established,
were described by me in *The Proceedings of the Royal Society. A,*
Vol. 124, 1929. It is an example of diffusion, and is similar
to the motion of the molecules of a gas, and leads to the same
form of gradient of density as exists in the atmosphere. This
form is such that for equal increases of height the density decreases

by the same fraction. With solid particles suspended in turbulent water, the rate of decrease of their concentration with height is related to the velocity with which they fall through still water. Coarse particles fall faster than fine ones, so the concentration of coarse particles falls off more rapidly from the bottom upwards than the concentration of fine ones. By the time the Nile gets down to Egypt and its velocity has been slowed down, the coarse sand is only found near the bed, the fine sand decreases rapidly in concentration from the bed upwards, but the very fine silt and clay particles hardly decrease at all in concentration from bed to surface. The various grades of sediment are defined by the rates at which they fall in still water, and the finest grade, the clay, is that which takes more than eight hours to fall 10 centimetres (4 inches). Sand falls 10 centimetres in less than four minutes forty-eight seconds, while silt is the class between these two. The term silt is applied to this grade of particles, but it is also applied loosely to the suspended matter in general.

The maximum content of suspended matter which has been measured in the Nile where it enters Egypt, is about 4,000 parts per million by weight, or 4 kilograms per cubic metre. The average amount carried during the period of flood, August to October, is about 1,600 parts per million. This is much less than is carried by many other rivers, for example the Colorado, the Rio Grande of Mexico, the Orange River and the Indus.

Fig. 24 shows the concentration and amount of suspended matter in the Nile.[1]

The presence of silt has an important bearing on irrigation, since, as has been mentioned, it limits the time during which storage reservoirs on the Blue or Main Niles can be filled. In the case of the Aswan Reservoir, to avoid any risk of silting up the reservoir, filling takes place after the crest of the flood has passed, and the quantity of silt in the water has decreased considerably. Owing to the increase in capacity of the reservoir due to the two heightenings of the Aswan Dam, the date at which filling commences has been advanced, and is now usually about the middle of October. At this date the normal silt-content is about 700 parts per million.

[1] This has been compiled from " The Suspended Matter in the Nile " by Y. M. Simaika. Physical Department Paper No. 40. Cairo, 1940.

There remains much work to be done on the suspended matter in the Nile, and an interesting line of research has been started by the geologists. The composition of a sediment sometimes gives a clue to its origin, and the presence of some particular mineral will prove, for example, that the silt came originally from a certain district of Ethiopia. Minerals are recognized by microscopic examination, sometimes with polarized light, or by identification of crystals. This identification of the origin of a sediment may help in building up the past history of the Nile, which is being slowly put together.

In flood-time all the canals carry silt in the water, and some of this is dropped on their beds so that periodical clearance is necessary. Clearing is carried out during the winter closure (January), and a good deal of the work is still done by hand. Research in Egypt, India and other countries has been devoted to the design of canal intakes so as to reduce the quantities of silt which enter the canals. It is a universal belief amongst cultivators that the silty flood water is of greater benefit to the crops than clear water of the low-stage. This is a complicated question on which there has been a great deal of discussion, but the effect of silt, as such, is difficult to separate from the concomitant circumstances, particularly in the Basin areas. It is a subject for agricultural chemists rather than for hydrologists.

The earth which is cleared out of canals is piled on their banks, and unless the quantity is excessive it is gradually used up by the cultivators to fill borrow pits and to raise the level of low patches of land, and so goes to the general improvement of the land. The cost of clearance to the Government is something like £E.350,000 annually.

9. THE MATTER IN SOLUTION IN THE NILE

The composition of the water of the tributaries of the Nile varies slightly from stream to stream, and also throughout the year. Thus Blue Nile water is slightly different from White Nile water, and the waters of the Central African lakes vary considerably in their content of dissolved substances. The following are the approximate quantities of solids in some Nile waters, based on the analysis of a few samples. The information is taken from various sources.

	Parts per million by weight.
Lake Victoria	80
Victoria Nile below Lake Kioga . . .	100
Lake Edward	670
Lake Albert	590
Lake Tana	170
Albert Nile below Lake Albert . . .	160
Blue Nile at Khartoum	140
White Nile at Khartoum	130
Atbara	200
Nile at Cairo	170

The following table, giving the monthly variation of the contents of Nile water in Cairo, was supplied by Dr. W. T. H. Williamson from the results of analyses by the Chemical Section of the Ministry of Agriculture, to whom, and to Dr. D. S. Gracie, I am indebted for interesting talks and valuable information.

The Nile does not contain a great amount of matter in solution, in fact about half that in the Thames, but more than in many other British rivers. Its content is greatest from April to July, but falls off in August as soon as the river begins to rise in flood, and reaches a minimum in October. The variation is accounted for by the difference in salt-content of the White and Blue Niles, and the varying proportions of their contributions to the main Nile. Thus, when the proportion of White Nile water is high, from April to July, the salt-content is at its maximum, while when the greater proportion comes from the Blue Nile it is at its minimum. The principal constituents are bicarbonates of calcium and magnesium, and the hardness of the water is measured by the quantity of these substances present. It varies from moderately soft to slightly hard. Sodium salts are also important, and dissolved salts and their influence on the land and agriculture have been mentioned several times in the book. It may be stated that according to an American classification of waters with regard to their salinity and fitness for irrigation, there is no important tributary of the Nile whose water is not excellent.

ANALYSIS OF NILE WATER AT CAIRO

Mean of Bi-monthly Samples for the Years 1933–36

(Results are expressed in parts per millions.)

	January	February	March	April	May	June	July	August	September	October	November	December	Year
Total soluble solids dried at 120° C.	151	160	174	200	204	194	212	174	137	130	135	138	167
Calcium (Ca)	22	23	25	26	26	24	23	22	22	20	21	20	23
Magnesium (Mg)	8	8	9	11	10	10	10	9	8	8	7	8	9
Sodium (Na)	16	17	21	26	28	31	37	21	8	8	10	12	20
Carbonate (CO$_3$)	3	1	3	4	6	7	7	4	3	2	2	2	4
Bicarbonate (HCO$_3$)	116	121	132	143	146	149	168	135	102	101	105	108	127
Chloride (Cl)	10	10	15	20	22	17	17	10	3	3	4	7	12
Sulphate (SO$_4$)	9	9	12	12	11	9	10	11	7	8	6	10	10
Silica (SiO$_2$)	26	22	22	24	19	17	13	24	24	22	21	21	21

Chapter Sixteen

GENERAL CONSIDERATIONS RELATING TO THE MAJOR NILE PROJECTS

1. SUMMARY OF PROPOSALS

THIS and the following chapter have been the most difficult to write, and will probably be the most difficult to understand. However, the magnitude and complexity of the projects for the full development of the Nile justify an attempt to give some account of the principles underlying them, and of the hydrological problems which had to be solved, apart from problems of design and construction, and which are, from the utilitarian point of view, the reason for the previous studies and a justification for the money spent upon them. But to those who have spent their lives in the study of the Nile there is a satisfaction in the solution of the many problems which have presented themselves, apart from the practical value of the solutions. This artistic satisfaction is some recompense, even if the practical applications of their labours are never fully developed. The following short summary with the aid of the diagram in Fig. 25 will make the succeeding description and theory easier to follow.

The Nile is a geographical unit, and the projects for its full development must also form a unity, the parts of which work together. The basic idea of the scheme, an account of which follows, is over-year storage, or as we have called it " Century Storage," and the following are its component parts. A large reservoir in Lake Victoria, controlled by a dam at the Owen Falls, will form the main reservoir for Century Storage, and will also provide hydro-electric power for use in Uganda. By means of this reservoir water will be stored in good years to supplement the supply of bad ones.

An auxiliary of this reservoir will be a regulating barrage downstream of Lake Kioga. By keeping the lake partially full, an increase of the discharge from Lake Victoria can be passed on without having first to raise the level of Lake Kioga, thus avoiding a delay of two or three months. A reservoir in Lake

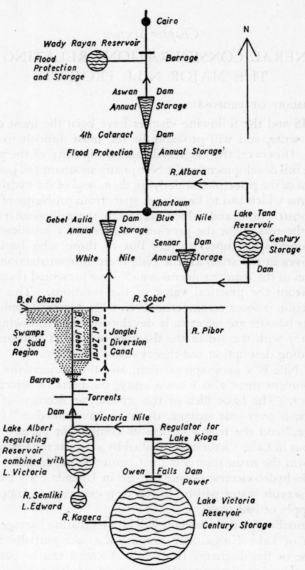

FIG. 25. Diagram of major Nile projects.

Albert is required to control water from the Semliki River, and also the large quantity which in times of unusually heavy rain comes from the tributaries of Lake Kioga. The Lake Albert Dam will be the regulator which controls the amount of water sent down from the Lake Plateau to the Sudan and Egypt.

The Jonglei Diversion Canal will carry a large quantity of water which would otherwise flow in the Bahr-el-Jebel and spill into the swamps of the Sudd region, where it would disappear by evaporation and transpiration by plants. Thus the regulated water from Lake Albert will be able to pass the swamps with only a normal loss instead of the 50 per cent., as at present.

The Gebel Aulia Reservoir will continue to act as it does at present, and hold back water mainly from the Sobat flood for use in Egypt at the low time of the year.

A dam at the outlet of Lake Tana, if the lake is used to its full capacity, can provide water for increase of cultivation in the Sudan, a measure of Century Storage, and a reserve in case of an emergency in Egypt, such as was caused by the record low flood of 1913.

The Fourth Cataract Dam will provide a reservoir for flood protection with, in addition, some stored water from all floods, except the low ones, for use in the following low-stage. It will act as a regulator on the water coming down to Egypt.

A new project, at present being studied, for the Wady Rayan, is to form a flood protection reservoir and to store some additional water from the flood.

The Aswan Power Scheme is at present under construction to provide hydro-electric power. Any of the dams previously mentioned are also possible sites for hydro-electric schemes.

2. EXISTING WORKS

The Nile in its natural state and without any control works could only support a small population. The reason for this is the great variation of the river between flood and low-stage, both in level and quantity of water. The natural discharge entering Egypt in an average year ranges from 700 to 45 millions per day, and the natural levels have a range of about 5 metres at Cairo, while in a very low year the discharge might fall to 30 mlpd. for a couple of months. The conditions of irrigation before, prior to any control of the river have already been described, and the difficulty of making full use of a very small flow deep down in the trough of the river will be realized. The result was that a great part of Egypt could have no summer crops.

The first project, the Delta Barrage, was intended to raise the level of the river at the low time of the year so that the main Delta canals could provide water for summer crops. This was followed by the Aswan Dam, the first project for storing some of the autumn surplus of clear water for use in the following summer. At the same time a barrage was built at Assiut, followed by others at Esna, Zifta and Nag Hammadi, for raising the river level to give command to other canals. The Aswan Dam was followed by dams at Sennar on the Blue Nile and at Gebel Aulia on the White Nile, all with the object of holding back water from the time of plenty for use in the low season. These we may call annual storage works. Their effect is shown by the following figures:—

Irrigated Areas in Feddans

EGYPT

	Basin	Perennial
1886	2 million	2·9 million
1946	1 ,,	5 ,,

SUDAN

1886	negligible
1946	10,000 to 100,000	1 million

The conversion of one million feddans from basin to perennial irrigation means that on this area two or three crops are produced in place of one.

Projects with a different object are those for the protection of Egypt against the disaster which might arise from a high flood. So far this object has been achieved by continued attention to the Nile banks, which rise well above land level in Middle and Lower Egypt, and more recently, by reducing the crest of the flood by retaining some of its water in the Aswan Reservoir until the critical time was past. A project of a recent date is the Aswan Power Scheme, which is now under construction, and which will make use of the head of water provided by the dam to drive turbines.

There are two factors which put a limit to the extension of annual storage. The first is that the waters of the Blue Nile, Atbara, and Main Nile, carry, in flood time, silt, which tends to deposit in a reservoir when the velocity is checked by the filling. The result of storing flood water in other parts of the world has been the gradual filling of the reservoirs with sediment. To avoid this, the Aswan Reservoir filling is delayed until the river falls to a certain level on Aswan Gauge, which usually occurs in October, by which time, as will be seen from Fig. 24, the silt-content of the water has fallen considerably and is decreasing. The level in the Sennar Reservoir is raised from the middle of July to command the Gezira Canal, and the filling of the reservoir is completed in November, when there is little silt in the water. The Sennar Reservoir has only a small volume, and although there are deposits of silt during the flood they are mostly washed away by the final emptying of the reservoir from the canal command level to the natural level of the Blue Nile. The White Nile carries a negligible quantity of silt, and as I have said, is ponded up naturally by the rise of the Blue Nile. This ponding is increased by closing sluices in the Gebel Aulia Dam until full level is reached in October. After which full level is maintained by regulation of the sluices, and the natural fall of the White Nile is prevented, so that much of the water which would have flowed down to Egypt is retained in the reservoir until it is required. This is usually in February, and the water stored in Gebel Aulia is used by Egypt before that at Aswan, in order to reduce the heavy losses caused by evaporation over the large surface of the Gebel Aulia Reservoir. It is usually empty by early in May. The Aswan Reservoir water is then drawn upon, and this lasts until towards the end of July, when the rising river meets the requirements of the crops, and the surplus water is diverted down the two branches through the delta to the sea. The difficulties of regulation of the river during the critical time in June and July have already been mentioned.

The second factor which limits annual storage is the occurrence of very low years. These cannot be predicted in advance, and it is only in September that it would be known that a flood was likely to be a low one, and that it would, therefore, be advisable to begin to fill Main Nile Reservoirs. This means that even with the present day cultivation there will be years when it is not possible to fill both Aswan and Gebel Aulia Reservoirs, thus increasing the shortage in the following summer. If further annual storage is provided it will be possible to reclaim new land and extend cultivation in Egypt in many years, but it will be at the expense of increased losses in the very low years. It should be noted that there have been two years in the last fifty whose recurrence, even under present conditions, would cause serious loss to Egypt, and the disaster would be worse with an expanded area of cultivation (see Fig. 26, p. 290). The rapidly increasing population both in Egypt and the Sudan, however, makes the increase of the cultivated area imperative. Expansion, however, is not a final remedy, since population increase at the present rate will outrun any possible extension of cultivation. The dilemma of increasing the cultivated area on the basis of annual storage can be met by creating over-year storage, so that the high years can help the low ones, but the menace of a rapidly increasing population can only be met by birth control.

3. BASES FOR EXTENSION OF IRRIGATION. SCHEMES FOR CONSERVATION AND CONTROL

At the end of the recent war the Minister of Public Works[1] asked my department to make an examination of the possible development of cultivation in Egypt, the water needed for such development, and the conservation projects necessary to store the water. My colleagues and I therefore made an investigation to see what could be done, and the results were published in Vol. VII of *The Nile Basin* (Hurst, Black and Simaika, Cairo Government Press). For this we made a review of the many projects which had been proposed at different times,[2] and introduced some new ideas. For the first time the full development of Egypt was considered in detail, and it was made clear that it was not possible to proceed by small stages leaving the ultimate development for future consideration. The new ideas, particularly that of " Century Storage," showed that on some important points a decision had to be made without delay. The main

[1] Abd el Qawi Ahmed Pasha.
[2] An account of the ideas about project as they were in 1938 can be found in "The Training of the Upper Nile." F. Newhouse. Pitman. London. 1939.

projects were seen to be closely connected parts of a whole, but the connection is a complicated one. The idea of over-year storage was not new, but how much storage capacity was required, or how it would be operated, was not known. The general problem of what storage was needed to enable the variations in the annual flow of the river to be evened out, so as to produce a steady amount year by year, had interested me for a number of years. In Vol. V of *The Nile Basin* I was able to give the beginnings of a solution which was elaborated in Vol. VII and later published elsewhere.[1] Some account of this will be given later.

Another new suggestion was the possibility of using Nile water to irrigate portions of the desert fringes in Egypt, provided that cheap power would be available. Previous estimates had put the cultivable land of Egypt at 7·1 million feddans. Our estimate based on reasonable possibilities of pumping on to the desert and of reclamation of land in the delta, added 400,000 feddans to this figure. Others since, on what grounds I do not know, have added another $2\frac{1}{2}$ million feddans, to make a total cultivable area of 10 millions. Our conservative estimate of $7\frac{1}{2}$ million feddans may after careful investigation be extended a little, but 10 million feddans of perennial irrigation, together with development of the Sudan, would take more water than any scheme of projects could get out of the river. Such optimistic estimates do not take account of the variability of the river flow and the limitations on over-year storage, or whether this area of cultivable land exists where it is accessible to water.

The scheme of projects which we proposed in Vol. VII was examined by a committee of three former ministers of Public Works, who recommended its adoption. It was finally approved by the Council of Ministers in 1949, and became the policy of the Egyptian Government.

Egypt and the Sudan are interested in irrigation from the Nile, and development in the Sudan, and the construction of the Gebel Aulia Reservoir by Egypt have taken place under the Nile Waters Agreement of 1929 between Great Britain and Egypt. All the countries in the basin, however, are affected to

[1] Hurst. *Long-term Storage Capacity of Reservoirs.* Transactions of the American Society of Civil Engineers, 1951, Vol. 116, p. 770.

some extent by the Nile. Uganda and Ethiopia have interests as potential users of power, and therefore in the storage reservoirs which it might be desirable to construct in their territories. Reservoirs in the Great Lakes would also affect Kenya, Tanganyika and the Belgian Congo. Besides those of irrigation and power there are also interests in navigation.

It is clear that the full development of the Nile for irrigation in Egypt and the Sudan can only be carried out by agreements between the countries of the Basin, having regard to all interests. Insofar as engineering matters are concerned the Nile is a unity, and must therefore be dealt with as a unity, in order that its waters may be used to the greatest advantage of all parties. Negotiations have been going on for some time between Egypt and Uganda, and they have agreed to build a dam at the Owen Falls just below the outlet of the Nile from Lake Victoria. This will turn Lake Victoria into a reservoir for over-year storage of irrigation water, and will provide power for industry in Uganda, and work on the project has already started.

For many years a reservoir in Lake Tana has been a suggested project for the joint benefit of Egypt and the Sudan, and there is an agreement between Egypt and the Sudan on some of the technical points. A combined delegation visited Addis Ababa and had conversations with members of the Ethiopian Government, but the Italian invasion of Ethiopia put an end to discussions. For some time past there have been talks about re-opening the question with Ethiopia, but unfortunately the clear-cut engineering aspects have become clouded by political considerations.

We now deal with the facts on which projects must be based. They are:—

1. The rate at which population is increasing.
2. The area which it is possible to cultivate.
3. The quantity of water flowing in the river, together with the possibility of increasing it by the prevention of waste in swamps, and the amount of this which can be turned on to the land.
4. The cost of utilizing water and the return to be expected.

The following are the results of censuses of the population of Egypt given in the *Annuaire Statistique*.

Year of Census	Number of people millions	Factor of increase in 10 years
1897. . .	9·71	
1907. . .	11·29	1·163
1917. . .	12·75	1·129
1927. . .	14·22	1·115
1937. . .	15·93	1·120
1947. . .	19·09	1·200

The rate of increase shown in the table decreased slightly from 1897 to 1937, and then increased considerably in the census of 1947. This phenomenal increase which covered the period of the war is hard to explain, but even if we take the lowest factor of increase, 1·115, it means that the population would double itself in sixty-one years. If we take the factor of increase per decade as 1·2 the population would be doubled in thirty-eight years. The factors which influence population are birth-rate and death-rate. Amongst recorded birth-rates Egypt has nearly the highest, and its death-rate is also high, largely due to the heavy death-rate among children. It is probable that the attention given to public health will cause the death-rate, particularly that among children, to decrease in the immediate future, so that unless something happens to decrease the birth-rate the rate of increase will become still larger.

Egypt is mainly an agricultural country, and in 1946 the value of its principal exports was:—

Agricultural products . . £E.58 million[1]
Mineral products . . . £E.2½ ,,
Animal products . . . £E.1 ,,

Excluding from these figures of exports rice and minerals, the amount of goods which were manufactured or processed in some way in the country was 3½ million Egyptian pounds.

To meet as far as may be the needs of this rapidly increasing population the possibilities are: increase of the cultivated area, 5·7 million feddans in 1946, to 7·5 million: improvement of methods of cultivation and quality of the crops: the economy of water so that, if suitable land and power for pumping exist, the

[1] One Egyptian pound = £1 0s. 6d.

area can be extended: and finally, the development of industry as far as may be possible.

The area cultivated by irrigation in the Sudan is at present about a million feddans, and the population there is also increas-

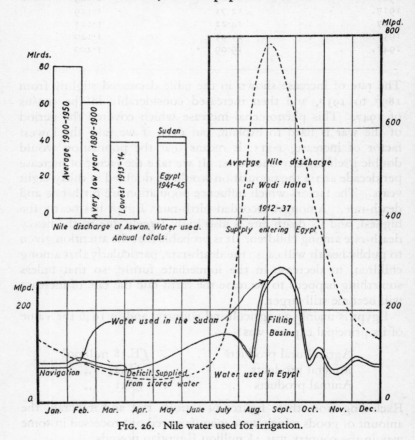

FIG. 26. Nile water used for irrigation.

ing. It is not possible to say what area can ultimately be cultivated and in our estimates we tentatively assumed two million feddans. At the present time the Sudan Government is making a survey to find how much land lies at levels suitable for irrigation, and what proportion of this is of good enough quality to be worth the cost of the necessary irrigation works. Fortunately, from some distance south of Khartoum the whole of the Nile Basin can produce rain-crops.

A rainfall of 400 millimetres (16 inches) is found about 160 miles south of Khartoum, but the greater part of it falls in about four months. The line indicating 400 millimetres of rain runs approximately along the railway from Sennar to Kosti, and practically all irrigation is north of this. The rainfall and its duration increases as one goes south, and on the Lake Plateau it is fairly well distributed through the year. The irrigation season in the Sudan is from July to April, and so far the bulk of its water is taken while there is an excess in the river, but increasing demands both of Egypt and the Sudan are shortening the time of excess and lessening its amount.

The basis of the estimate of the water needed for irrigation in Egypt in the future, is the amount which has been used in the recent past. The estimates used in Vol. VII of *The Nile Basin* were obtained by a careful analysis of the quantities used just before the last war, which were increased to cover an area of 7·1 million feddans. The quantities used in the years 1941–45 are plotted in Fig. 26 in order to show how the water is distributed throughout the year, and how the total compares with the average natural supply, and shown as discharge entering Egypt at Wadi Halfa. Following the year through, irrigation begins in February after the winter closure of the canals for silt clearance and repairs to locks and regulators. During the closure, however, water is needed for navigation in the river. At an early date in February the natural river supply in the river at Aswan usually falls below the requirements of the cultivation, and is supplemented first by water stored in the Gebel Aulia Reservoir, and later by that in the Aswan Reservoir. In the latter half of July the river supply is again adequate, though when the river is late in rising availability may be delayed until August. The requirements increase in May and June owing to the planting of rice and, later, the irrigation of fallow land. The large hump in September on the curve of water used, is due to the filling of the basins from which there is some return later. Demand then falls off until just before the closure. During the closure no water is taken for crops, consequently it is usual to give an extra heavy watering just previously. The water used by the Sudan is shown

U 2

as a thin band on the diagram above that used by Egypt, and includes the amounts used in the Gezira, in the basins of the Northern Sudan, and those taken from the river by pumps.

The inset diagram shows the total used for irrigation in Egypt and the Sudan, including the amount necessary to maintain navigation in the Nile during closure. It also shows the average natural river supply and the supply in the two lowest years.

It will be seen that the total water at present used, is about half the supply in an average year, and about equal to that in the lowest. It must not be supposed, however, that, even in the lowest year, the whole supply is available for irrigation. The diagram does not give the whole picture, which is complicated by the fact that shortage is not evenly spread through the year, but occurs, as the diagram shows, from February to July. In all, except the lowest years at present recorded, deficits during the low stage can be met from the water in the Gebel Aulia and Aswan Reservoirs, stored during and after the preceding flood. In the very low years, however, these reservoirs cannot be completely filled. This is partly due to the inability to forecast a low flood until it has reached the Sudan boundary, and partly to the restrictions against filling Aswan with flood water containing a lot of silt. To store muddy water occasionally will not do much harm, but it cannot be done every year, and the difficulty is to recognize the low year early enough so that storage can begin in time to fill Aswan as well as Gebel Aulia. With the present annual storage reservoirs, the greatest skill in forecasting, regulating and distributing the water in very low years could not avoid heavy losses to Egypt. The Sudan, too, would suffer losses, but not to the same extent. The ill-effects of such years will be increased by the expansion of cultivation based only on annual storage reservoirs, and it cannot be said too often that, without over-year storage, there will sooner or later be a disaster. The provision of such storage is therefore urgent.

Caution, for the following reasons, is necessary with regard to Fig. 26. It must not be taken to mean that cultivation can be expanded to nearly twice its present area. Whatever measures of conservation are undertaken, it can never be the case that the whole of Nile water can be used. Storage implies unavoidable losses, though some of these may be neutralized by reducing the areas of swamp on the Upper White Nile. However, if the whole flow of the Nile could be equalized, and this would be a colossal, and probably impossible operation, we should still not be able to make use of all the Nile water. One reason is that a good proportion of this storage would have to be on the Main Nile, where evaporation losses would be very considerable. Another is that, even with this very large over-year storage, one cannot eliminate entirely the possibility of a dangerous flood arriving when the reservoirs are full, or nearly so. As normally no water would flow down the river branches to the sea, cultivation would take place in them, and wind-blown dust would also accumulate. Thus their channels would gradually diminish in section, and their banks deteriorate. There would therefore be grave danger, if they ever had to be used to carry off a great flood, that they would be unable to carry the water; this would mean flooding and disaster for Lower Egypt. To avoid this it would be necessary, as a precaution in every year, to escape a sufficient quantity of water to maintain the river branches as efficient channels. The minimum amount required to do this has never been investigated.

In Vol. VII of *The Nile Basin* we first put forward the idea that it might be possible, ultimately, to cultivate some of the lower desert slopes. The conditions necessary for this are the existence of cheap power for pumping, and a suitable soil on which to put the water. Our suggestion has led to very exaggerated ideas and statements of the area which can be cultivated with Nile water. The preceding remarks have therefore been made as a warning against over-optimism as to the amount of desert which it is possible or practicable to cultivate.

In our estimates of water requirements given in *The Nile Basin*, Vol. VII we assumed an area of 7·1 million feddans in Egypt, and ignored a possible further 400,000 feddans which we thought might be cultivable, on the ground that as this was only an extra 5 per cent. its needs might be met by improvements in water distribution. Our estimates were:—

August 1st to January 31st. Natural supply sufficient.
Requirements at Aswan. . . . . . 30 milliards
February 1st to July 31st. Natural supply insufficient.
Requirements at Aswan. . . . . . 28 ,,
Total 58

These water requirements are not optimum requirements for the crops, but are based on the average quantities which, in a number of recent years, have produced crops. It has been found by experience that crops have a considerable tolerance with respect to amount of water, and that a variation of 10 or 15 per cent. on either side of the optimum makes little difference to the yield of cotton, the principal summer crop; the same applies to other crops.

The estimate of two million feddans cultivable in the Sudan, made in 1945, now seems likely to be exceeded. It was based on the idea that only the more valuable land would be worth irrigating. In *Nile Control* (1920) it was suggested that three million feddans in the Gezira were irrigable. However, I adopt our previous estimate, which has been used since 1932, until definite figures are available for a better one. On this basis the Sudan water requirements reckoned at Aswan are:—

Sudan. Area 2,000,000 feddans.

July to December	3·7 milliards
January to July (Sudan dates)	2·3 ,,
	6·0 ,,

This division of the year in the Sudan corresponds approximately to the division of the year taken for Egypt's requirements, owing to the fact that water takes about a month to travel from Sennar to Aswan. Roughly, the totals for Egypt and the Sudan are, as measured at Aswan,

August to December	34 milliards
January to July (time of shortage)	30 ,,
Total	64 ,,

We have now to see what the river can do to provide these requirements. Here we meet a notable fact, which is not generally appreciated. It is the variability of the average discharge of the river. This is particularly striking over the period 1870 onwards, for which we can claim to have reasonable estimates of the Nile discharge. During the period 1870 to 1899 the average annual quantity of water passing Aswan was 109 milliards, while in the succeeding period, 1900 to 1949, the quantity was

83 milliards. There is a difference of 24 per cent. between these two means, but even the lower would easily meet requirements, if it occurred regularly every year. About half the years, however, are below the mean, and the remedy is to increase the supply of these low years. This can only be done by storage from the good years. A point may here be emphasized. In the Southern Sudan, as I have said in previous chapters, a good deal of water is lost by evaporation and transpiration from swamps. In the past much attention has been devoted to schemes for preventing some of these losses, and so increasing the natural river supply. These losses are from the White Nile, which is the main source of the low-stage supply. They are greatest in high years and small in low years, so that economies help the low years very little. Hence schemes for preventing losses must be backed up by over-year storage reservoirs in order that economies can be used in the low years, when they are most needed. It is necessary therefore, to consider the very complicated question of over-year storage, complicated technically and politically. However, it is, in this book, fortunately the technical side only which concerns us.

4. THE THEORY OF OVER-YEAR STORAGE

This section may be skimmed by those who dislike anything mathematical; but it is nevertheless of considerable practical and theoretical interest. To put the problem of over-year storage in its simplest form, we consider the case of a river whose flow varies from year to year, and investigate the capacity of the reservoir, which will be required to equalize the flow year by year over a number of years. To fix ideas, let us suppose there were ten years whose discharges were 5, 8, 3, 7, 1, 2, 9, 5, 6, 4. The average discharge is 5, and if this were given every year the total amount passing in the ten years would be the same as the amount which actually passed. By giving 5 each year we should store in the first four years: $0 + 3 - 2 + 2 (= 3)$, and we should then draw $4 + 3$, leaving a deficit of 4, which would be wiped out the next year. In the ninth year there would be an excess of 1 and we should finish all square at the end of the period. In this case if the reservoir had a capacity of 7 and we started with 4 units of stored water, after two years we should fill the reservoir, it would be again full at the end of the fourth year and back to 4 again at the end of the period. In this case, with the figures in front of us we can calculate that we need a storage of 7. It will be seen that the storage can be found by adding up consecutively the departures from the mean to form a running total, then the difference between the highest and the lowest totals is the storage which can give the average discharge throughout the period. But this does not tell us much about the future, since the same sample is not likely to be repeated. For example, we might have the same average with the high years occurring in the first half of the period and the low ones in the second. In this case we should need a storage of 10 to meet the deficits. It might also be the case that the next ten years had an average of 4 instead of 5, or that instead of varying from 1 to 9 in individual years they might only range from 3 to 7. In both these cases the answer would be different. These numbers illustrate what does occur with natural phenomena, and at the same time show the complexity of the problem.

As an illustration of what has actually occurred, we may take the recorded discharges of the Nile at Aswan from 1871 to 1945. If we divide this into two equal periods and calculate how much storage would equalize the flow in each case, we find:—

	Average discharge mlrds.	Storage mlrds.
1871–1908	103	201
1909–1945	83	83
1871–1945	93	476

Apart from the variation of the average discharge, to which we have already drawn attention, we see that, in the first period, two and a half times as much storage would be required to equalize the flow, as in the second. Also, considering the whole period, a still bigger storage is required. It is clear that in view of the variability shown by the discharge at Aswan, and other phenomena, we must seek a wider basis on which to determine a suitable storage, and if we can find this suitable storage we must know what risk there is of its proving insufficient, and what precautions we must take as safeguards.

This problem occupied me at intervals for twelve years. There were obviously two lines of approach. One was the experimental and statistical one of collecting the discharges of a number of rivers and calculating the storage capacity required to equalize the discharge in each case. The other was a mathematical approach through the theory of probability, assuming that the variability of the discharge of a river is similar to the variability of chance events. The first method led to an enormous amount of computation, since to deal statistically with a question one must have a mass of material. For this purpose records extending over many years were required, and these are not numerous in the domain of rivers, so work was extended to rainfall statistics, which appeared to be similar in their characteristics. Then followed the inclusion of temperatures and barometric pressures. The common characteristic of all these is that they have similar frequency distributions. The idea of a frequency distribution is a simple one, with wide applications to many subjects, including biology, social science, and engineering, and has already been described in connection with Roda Gauge (p. 261). The use of temperature or any other statistics merely means that we go through the same arithmetical process as we should if they represented quantities of water, and we arrive at a figure which, in the case of water, would be the required storage capacity. That is, we are using a property common to similar sets of numbers—a usual practice of mathematicians and physicists. The longest series of river or rainfall records, excluding those of the Roda Nilometer, do not reach 200 years, and the same is true of temperatures and pressures. In order to get longer series of figures, it was necessary to make use of the work of Dr. A. E. Douglass in measuring the annual growth rings of giant trees in America,[1] and also of the measurements made by Baron de Geer, of the thickness of varves.[2] These are the annual layers of mud deposited on ancient lake beds. The tree rings extend to nearly 1,000 years, and the varves in some cases to 4,000 years. In all, seventy-five different phenomena were analysed, and 690 computations made of storage capacity. This very large amount of work, however, yielded the required result for practical application.

---

[1] *Climatic Cycles and Tree Growth.* Publication 2890, Carnegie Institution, Washington, D.C., 1928.
[2] *Geochronologia Suecica Principles.* Almqvist and Wikoells, Stockholm.

The mathematical work was undertaken because, for some purposes, river discharges can be treated statistically as if they were chance events, which they resemble in some respects. Assuming that this is the case, it is theoretically possible to find a solution, and with some difficulty a solution was found which was confirmed by experiments with chance events. However, when this solution was compared with the storage capacities calculated from observations of natural events, it was clear that the storage required in the case of river discharges, rainfall, etc. was greater than that which would fit pure chance events. This is due to the tendency, already mentioned, of natural events to group themselves in runs in which high or low values preponderate.

The theoretical solution, although it was not useful in the way expected, did show clearly the difference between natural and chance events, and emphasized that the old idea that thirty or forty years' records of rainfall or river discharges are enough for all purposes, is erroneous. A note at the end of this chapter summarizes the mathematical results of the investigations.

The points of practical interest which emerge from the many calculations are: that the storage (R) required to equalize the flow over a number of years varies a good deal from one phenomenon to another, and in the case of the same phenomenon it varies from one period to another; it increases with the length of period considered. Now R is the storage required to give a steady discharge equal to the average over a number of years. In practice it is not possible to give the average discharge indefinitely, firstly, because there is no such thing as a fixed average, and secondly, the storage required increases with the length of the period, and does not tend to reach a steady value. However, if we are content with something less than an average as a minimum quantity, we can have a factor of safety, since a small reduction from the average discharge produces a much bigger proportional reduction in the storage required to guarantee it.

The procedure in practice is to choose a reasonable length of period determined by the conditions, and in the case of Nile reservoirs we choose 100 years. R can then be calculated by using the variability of the discharge, computed from the available observations and substituting it in the average formula derived from the natural events. This is given in the note at the end of this chapter. Having obtained R it will be necessary to apply a factor of safety, as is always done in engineering matters. This is a complicated procedure, and cannot be dealt with here. It must be decided by the circumstances of each case. The main factors are the water requirements, the cost of providing the storage, and the effect of storing water on the interests of other parties. The factor of safety will probably be applied both to the storage R, and to the discharge expected as a minimum. In doing this it must be remembered that with a steady draft less than the average discharge, the reservoir will ultimately be filled, and the normal discharge will then be exceeded. Provision must be made so that this extra flow can take place without serious damage to the country below the reservoir. The theory of over-year storage given in this book is of considerable importance wherever the question of long-term storage arises. Not only does it apply to water, but also to stocks of food, clothing or raw materials. Its most obvious application is to municipal water supplies, which in some cases in England, are so inadequate that any dry summer exhausts them, to the great inconvenience of the inhabitants. On the other hand a rainfall a little above the average causes floods in some districts, when the urgent need then is to get rid of valuable water. It looks as if a national long-term water conservation policy is badly needed in England.

5. MATHEMATICAL NOTE ON OVER-YEAR STORAGE

Suppose we have a series of N quantities in order, which may be successive annual discharges of a river, annual rainfall totals, or other phenomena. We then write down the differences of these numbers from their mean, reckoning the difference positive if the quantity is greater than the mean, and negative if it is less. We add up these differences and write down their successive accumulated sums. The difference between the highest and the lowest of these accumulated sums, which is the range, we call R. In the case of a river, R is either (*a*) the maximum accumulated storage when there is never a deficit; (*b*) the maximum accumulated deficit when there is never any storage, or (*c*) their sum when there are both storage and deficit. This range R is the storage required to maintain the average discharge. In the case of chance events I have shown [1] that

$$R = 1·25 \, \sigma \, \sqrt{N}$$

σ is a measure of the variability of the original numbers, and is called the standard deviation. It is such that σ^2 is the average of the squares of the departures of the numbers from their mean. This formula was verified experimentally by tossing a set of ten coins 1,000 times, by cutting cards 1,000 times from a special pack, which I called a " probability pack," and by using a set of 1,000 random numbers made up from the published numbers of bonds drawn for redemption. In all these cases there was good agreement between theory and experiment.

In the case of natural events, as already mentioned, it was found that R increased with N faster than was the case with chance events. A formula which fitted the facts was

$$R = 0·61 \, \sigma \, N^x$$

x varied considerably in different cases, but grouping the phenomena together the mean values were:—

	x
Rainfall and river discharges and levels, 267 cases	0·72
Temperature and pressure, 115 cases . .	0·70
Annual growth of tree rings, 85 cases . .	0·81
Thickness of varves or mud layers, 204 cases.	0·72

The value of x finally adopted was 0·72, and the formula becomes

$$R = 0·61 \, \sigma \, N^{\,0·72}$$

If N is 100, the formula for chance events gives $R = 12·5 \, \sigma$, while the formula for natural events gives $R = 16·8 \, \sigma$.

[1] Hurst. *Long-term Storage Capacity of Reservoirs.* Transactions of the American Society of Civil Engineers, 1951, Vol. 116, p. 770.

Chapter Seventeen

PROPOSED PROJECTS

1. PROPOSALS FOR CENTURY STORAGE

THE most suitable sites for Century Storage are in the Great
Lakes, principally because of the large areas of Lakes Albert
and Victoria, where a small increase in their depths means a large
volume of water stored. Lake Albert has an area of 5,300 square
kilometres, and Lake Victoria 67,000 square kilometres, so a
metre increase of level in the one case means 5·3 milliard cubic
metres, equal to the amount stored in the present Aswan Reservoir, and in the case of Lake Victoria, 12½ times as much. Consequently low dams will store large quantities of water, and the
cost of storage per cubic metre will be relatively cheap. A
second point is that on the Great Lakes, evaporation and rainfall
are nearly equal, so that the increase of surface area caused by
raising the lake level does not lead to greatly increased losses.
Disadvantages, which, however, are of lesser weight, are that
the lakes are a long way from the Sudan and Egypt, and are not
in the territories of either, and, in addition, they can only control a
portion of the Nile supply.

Our original proposal in *The Nile Basin*, Vol. VII, was to
convert Lake Albert into a large storage reservoir, and to use
Lake Victoria as a supplementary regulator. The reason for this
was that we thought there would be less disturbance of local
interests by making the main reservoir in Albert rather than in
Victoria. However, when the Egyptian representatives, under
Hamed Pasha Suleiman, arrived in Uganda for discussions, we found
that a large reservoir in Lake Albert was not acceptable to Uganda
because of the increased area which would be flooded, but that
the three territories around Lake Victoria would agree to the
raising of its maximum level by 1·3 metres, or about 4 feet.
Uganda, however, was prepared to agree to the creation of a
reservoir of small capacity in Lake Albert, for use as a balancing
reservoir to assist regulation, so that water could be sent down

the White Nile as required. It was later agreed between Great Britain and Egypt that a dam be built at the Owen Falls, about a mile and a half below the exit of the Victoria Nile from Lake Victoria, to store water for the use of Egypt, and to produce power for Uganda. Sir Alexander Gibb and Partners and Messrs. Kennedy and Donkin have designed the dam and power station, and the work has already begun. Lake Victoria will thus become the largest reservoir in the world as to area, and perhaps as to volume, and will provide a usable storage of about 100 milliards of cubic metres (roughly 80 million acre feet). The dam will produce about 20 metres of head, owing to the drops of level due to the Ripon Falls, the Owen Falls, and other smaller rapids. The power station is designed for 10 units, each consisting of a Kaplan Turbine driving an alternator to produce 15,000 kilowatts, but, initially, only 6 of these are being installed.[1] The power will be used for industry in Uganda. The raising of the level of Lake Victoria will necessitate some changes in the lakeside ports, and will cause the removal of a certain number of huts and the embanking of a few cultivated areas, for which compensation will be paid.

With the main storage in Lake Victoria a subsidiary regulator below Lake Kioga will be necessary in order to avoid delays in the passage of water down the Victoria Nile. An increase of discharge out of Lake Victoria, would only be fully effective in Lake Albert after Lake Kioga had been filled to the level necessary to force the discharge through the lower part of the Victoria Nile, and this would introduce a delay of two or three months. If, however, a barrage were built across the Victoria Nile below Lake Kioga, it would be possible to store some water in the lake, so that as soon as an increase of discharge took place at the Owen Falls Dam, a similar increase could be made at the Lake Kioga Regulator, thus cutting out the necessity to fill Lake Kioga, and the delay which this would involve. The barrage would be a small work to hold up a maximum of 3 or 4 metres of water, on the same kind of design as the barrages in Egypt.

The original proposal was for a dam at Nimule on the Bahr-el-Jebel just inside the Sudan, which is the most suitable site from an engineering point of view. Its advantages are that it would control completely the torrential streams which enter the river

[1] It is hoped to complete the dam by 1953 and instal 6 generators by 1956.

between Nimule and the lake, and give some indirect control of those which enter below Nimule, while it would make navigation from the lake to Nimule easy at all times without any waste of water. The control of the torrents in high years will be important for the Sudan.

This site was not acceptable to Uganda on the ground that valuable land alongside the river, which is now cultivated, would be lost by flooding, but there was no objection to the alternative site at Mutir, which is at about one-third of the distance from the lake exit to Nimule. There are suitable rock foundations at both sites. It has been suggested by Uganda that the maximum level in Lake Albert Reservoir should not exceed 9½ metres or so above the lowest recorded level of the lake, but agreement on this point has not been reached.

The regulation of the combination of a large reservoir in Lake Victoria and a smaller one in Lake Albert, will be much more complicated than that of a single large one in Lake Albert. This is partly because of the limitations on the use of Lake Albert, and partly because the greater part of the variation of the level of Lake Victoria will be due to the natural lake, and not to the regulation. As we have seen in Chapter XV, it is not possible to forecast future lake levels, nor is it possible to say that the mean discharge of the next fifty years will be the same as that of the last. The old idea was that the mean of a long series of years tended towards a fixed quantity looked upon as the " true mean." The experience obtained from the examination of the long-term records in the over-year storage investigation, however, shows that this idea is entirely erroneous. As an example we refer again to the eighty years' record of the Nile at Aswan, where the average discharge of the second half was 25 per cent. less than that of the first. A number of possible regulations of Lakes Victoria and Albert Reservoirs, based on the recorded fifty years, have been made, but these only give a general indication of what may happen. Moreover, it is one thing to regulate the past with all the records in front of one, and another to regulate for a future which is only known within wide limits. The only course, therefore, is to allow a good factor of safety, as is sound engineering practice all over the world. My advocacy of this at one of our discussions on these storage projects, led to the facetious remark, that I was like a man who wears a belt and braces and then has his trousers sewn on to his shirt.

The regulation would be directed to trying to make up the supply in bad years, and to store water in good ones. At the same time there would also be regulation to hold back water during the flood on the main Nile, and release it during the low stage. During the period when the Nile is in flood there is normally plenty of water from the Blue Nile, so the discharge out of the Lake Albert Reservoir will be limited to the amount necessary for navigation of the Bahr-el-Jebel in Uganda and the Sudan— about one third of the annual supply. During the time of low supply in Egypt (December to May at Lake Albert), two-thirds of the steady annual supply will be sent down. This will be the normal proceeding, but it will be modified when it is known that the low stage supply of the main Nile is likely to be unusually good or bad. For example, the year 1913–14 was phenomenally low on the main Nile, and if it should occur again in the future it will be impossible to fill the present reservoirs of Aswan and Gebel Aulia. In such a year all possible stored water will be required to lessen the disaster, and it would certainly be known by the end of September that the reservoirs could not be filled, so extra water would begin to be sent down from Lake Albert three months before the usual time. The year 1917–18 was a high year on the Blue Nile, the Sobat, and on the lakes, and when it occurred the White Nile did not reach its maximum until March, instead of at the beginning of November, as would normally be the case. In such a year it would be possible to keep the Lake Albert discharge down to navigation level throughout the year, and so store the excess. Thus, the fact of excesses on the Blue Nile and Sobat allows Bahr-el-Jebel water to be stored. This is called Virtual Storage of Blue Nile and Sobat water in Lake Albert.

2. REDUCTION OF WATER LOSSES AND CANALISATION OF THE SUDD REGION

The heavy losses of water in the Sudd region have already been mentioned, and Fig. 27 shows that at low levels of the Bahr-el-Jebel they are not excessive, but increase rapidly as the river rises, until at the highest levels they amount to about two-thirds of the water passing Mongalla. On the average the loss is about a half. The necessity for reducing these losses was first discussed by Sir William Garstin in 1904,[1] and as a result the region has been studied for many years by the Sudan branch of the Egyptian Irrigation Service.

It is obvious that storage schemes in the Great Lakes are useless while the Sudd region remains as it is at present, since half the water would be lost, and the regulation would be so distorted

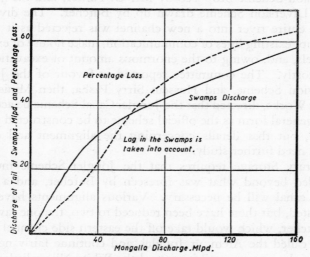

FIG. 27. Water losses in the Bahr-el-Jebel swamps.

by lag as to be largely ineffective. Various schemes have been proposed, which are of three kinds (*a*) embanking the Bahr-el-Jebel; (*b*) cutting a new channel to carry the whole supply, leaving the swamps as a flood escape, and (*c*) leaving the Bahr-el-Jebel to carry as much as it can without undue loss, and cutting a new channel to carry the remainder.

The cheapest scheme would probably be one for embanking the Bahr-el-Jebel, and a scheme for this purpose was drawn up by Mr. A. D. Butcher. The banks were to follow the general course of the river, but not its many windings, so that they would

[1] *Report on the Basin of the Upper Nile.* Cairo Government Press, 1904, and *Blue Book, Egypt,* No. 2, 1904.

usually be some kilometres apart. The head on the banks for most of their length would be about 2 metres. This, however, would have to be increased to carry the discharge under Century Storage conditions. Butcher did not recommend this scheme because of the difficulty of maintaining the banks in this inhospitable region, and also of the uncertainty as to what might happen in a year of high flood. A committee of the Ministry of Public Works examined the Banking Scheme, the Veveno-Pibor Diversion Scheme proposed by Mr. G. Parker, and the Jonglei Canal Diversion Scheme drawn up by Butcher. The diversion of the entire river into a new channel was rejected as it would interrupt existing lines of communication, make no use of existing channels, and, owing to the enormous amount of excavation, be very costly. The committee reported in favour of the Jonglei Diversion Scheme, and Hussein Sirry Pasha, then Minister of Public Works, directed that the Jonglei Canal Scheme be accepted in its general form as the official scheme to be constructed in due course, but that details concerning the alignment and design would need further study.

Century Storage requires that the Jonglei Scheme must be extended beyond what was foreseen by Butcher, and a much larger canal will be necessary. Various alignments have been suggested, but these have been reduced to two, the one favoured by Butcher, which would take off the eastern side channel of the Jebel, called the Atem, at Jonglei, and continue fairly near the edge of the swamp until it entered the White Nile a little to the east of the mouth of the Bahr-el-Zeraf. This canal would be cut by dredgers working on several sections at once, which it would be possible to enter by means of short cuts from the Bahr-el-Zeraf, and from the Atem. The other line is the direct one from Jonglei to the White Nile at the Sobat mouth. If this were chosen the work would be done by excavators working on land. The country is flat plain, and the choice of which line to take is largely the question of dredgers *versus* excavators. In order to settle this the Egyptian Government will shortly appoint an International Committee of three experts, American, British and Dutch.

It is probable that the Jonglei Canal will be cut in stages, beginning with a small channel right the way through, which will be gradually enlarged to the final width. The distance from Jonglei to the Sobat mouth is 280 kilometres, or 175 miles, and this is the shortest line. The final cut will be 120 metres wide at its bed and 5 metres deep, and when finished it will be one of the large canals of the world. The first cut will only need a regulator at its head, but the final stage will need an embanked channel from the main stream at Bor to Jonglei, and some embanking of the main stream above Bor. A barrage will be necessary where the canal and river separate, so as to be able to regulate accurately the amounts going through the canal, and down the river through the swamps.

The effect of Century Storage and the canalization of the Sudd region will be to produce more uniform conditions on the Bahr-el-Jebel and in the swamps, but they will be different from those now existing. The average regulation will send down approximately two-thirds of the supply during the months January to June, and the other third in the remainder of the year. This third will be increased by some of the water from the torrents which enter north of the Lake Albert Dam. The general result will be to make the annual supply very much more uniform, but to invert the seasons by making the discharge of the low season high, and that of the high season low. The rainfall on the swamps and neighbouring country will not be altered. This change of the régime of the river will have far-reaching effects on the country and the life of its inhabitants, as far even as Kosti on the White Nile.

For some years now a group appointed by the Sudan Government, and known as the Jonglei Team, has been studying the population problems raised by these great projects. The team has included irrigation engineers, political officers, surveyors and a veterinary expert, and has had assistance from experts on other subjects, e.g. fisheries. It has had to deal with a wide range of subjects and a very large area. Its labours, which have been arduous, have included a good deal of exploration of the fringes of the swamps of the Bahr-el-Jebel amongst mosquitoes and malaria, and an attempt to penetrate the Machar marshes, one of the very few unknown areas remaining in Africa. Apart from the importance of these studies in connection with the project, a great deal of information about the country has been collected, and which will be of lasting value for the people. In particular the pastures and their grasses, and the fisheries in the lagoons and branches of the Bahr-el-Jebel, have been studied, while much information about the people and their cattle has been collected. It is estimated that roughly 700,000 people, who own 700,000 cattle and 700,000 sheep and goats, will be affected by the project.

The paramount importance of cattle in the life of the Nilotic people of the southern plains has been described in Chapter XII, and the main effect on them will be through the loss of grazing in some of the areas. The area affected by the scheme has been divided by the Jonglei Team into three sections. The northern section extends from Kosti on the White Nile to a little south of Malakal, and includes the east and west reach of the White Nile, and the tails of the Bahr-el-Zeraf and Bahr-el-Jebel. In this area the river will be high in the dry season, and not so high, as it is at present in flood, consequently some of the land used for dry-season grazing will be covered, and the grazing lost. This will affect some Nilotic people, but also a good many Baggara Arabs north of Renk, who own large herds of cattle, sheep and goats. The central section includes the Jebel and Zeraf, and their fringes, as far as the latitude of Jonglei. This is a wide complex area, and it is difficult to say exactly what will be the effects. The regulation of the Bahr-el-Jebel throughout the year will be directed to preventing the loss of large quantities of water by spilling. The swampy areas will therefore be much reduced, and some which are now flooded in the rainy season and are grazed later, will no longer receive this water from the river. On the other hand, they will still receive the natural rain which produces abundant grass on the plains, and some low-lying areas which do not yield grazing at present, may do so at lower river levels. The probability is, however, that there will be some reduction of grazing. Possible remedies are, the production of pasture by irrigation—which might be costly—and making available grazing, which is now impossible for lack of drinking water. Another possibility is the provision of new grazing by measures of reclamation in the Machar marsh. The conditions in the southern section, from Jonglei to Juba, will be similar to those in the central section, but the difficulties will probably not be so great.

In view of the complexity of the problem and the large area concerned, it is not possible to speak with certainty on the detailed effects of the scheme. Fortunately the diversion scheme will proceed by stages spread over a number of years, and changes in the life of the people will take place gradually. Also the working of the first stages of the scheme will give the answer to many questions which are now obscure, and will enable remedial measures to be developed as experience recommends— certainly and economically.

A danger to be guarded against is that of flooding when the large areas of the present swamp have become dry, and are perhaps occupied by re-settled communities. This could happen if conditions similar to those of 1916–18 recur when the reservoirs in the Great Lakes happen to be full. In 1916–18 the lakes rose to their highest recorded levels, and in addition there was a great inflow into the Bahr-el-Jebel from torrents below Lake Albert, as well as a good deal of rain on the Sudan Plains. Lake Victoria rose and fell a metre, and Lake Albert rose 3 metres and fell 2 during the period. The occurrence of such an event after the canalization of the swamps had been completed, if uncontrolled, would be a disaster for the Sudan. It could only be controlled if storage were available in the lake reservoirs. Such storage would be available provided that a reasonable estimate of over-year storage is adopted, and there is, in addition, some reserve above the normal high water marks of the reservoirs for the case of exceptional rains occurring when the reservoirs are full to their normal levels.

3. THE LAKE TANA RESERVOIR

Lake Tana has been described in Chapter VI, and there is a mention of the various expeditions to study the lake in order that a reservoir project might be drawn up. Such a project was designed, and negotiations were begun with the Ethiopian Government, but the Italian invasion put an end to them. Now it is hoped to renew negotiations, but for political reasons they have not so far been started. The project, a joint one, is to store water for the benefit of Egypt and the Sudan, and combined with a power scheme, could also benefit Ethiopia, though the power would be a long way from where it could be useful. The proposal is to convert the lake into a reservoir by a relatively low dam at its outlet.

The original proposal was for a small reservoir for annual storage. Water would be stored in the lake in the rainy season, and released for the use of the Sudan and Egypt in the " timely " season, from January onwards. " Timely " water, an apt term coined by Mr. F. Newhouse, is what comes down when the natural flow of the river is insufficient for irrigation, and " untimely " water is what comes down when there is already enough.

Our investigations have shown, however, that the lake has much wider uses than this. A large reservoir can be used for Century Storage so as to provide an annual quota, instead of the variable supply produced by annual storage, which is least when it is most needed. In very low years its reserve can be drawn upon to provide emergency water for Egypt without a great delay, since the time of travel from Tana to Aswan would not be much more than a month. This reserve could be built up again in the following seasons, by storing Egypt's quota from Tana, and drawing the water required to replace it from the equatorial lakes. Another possibility will be mentioned when we come to discuss main Nile reservoirs. Tana has the advantage over Albert in that the Blue Nile channel can carry all the water required with only normal losses, so that its efficiency is not limited by the cost of having to make a new channel.

The area of the lake is about 3,100 square kilometres, or 1,200 square miles, so that it has about three-fifths of the area of Albert. The annual discharge out of the lake is only about one-sixth of that from Lake Albert, and about one-thirteenth of the total discharge of the Blue Nile. As a reservoir it will have a much smaller capacity than Albert, but in virtue of its position, it has some compensations, one of which has been mentioned. Another is that it will enable an increased area in the Sudan Gezira to be cultivated. This area can only be watered from the Blue Nile, since the slope of the country is downwards from the Blue Nile to the White. The scope of the project depends upon what agreement can be made with the Ethiopians.

4. MAIN NILE RESERVOIRS AND FLOOD PROTECTION

For seventy years Egypt has suffered no disaster from flood, and there can be few people now alive who remember the damage to life and property caused when a serious breach in the Nile banks last occurred. Consequently to many people, and particularly to town-dwellers, the subject may seem only of remote interest. However, many old records testify to the importance of protection when a high flood arrives. Between 1860 and 1880 serious damage and loss of life resulted from at least four floods, and by examining the old records these examples can be multiplied. As we have said, we have been passing through a period of low floods, but no man can say when high ones will recur.

Sir William Willcocks, one of the British irrigation engineers who came to Egypt from India, has left a description in his book *Egyptian Irrigation* [1] of an incident during the first big flood to be passed safely through the country to the sea without a serious breach in the river banks. He says:—

" The terror reigning over the whole country during a very high flood like that of 1887 is very striking to anyone seeing a flood for the first time. On the settlement of a culvert in the Nile bank near Mit el Kholi, and the consequent first rush of water through the bank, one witnessed a scene which must have been common in Egypt on the occurrence of a serious breach, but which fortunately was rare in 1887. The news that the Nile bank had breached spread fast through the village. The villagers rushed out on to the banks with their children, their cattle and everything they possessed. The confusion was indescribable. A very narrow bank covered with children, buffaloes, poultry, and household furniture. The women assembled round the local sheikh's tomb beating their breasts, kissing the tomb, and uttering loud shrieks. And every five minutes a gang of men running into the crowd, and carrying something wherewith to close the breach. The fellahin, meanwhile, were not in the least confused, but in a steady, business-like manner were working at the breach, and closed it in half-an-hour."

At present there is no reliable method of forecasting a high flood until the rain has actually fallen in Ethiopia, and then the first warning is given by Roseires Gauge on the Blue Nile, seventy miles from the Ethiopian frontier. A high peak at Roseires will reach Aswan in about ten days, and Cairo five days later, so the time available for making decisions is short. High floods appear to be more frequent in some periods than in others, but there is no regularity about their occurrence which might enable their coming to be predicted. For instance, between 1869 and 1900

[1] *Egyptian Irrigation.* Third edition, by Willcocks and Craig. Spon., London, 1913.

there were seventeen floods with a ten-day mean discharge exceeding 900 millions per day, which in these days would be considered high, while from 1901 to 1950 only eight have exceeded 900 mlpd. Of the floods of this century, only that of 1946 compares with the really high floods of the previous century. There is, however, a little uncertainty in comparing present-day floods with those of last century, owing to the changes which have taken place. The greatest flood of which we have record was that of 1878. In those days there were no measurements of the discharge, though the levels have been recorded at a number of stations, so for an estimate of the quantity of water which passed, we are dependent on a present-day curve giving the relation of the discharge to the level on Aswan Gauge. In this it is assumed that the relation was the same seventy years ago as it is now. We cannot compare the levels directly, because in 1946 the Aswan Reservoir was used to hold back flood water, and so reduce the quantity passing at the crest through Egypt to the sea. The best estimate we can make is that three floods have had greater volumes of water passing than that passed in 1946, after a dangerous level (900 millions a day) had been reached. These were in order of size those of 1878, 1874 and 1892.

The estimated quantity of water flowing at the peak of the flood in 1878 was 1,140 million cubic metres a day. A day's flow at this rate could flood an area equal to that of Greater London, to a depth of 2 feet. However, conditions in Egypt have since changed. In the past a high flood was diminished by having to fill two million acres of basins. To-day these basins are reduced to one million acres, and as I have said before, in some of them cotton is now cultivated, the picking of which delays the time of filling. In the case of a dangerous flood, a lot of cotton might have to be sacrificed owing to the necessity for filling the basins earlier. This would be very unpopular with the cotton growers, who would probably not be in any danger of their own lives.

Prior to 1880, a high flood nearly always caused breaches in the Nile banks, but since that date no serious breach has taken place. A high flood produces different effects in Upper and Lower Egypt. In Upper Egypt the basins would be over-filled, and the banks dividing them might be over-topped and receive some damage. In the villages standing on their islands in the basins, the lower houses might be flooded, and life would be very uncomfortable for people and cattle. On the other hand the extra flooding would help the higher lands, more mud would be deposited, and the winter crops would be good. In a very high flood the damage to basin banks might be considerable, and the late Sir Ismail Sirry Pasha, for many years Minister of Public Works, told me that he remembered the flood of 1878, which occurred when he was a boy at school. In this flood the river breached its banks above Cairo, and it was possible to sail on the inundation from Minia to Cairo, while water returned to the Rosetta branch north of the barrage. In the high flood of 1887, old men in Upper Egypt can remember that in places the valley was a sheet of water from desert to desert, while the villages on their mounds were awash, and most of their inhabitants were camped on the desert edges with their cattle and all their movable property.

In Lower Egypt there is no flood irrigation, nor is the country divided into basins by high banks, as in Upper Egypt. The banks are those of canals, drains and railways, which are usually only a metre or so above land level. The river banks, however, are well above land level since they are maintained at a metre above the flood levels of 1874. In the Central Delta these levels are in places 4 or 5 metres above the level of the land. In 1878 there was a breach on the Damietta branch north of Zifta, and a great loss of life and crops resulted, as the inundation swept northwards to the sea. Another disastrous breach occurred in 1863 on the Rosetta branch, when water travelled over a country in which there were no canal banks which could be used as refuges, and many people and cattle were drowned.

Conditions have changed very much since the last century, but the custom still remains, when a high flood occurs, of placing watchers at intervals of about eighty yards all along the banks. These men live in temporary huts made of palm branches, or of sticks and straw, and in case of danger pass the word from one to another. Formerly they were not paid, and, according to Willcocks, amused themselves by annoying the government officials in charge of the banks, preventing them from sleeping at night by shouting false alarms of breaches. He also records the story of a very high government official sending a message along the bank that he needed another official's horse. In transit, however, the word " horse " was changed to " wife."

Several factors combine in these days to lessen the danger from a high flood. For one thing the banks have been strengthened and improved, and many old culverts, always a source of danger, have been removed. There are now second lines of defence in the form of canal and railway banks, by which the inundation would be prevented from sweeping freely over wide areas of country, as it did formerly. In addition, modern transport would enable large quantities of men and materials to be concentrated at a dangerous point. Stocks of stone, timber, and tools, are accumulated at intervals along the banks ready for an emergency, and each section of bank is in charge of an engineer with motor transport at his disposal.

The high flood of 1946 was passed to sea without any breach of the Nile banks. It was, however, a very anxious time, and the minister, Abdel Qawi Ahmed Pasha, took up his quarters at the Barrage along with his staff, and from there he was able to estimate the position and move quickly to any threatened point. His decisive handling of the situation was largely responsible for the safety of the country. It was a terrifying sight, travelling along the Nile bank in early September, to see the river on one side nearing the top, whilst on the other the land was 10 or 12 feet below. One of the dangers of a flood is that, if high levels are prolonged the banks gradually become saturated, and slipping, which will cause a breach, may occur.

In some ways the changes of the last fifty years have tended to lessen the danger from a high flood, whilst in other ways the development of the country and increase of the population would make the damage caused by a breach of the river bank greater. The danger is recognized, and much thought has been devoted to the subject of flood protection. At present the principal defence is improved river banks, and the Aswan Reservoir can render a little help in reducing the crest of the flood. There has always been the desire to find methods of reducing further the flood volume, either by means of a diversion or by holding up more of the water in reservoirs. The diversion of part of the flood necessitates an escape channel from the river, and a depression into which the water can be poured. Both banks of the Nile from Khartoum to Aswan have been examined to see if any suitable depression exists. The Wady Mugaddam and the Wady-el-Kaab west of the Nile in the Dongola district have been explored, but were found to be unsuitable. The country along the Atbara has not been exhaustively searched, but a general inspection of the river banks does not show anything suitable.

In Egypt south of the Fayum there is a considerable depression, the Wadi Rayan, whose lowest point is about 50 metres below sea-level, and whose area at high levels is about 700 square kilometres. Many years ago this was first suggested as a possible flood escape, and from time to time projects have been drawn up for this purpose. Coupled with its use as a flood escape is the possibility that it may provide some addition of stored water to the summer water supply. In general form the project would require a barrage on the Nile somewhere in the neighbourhood of Beni Suef, and a large canal crossing the cultivated valley and cutting through the rocky ridge between the valley and the Wadi. The canal and barrage would allow quantities of water to be diverted from the river into the Wadi. A little stored water can be returned by the channel to the river when it falls, or some could be used in the Fayum, and it has sometimes been suggested that a second channel back to the river be cut lower down; and quite recently to make use of pumps.

The objections which have been raised to the project in the past have been the expense, and the possibility of infiltration from the Wadi into the Fayum. When the Wadi is full, the water at its nearest will be within about a mile from the edge of the cultivated land in the Fayum, and at a much higher level. My colleagues and I did not regard the possibility of infiltration as a serious objection. We reasoned that the fine mud in suspension would soon cure any porosity of the rock, and that if actual cracks showed themselves they could be dealt with easily. The objection has now been disposed of by the very thorough geological examination of the Wadi by Sir Cyril Fox. A reservoir within the boundaries of Egypt is naturally very attractive to Egyptians, and an added attraction in these days is the fact that there need be no negotiations for a concession from other countries to introduce disagreements and delays. Another point is that, under some conditions, water from the rising flood can be stored without troubling about silt, since if the reservoir ultimately silts some good cultivable land will have been added to Egypt. H. E. Osman Moharram Pasha, Minister of Public Works, has recently given instructions that fresh investigations into the project shall be made, and these are now being carried out.

As opposed to diversion schemes, there is the type of scheme which proposes to hold back part of the flood in a reservoir in the Nile Valley. Of this type is the scheme to build a dam at the Fourth Cataract, proposed by Mohammed Sabry el Kordi Bey, and which is now a part of the Government Scheme of Projects. The site has been surveyed and examined geologically, and designs are being made for a dam of such a height as to be able to impound 8 milliards at the top of the flood. The stretch of valley which would be flooded is very thinly populated, and would stretch from about twenty-five miles upstream of Merowe to Abu Hamed. We have calculated in Vol. VII of *The Nile Basin* that the abstraction of 8 milliards at the peak would reduce a flood of the volume of that of 1878 to safe dimensions. The other projects which are part of the Government's Scheme will add some additional security, since they will automatically be impounding water in flood-time, and so offer some factor of safety against a higher flood than the previous highest known to us. Making use of all these reserve storages means that it would be possible to deal with a flood 10 per cent. greater than that of 1878.

In the high flood of 1946 an unforeseen relief to Egypt occurred, which, however, caused great damage in the Sudan. The main Nile between Khartoum and Atbara over-topped its banks over long stretches, and large areas of country were flooded, particularly on the west bank. Air photographs showed flooding extending for several kilometres in some places, and there was considerable damage to houses. Presumably something of the same sort occurred in 1878, and may have partly accounted for the flood peak at Aswan occurring nearly a month later than the normal. I have not come across any reference to the effect of the flood of 1878 in the Northern Sudan, though possibly a search of old newspapers and journals might produce something. The inundation of 1946 draws attention to the value of some measure of flood protection in the northern Sudan, to which, in the present scheme, only Lake Tana and the Equatorial Lakes would contribute anything, and that not of great amount. It is difficult to see what form protection could take. The raising of the river banks would be a costly procedure in a poor country, and maintenance in a dry windy climate, for an event which may not happen again for fifty years, might be uncertain.

Returning to the question of the Fourth Cataract Reservoir, in addition to its use for flood protection it would, except in the very low years, impound water from the tail of the flood for use in the low season. A still more important use would be in connection with the Century Storage Reservoirs, to which it would act as an auxiliary regulator. In this capacity it could hold up excess water which might come down, delay water which might have been released against an emergency a little prematurely, or in some cases, anticipate the arrival of water from the south. Further, it could be used, in connection with Century Storage, for what we have called virtual storage, and for re-building the reserve in Lake Tana after an emergency had drawn it down. In this case, water impounded at the Fourth Cataract from the flood, or sent down from Lake Albert, would be used in Egypt, instead of Lake Tana water (see p. 309).

5. THE WORKING OF THE PROJECTS IN COMBINATION

The following gives an idea of what the various projects will do if they can be carried out so that their capabilities are fully utilized. The time of the year considered is February to July, during which the natural river supply is insufficient for irrigation in Egypt and the Sudan. The quantities of water are reckoned at Aswan, i.e. transit losses have been deducted in the case of water from upstream reservoirs.

Average flow of natural river (February to July).	15·4 milliards
Water stored in reservoirs at Aswan, Gebel Aulia, and Sennar	8·1 ,,
Water stored in new Main [1] Nile reservoirs	3·0 ,,
Water taken from storage in Lakes Victoria and Albert .	5·2 ,,
Water taken from storage in Lake Tana	2·1 ,,
Total	33·8 ,,

[1] This includes part of what could be stored in Wadi Rayan, which, however, might store a little extra on the rising river.

Requirements of cultivation with 7·1 million feddans in
Egypt, and 2 million feddans in the Sudan (see Chapter XVI, section 3) . . . . 30 milliards

In an average year it appears that there will be water to spare. If,
however, surveys show that parts of the Egyptian deserts and
larger areas in the Sudan can be profitably cultivated, this excess
will disappear. Moreover the July natural river supply depends
on the rising flood and cannot be foreseen, so that it is necessary
to keep a reserve for July, and in many years some of this is not
used. But what of the low years? Records show that on the
above areas and requirements, in twenty-nine years out of seventy-
five there would have been a deficit. In the worst of these years
some of the reservoirs on the Main Nile would not have been
filled, and this makes a shortage in addition to the natural river
shortage in the period. The steps to meet the shortage would
be a drastic cut in the rice area in Egypt, and a general economy
of water which could amount to a general 10 per cent. cut of
requirements. Even so there would still be seven years with a
deficit. In these years, if the shortage was foreseen in time, a
little extra could be got from the Great Lakes, and a little from the
Lake Tana reserve. In a year like 1914, the lowest recorded year,
after reductions of requirements had been made, the Lake Reservoirs would be called upon to do their best to meet a shortage of
6 milliards. Very good judgment and management would be
required to avoid a disaster in such a year. The projects would,
however, if well operated, reduce the really dangerous years to
about one in twenty-five.

6. HYDRO-ELECTRIC SCHEMES

The Owen Falls Scheme has already been mentioned, and the
construction of a power plant at Aswan has been going on for
some time. The work is complicated by the fact that the power-
house and intakes of the turbines have to be built on to the
existing dam, so that difficult problems of construction have had
to be solved. The problem is simpler when power-house and dam
are designed together, and the dams of the future must be considered in relation to power. Unfortunately those at present
projected are at considerable distances from locations where
power is likely to be used. As far as the development of power is

concerned there are many potential sites. In fact wherever the river has a steep slope it is possible, but not always economical, to develop power. On the Blue Nile and its tributaries in Ethiopia, there are many possibilities. Between Lakes Victoria and Albert and on the Bahr-el-Jebel between Nimule and Rejaf, power development is possible, and the same is true of the Batn-el-Hagar on the Main Nile.

Some twenty-five years ago the late Dr. John Ball, then Director of Desert Surveys, and also an able geologist and engineer, suggested that a site for a power scheme, much closer to the Delta where power might be used, could be found at the Qattara Depression in the Western Desert, that same impassable depression which covered the flank of the 8th Army at Alamein. Ball's scheme was to admit the Mediterranean Sea water by means of a canal or tunnel or both, to the depression, the lowest point of which is at 137 metres, or about 450 feet, below the sea, and allow the water to evaporate there. The energy of the water falling into the depression could be used to generate power. Others have suggested that the slopes of the depression might be cultivated by Nile water.

Between the depression and both the Nile and the sea there is a considerable stretch of land (about ten miles wide) lying at a level of 100 metres or more above sea-level, and this introduces a formidable difficulty into both Ball's and the cultivation scheme. As, however, the population problem presses ever more heavily, both these schemes merit careful consideration. If the power scheme is feasible, the cultivation scheme is much simplified, and it may well be that a combination of the two will be the final solution. As I have already said, the limitation of the population by birth control to the number which the country can support will operate only slowly. The production of power, however, would assist the development of manufactures, and so increase the resources of the country. This would enable it to support a larger population and improve their standard of living. This improvement of the conditions of life would tend automatically to reduce the rate of increase of population. When new dams are designed the importance of navigation should not be lost sight of, and any dam on the Main Nile north of Khartoum can make some local improvement in this respect. In designing a dam it is therefore important to consider the potential value of locks.

7. OTHER SCHEMES

I have just received (November, 1951), a pamphlet by Mr. Adrian Daninos proposing a new dam at Aswan of such a height as to form a reservoir capable of performing Century Storage on the Main Nile, and at the same time providing an enormous amount of power, by means of which Egypt might become an industrial country. If this idea could be realized it would provide a simple solution to many complicated problems and avoid some political difficulties. But, as is always the case, in avoiding some difficulties one encounters others. The pamphlet is rather like the prospectus of a company in which the claims are somewhat exaggerated and the difficulties passed over. It is a very long way from this stage to the presentation of a final project, in which pros and cons have been duly weighed and detailed designs can be prepared for the construction. Nevertheless the proposal is worthy of some examination to see whether the difficulties are as formidable as they first appear.

8. CONCLUDING REMARKS

This book is a record of what exists and what has been done in the Nile Basin. I may perhaps conclude with some remarks drawn from my own experience of thirty-five years' work on Nile projects, and some suggestions for future work. Most of the remarks are obvious, but are very often not remembered when they should be applied to practice.

It is often said that it is impossible to carry out some particular work, and I can remember a number of instances of this attitude. One of these was the second heightening of the Aswan Dam, and of which some people said it was impossible on structural grounds, whilst others observed that if it were heightened the reservoir could not be filled. Both these statements proved to be incorrect, for the dam was successfully heightened, and has been working these last seventeen years. A job may be difficult, too expensive, or undesirable, but except when a logical contradiction is involved, it is rarely impossible. It is remarkable how often the execution of projects is delayed by difficulties in deciding between rival ways of doing things, and quite trivial differences may cause entirely disproportionate delays. It is well to remember Kipling's lines:—

" There are nine and sixty ways of writing tribal lays
And every single one of them is right! "

It is usually better to do something which is 95 per cent. effective immediately, rather than wait several years to improve the solution by 4 per cent. Another point I would emphasize is the importance, when projects are in question, of personal knowledge of the river and personal visits to the sites. Making projects from a map of a country one has not seen is amusing, but not on a much higher plane than the efforts of those diviners who claim to find water solely from a map.

With regard to future work it is important to maintain accurate measurements of the Nile and all its principal tributaries, together with regular publication of the results. Often have we been delayed in the past for lack of water measurements at important points, and it cannot be said too often that records grow greatly in value as their length increases. Unless, however, records are published up-to-date regularly they lose a lot of their usefulness, as everybody knows who has been compelled to work with manuscripts in files. The future regulation of the Nile will be much more difficult than it is at present, and will depend almost entirely on having good measurements and records, and on continuous study of the Nile Basin. Meteorological studies can help, and more rainfall observations in Ethiopia and in the northern part of the Lake Plateau are needed. The suspended matter in the Nile would repay further study, and sampling and analysis should be extended on the tributaries. Subsoil water, its levels and movements, have been studied in Egypt in the past. This is a complicated subject, and the work might with advantage be taken up again, so as to have a continuous record at a few representative places in Upper Egypt and the Delta, of the changes which take place. The height of the subsoil water table is a matter of great importance to crops, particularly to those grown on irrigated land, and also in studies relating to decrease of fertility.

There is no lack in Egypt of subjects for research connected with the Nile, the land, and the employment of water, and the same is probably true to a greater extent in other parts of the Basin, where the period during which scientific work has been carried on is shorter, and where there are much greater areas to be covered.

I conclude this book with thanks to all my colleagues, and good wishes to our successors; may they have as much pleasure from the work as we have had.

INDEX

INDEX

Leprosy, 130, 184
Life of Egyptians, 14–17
Lifting appliances for water, 43–45
Linant de Bellefonds Pasha, 46, 48, 49, 50
Linant de Bellefonds, E., 217, 218
Lol River, 123, 126, 129
Luxor, antiquities, 24
Lyons, Sir Henry, 1, 168, 224, 226

MacDonald, Sir M., 227, 230
Machar Marsh, 113, 307
Mahdi, 78
Mahmoud Pasha el Falaki, 255
Main Nile reservoirs, 310. *See also* Fourth Cataract.
Malakal, 105
Malaria, 96, 181
Marchand, General, 103, 129
Mathematical note on over-year storage, 299
McMillan expeditions, 88, 93
Mission to lakes, Egyptian, 137, 144
Tana, 98
Models, hydraulic, 67
Mohammed Ali Pasha, 46, 49, 50, 52, 206–208, 210
Mohammed Amin Bey, Dr., 144
Mohammed the Deftardar, 207
Mongalla, 119, 120
Mountains, heights of, 71, 96, 112, 132, 147
Mufumbiro or Birunga Mountains, 132, 144, 147
Murchison Falls, 149
Murray, G. W., 20, 189

Navigation, 25, 26
Newhouse, F., 114, 286, 310
Niavarongo River, 160–163
Nile, area of Basin, 4
Blue. *See* Blue Nile.
branches, 9, 12, 13, 37, 199
cataracts, 73–78
discharges, 8, 242–245
dissolved matter, 278
expeditions, 73, 78–80
fish, 21, 27, 127–129, 150, 154, 166
flood, origin of, 4, 255–258
length, 4
projects, 281–320
Projects controversy, 84, 85
rainfall, 5, 169, 175, 177
silt, 12, 275–278
sources, 92, 161, 163, 203, 213
Valley, early history, 35–38

Nile, Waters Agreement, 236, 287
White. *See* White Nile.
Nilotic people, 102, 308
Nuer, 102

Osman Moharram Pasha and Wady Rayan, 316
Over-year storage, 292, 295–304
mathematical note, 299

Parker, G., 306
Pearson, Colonel H. D., 98
People, basin, 189–193
Egypt, 14–17
Ethiopia, 99, 100
Ruanda, 146
Sudan, 76, 102
Perennial irrigation, 46, 54–62
Periodicity, 258
Petherick, 210–214
Phillips, Dr. P., 227, 231, 248
Pibor River, 108, 109
Plants, 116, 117, 126, 187
Population, 14, 70, 289
Porters, 121, 122
Portuguese, 92–94, 202–205
Prediction of flood, 258, 269
Projects, 84, 85, 281–320
Protection against sun, 185
flood, 284, 310, 314
Prowde, O. L., 98
Ptolemy, 200
Pyramid, 50, 68, 258

Qattara depression, 319

Rainfall, 169, 175–178
Rayan Wady, 283, 315, 316
Relapsing fever, 145
Relative humidity, 172, 173, 175, 176
Requirements, water, 291–294
Reservoir, Aswan, 26–31
Fourth Cataract, 74, 283, 316
Gebel Aulia, 104, 285
Lake Albert, 123, 283, 302
Lake Tana, 95, 283, 288
Lake Victoria, 123, 133, 153, 281, 288, 301
Sennar, 83, 285
Wady Rayan, 283, 315
Rey, Sir C. F., 93, 99
Rift Valley, 132, 165
Roda Gauge, 258–261
Roseires Gauge, 88